Real Numbers and Some of Their Important Properties

Real numbers, R

Rational numbers, Q
$\frac{3}{5}, -2, 3, \frac{11}{13}$, repeating decimals

Irrational numbers
$\pi, \sqrt{2}$, nonrepeating decimals

Integers, J
$\ldots, -2, -1, 0, 1, 2, \ldots$

Natural numbers, N,
or positive integers
$1, 2, 3, \ldots$

Zero

Negative integers
$\ldots, -3, -2, -1$

For a, b, c, and k any real numbers:

COMMUTATIVE PROPERTIES

$a + b = b + a$

$ab = ba$

DISTRIBUTIVE PROPERTIES

$a(b + c) = ab + ac$

$(a + b)c = ac + bc$

ZERO PROPERTY

$ab = 0$ if and only if $a = 0$ or $b = 0$

ASSOCIATIVE PROPERTIES

$(a + b) + c = a + (b + c)$

$(ab)c = a(bc)$

FUNDAMENTAL PRINCIPLE OF FRACTIONS

$\dfrac{a}{b} = \dfrac{ka}{kb}$ $b, k \neq 0$

ELEMENTARY ALGEBRA
Structure and Use

FIFTH EDITION

ELEMENTARY ALGEBRA
Structure and Use

Raymond A. Barnett
Merritt College

Thomas J. Kearns
Northern Kentucky University

McGRAW-HILL PUBLISHING COMPANY

*New York   St. Louis   San Francisco   Auckland   Bogotá
Caracas   Hamburg   Lisbon   London   Madrid   Mexico
Milan   Montreal   New Delhi   Oklahoma City   Paris
San Juan   São Paulo   Singapore   Sydney   Tokyo   Toronto*

This book was set in Times Roman
by York Graphic Services, Inc.
The editors were Robert A. Weinstein and
James W. Bradley;
the designer was Joan E. O'Connor;
the production supervisor was Leroy A. Young.
The cover was designed by John Hite.
New drawings were done by Fine Line Illustrations, Inc.
R. R. Donnelley & Sons Company was
printer and binder.

ELEMENTARY ALGEBRA:
Structure and Use

34567890 DOC/DOC 9987654321

ISBN 0-07-003942-9

Library of Congress Cataloging-in-Publication Data

Barnett, Raymond A.
    Elementary algebra: structure and use / Raymond A.
Barnett, Thomas J. Kearns, —5th ed.
      p.   cm.
    ISBN 0-07-003942-9. —ISBN 0-07-003943-7 (answer
manual). —ISBN 0-07-003944-5 (student solutions
manual). —ISBN 0-07-003945-3 (print test bank)
    1. Algebra.   I. Kearns, Thomas J.   II. Title.
QA152.2.B37   1990
512.9—dc20   89-27175

ABOUT
THE AUTHORS

Raymond A. Barnett is an experienced teacher and author. He received his B.A. in Mathematical Statistics from the University of California at Berkeley and his M.A. in Mathematics from the University of Southern California. He then went on to become a member of the Department of Mathematics at Merritt College and head of that department for four years. He is a member of the American Mathematical Association, the National Council of Teachers of Mathematics, and the American Association for the Advancement of Science. He is the author or coauthor of 17 books in mathematics that are still in print—all with a reputation for extremely readable prose and high quality mathematics.

Thomas J. Kearns received his B.S. from the University of Santa Clara and his M.S. and Ph.D. from the University of Illinois. After several years of teaching at the University of Delaware, he was appointed to the faculty at Northern Kentucky University. He served as chairman of the Department of Mathematical Sciences there for ten years. He is a member of the professional organizations listed above, has coauthored four texts with Raymond A. Barnett, and has also coauthored texts in college algebra and elementary statistics.

CONTENTS

PREFACE

This is an introductory text in algebra written for students with no background in algebra and for students who need a review before proceeding further. The improvements in this fifth edition evolved out of generous responses from users of the fourth edition. Most of the changes in this edition have been made with an eye toward making the text even more accessible to students with minimal background and to provide a better transition to material covered in subsequent courses, intermediate algebra courses in particular.

PRINCIPAL CHANGES FROM THE FOURTH EDITION

1. **Sets** are treated informally in the text. A more detailed treatment is provided in Appendix A.
2. **Word problems** are more evenly dispersed throughout the text, rather than concentrated in one or two chapters. **Rate–time** and **mixture problems** are deferred until after systems of equations have been intro-

duced and both one- and two-variable methods are used to solve them (Sections 4-7, 4-8).

3. The review of **fractions, decimals,** and **percent** has been moved from the appendix to the text (Sections 3-1, 3-7), and **percent problems** have been added (Section 3-7).

4. The method of **solving equations by factoring** has been moved to an earlier section of the text (Section 6-7) and used thereafter when appropriate.

5. New sections on **solving radical equations** (Section 8-7) and **graphing quadratic equations** (Section 9-4) have been added.

6. **Order and inequality** are introduced briefly and informally early in the text (Sections 1-3, 2-4, 3-4). The more detailed treatment of **inequalities** is consolidated in a new chapter (Chapter 5), which can be covered anytime after Chapter 4. Material in subsequent chapters is not dependent on the material on inequalities.

7. **Calculators** are assumed to be available to students. Many of the problems in the text lend themselves naturally to calculator use and are made easier by such use. However, with the exception of very few exercises, the problems do not *require* use of a calculator and are not marked specifically as "calculator exercises."

8. A new appendix is included to provide an additional approach to **setting up word problems** (Appendix B).

9. The use of interval notation has been deferred to intermediate algebra.

10. Many **exercise sets** have been replaced and/or expanded. More problems involve **fractions** and **decimals**.

11. There are more **worked-out examples** with **matched problems**. There is more **boxed material** for emphasis, and **schematics** have been added for clarity. **Applications** have been kept current.

12. Areas that are a source of **common student errors** are highlighted with a special "caution" symbol.

IMPORTANT FEATURES RETAINED AND EXPANDED FROM THE FOURTH EDITION

1. The text is still **written for student comprehension**. Each concept is illustrated with an example, followed by a parallel problem with an answer (given at the end of the section) so that a student can immediately check his or her understanding of the concept. These follow-up problems also encourage active rather than passive reading of the text.

2. The order of topics has been chosen to provide a **smooth transition from arithmetic to algebra**. The beginning chapters gradually develop algebraic concepts and applications based upon known properties of number systems. The last half of the text extends this development.

3. An **informal style** is used for exposition. Definitions are illustrated with simple examples. There are no formal statements of theorems in this text.

4. The text includes **more than 3,200 carefully selected and graded problems**. The exercises are divided into A, B, and C groupings. The A problems are easy and routine, the B problems more challenging but still emphasizing mechanics, and the C problems a mixture of theoretical and difficult mechanics. In short, the text is designed so that an average or below-average student will be able to experience success and a very capable student will be challenged.

5. The subject matter is related to the real world through many carefully seletcted **realistic applications** from the physical sciences, business and economics, life sciences, and social sciences. Thus, the text is equally suited for students interested in any of these areas.

6. The text continues to use **spiraling techniques** for difficult topics; that is, a topic is introduced in a relatively simple framework and then is returned to one or more times in successively more complex forms. Consider the following:

   Factoring: Sections 1-5, 6-2 to 6-7, 7-1 to 7-3, and 9-1
   Word problems: Sections 1-2, 1-3, 2-7, 2-8, 3-6 to 3-9, 4-7 to 4-9, 5-2, 5-4, 7-4, 8-3, 8-7, and 9-6
   Fractional forms: Chapters 3 and 7
   Order and inequality: Sections 1-3, 2-4, 3-4, and Chapter 5

   The use of this spiraling technique continues into the companion text *Intermediate Algebra: Structure and Use (Fourth Edition).*

7. **Answers** to all chapter review exercises and to all odd-numbered problems from the other exercises are in the back of the book.

8. **Historical comments** are included for interest.

9. **Chapter review sections** include a summary of the chapter with all important terms and symbols, and a comprehensive review exercise. Answers to all review exercises are included in the back of the book and are keyed (with numbers in italics) to corresponding text sections.

ADDITIONAL STUDENT AIDS

1. **Common student errors** are clearly identified at places where they naturally occur (see Sections 2-7, 3-3, 3-4, 3-5).

2. **Think boxes** (dashed boxes) are used to enclose steps that are usually performed mentally (see Sections 1-4, 1-5, 2-6, 2-7).

3. **Annotation** of examples and developments is found throughout the text to help students through critical stages (see Sections 1-2, 2-4, 2-6, 2-7).

4. **Functional use of a second color** guides students through critical steps (see Sections 1-5, 2-6, 2-7).

5. **Summaries** of formulas and symbols (keyed to the sections in which they are introduced) and the metric system are inside the front and back covers of the text for convenient reference.

6. A **solutions manual** is available at a nominal cost through a bookstore. The manual includes detailed solutions to all odd-numbered problems and all chapter review exercises.

INSTRUCTOR'S AIDS

This supplements package contains a wide and varied assortment of useful instructor's aids. They include:

1. A **student's solutions manual** contains detailed solutions to every chapter review exercise as well as all other odd-numbered problems. This supplement is available to students at a nominal fee.
2. An **answer manual** (which slips inside the back of the text) contains answers to the even-numbered problems not answered in the text. This supplement is available to adopters without charge.
3. An **instructor's resource manual** provides sample tests (chapter, midterm, and final), transparency masters, and additional teaching suggestions and assistance.
4. A **computer testing system** is also available to adopters without cost. This system provides the instructor with numerous test questions from the text. Several test question types are available including multiple choice, open-ended, matching, true-false, and vocabulary. The testing system enables the instructor to find these questions by several different criteria. In addition, instructors may edit their own questions.
5. A printed and bound **test bank** is also available. This bank is a hard copy listing of the questions found in the computerized version.

ERROR CHECK

Because of the careful checking and proofing by a number of very competent people (acting independently), the authors and publisher believe this book to be substantially error-free. If any errors remain, the authors would be grateful if corrections were sent to: Mathematics Editor, College Division, 43rd floor, McGraw-Hill Book Company, 1221 Avenue of the Americas, New York, New York 10020.

ACKNOWLEDGMENTS

In addition to the authors, many others are involved in the publication of a book. The authors wish to thank the many users of the fourth edition for their kind remarks and helpful suggestions that were incorporated into this fifth edition. We particularly wish to thank the following for their detailed reviews: Edward Beardslee, Millersville University; John P. Bibbo, Southwestern College; Barbara Buhr, Fresno City College; Virginia M. Carson, DeKalb College; Norman Cornish, University of Detroit; Thomas M. Green, Contra

Costa College; Richard Langlie, North Hennepin Community College; and Mark Serebransky, Camden County College.

We also wish to thank Fred Safier for his careful preparation of the Solutions Manual accompanying this book; Richard Morel, a developmental editor, for his detailed reading of the manuscript, his many helpful suggestions, and for his work on several of the text's supplements; Sr. Margaret Anne Kraemer, Northern Kentucky University, and Marie B. Jump, Erlanger-Elsmere (KY) School District, for their detailed checking of examples and exercises; Karen Hughes, for her editorial and coordinating work on many of the text's supplements; Laura Gurley, for her coordination of the reviews and manuscript; and Robert Weinstein, mathematics editor, for his support and useful ideas about the series as a whole.

Raymond A. Barnett
Thomas J. Kearns

TO
THE STUDENT

The following suggestions will help you get the most out of this book and your efforts.

As you study the text we suggest a five-step process. For each section:

1. Read the mathematical development.
2. Work through the illustrative example. } Repeat the 1-2-3 cycle until the section is finished.
3. Work the matched problem.
4. Review the main ideas in the section.
5. Work the assigned exercises at the end of the section.

All of this should be done with plenty of paper, pencils, and a wastebasket at hand. In fact, no mathematics text should be read without pencil and paper in hand; mathematics is not a spectator sport. Just as you cannot learn to swim by watching someone else, you cannot learn mathematics simply by reading worked examples—you must work problems, lots of them.

If you have difficulty with the course, then, in addition to doing the regular assignments, spend more time on the examples and matched problems and work more A exercises, even if they are not assigned. If the A exercises continue to be difficult for you, see your instructor. If you find the course too easy, then work more C exercises, even if they are not assigned. If the C exercises are consistently easy for you, you are probably ready to start intermediate algebra. See your instructor.

Raymond A. Barnett
Thomas J. Kearns

ELEMENTARY ALGEBRA
Structure and Use

1

NATURAL NUMBERS

Arithmetic, as you have studied it thus far in school, involves numbers, certain operations on numbers, and problems in which these operations are used. The numbers involved are whole numbers $0, 1, 2, \ldots$, fractions such as $\frac{1}{2}, \frac{1}{3}, \frac{2}{3}, \ldots$, negatives of these, and perhaps other numbers such as $\sqrt{2}$ or π. The operations are the familiar operations of addition, subtraction, multiplication, division, and possibly the taking of square roots.

Algebra extends the concepts of arithmetic. In addition to specific numbers, algebra also involves symbols that represent unspecified or unknown numbers. These objects—numbers and symbols—are manipulated by the same basic operations used in arithmetic.

When arithmetic is extended to algebra, where the objects manipulated are not just specific numbers but unknown quantities as well, a wider range of problems can be attacked. For example, arithmetic alone can solve the following problem:

A rectangular field is 110 yards long and 65 yards wide. What is its area?

You can routinely calculate the area to be 7,150 square yards, by multiplying 110 by 65. A problem only slightly different, however, requires an algebraic approach:

A rectangular field is twice as long as it is wide and has area 6,962 square yards. What are its dimensions?

The answer, that the field is 59 yards wide by 118 yards long, is unlikely to be found quickly by guessing and arithmetic. It is, however, easily found by using simple algebra.

In this text you will encounter not only the basic objects and operations of algebra, but also many practical problems in which these objects and operations are used in their solutions. Since algebra uses many kinds of numbers, and symbols for these numbers, it is important that we go back and take a careful look at some of the properties of numbers that you may have previously taken for granted. We begin in this chapter using only the counting numbers $1, 2, 3, \ldots$. Algebraic ideas and methods will be extended to the integers $\ldots, -2, -1, 0, 1, 2, \ldots$ in Chapter 2 and to fractions and the rational numbers in Chapter 3.

1-1
THE SET OF NATURAL NUMBERS

■ The Set of Natural Numbers
■ Important Subsets of the Set of Natural Numbers
■ Least Common Multiple

We begin our development of algebra using only the simplest set of numbers, the **counting numbers** 1, 2, 3, ... These numbers are also referred to as the set of **natural numbers**, and the two names can be used interchangeably.

THE SET OF NATURAL NUMBERS

The word "set" here and throughout the text will be used as it is used in everyday language, meaning a collection. We want the collection to have the property that for any given object, it is either in the set or it is not. The word "subset" will also be used informally to mean part, or possibly all, of a set, much as a subcommittee is to a committee. We will often represent a set by listing its **elements** (objects in the collection) between braces { } or by giving it a capital letter name. Symbolically, the set of natural numbers will be represented by the letter N:

$$N = \{1, 2, 3, . . .\} \quad \text{Natural or counting numbers}$$

The three dots tell us that the numbers go on without end, following the pattern indicated by the first three numbers. This is a useful way to represent certain infinite sets. (A set is called a **finite set** if it can be counted and has an end; otherwise it is an **infinite set**.)

Example 1   Select the natural numbers out of the following list:

$$\tfrac{2}{3}, 1, \sqrt{2}, \pi, 5, 7.63, 17, 83\tfrac{7}{8}, 610$$

Solution   1, 5, 17, and 610 are natural numbers.

Problem 1   Select the natural numbers out of the following list: 4, $\tfrac{3}{4}$, 19, 305, $4\tfrac{2}{3}$, 7.32, $\sqrt{3}$.†

Assumption
We assume that you know what natural numbers are, how to add and multiply them, and how to subtract and divide them when the result is a natural number.

† The answers to matched problems are found at the end of a section, just before the exercise set.

You may recall that the results of addition, multiplication, subtraction, and division of numbers are called the **sum**, **product**, **difference**, and **quotient**, respectively.

IMPORTANT SUBSETS OF THE SET OF NATURAL NUMBERS

The set of natural numbers can be separated into two subsets called even numbers and odd numbers. A natural number is an **even number** if it is exactly divisible by 2 (that is, divisible by 2 without a remainder). A natural number is an **odd number** if it is not exactly divisible by 2.

Example 2   Separate the set of natural numbers $\{1, 2, 3, \ldots\}$ into even and odd numbers.

Solution   The set of even numbers: $\{2, 4, 6, \ldots\}$
The set of odd numbers: $\{1, 3, 5, \ldots\}$

Problem 2   Separate the following set into even and odd numbers: $\{8, 13, 7, 32, 57, 625, 532\}$.

When we add or subtract two or more numbers, the numbers are called **terms**; when we multiply two or more numbers, the numbers are called **factors**.

Terms	Factors
↓ ↓ ↓	↓ ↓ ↓
$3 + 5 + 8$	$3 \times 5 \times 8$

In mathematics, at the level of algebra and higher, parentheses ( ) or the dot "·" are usually used in place of the times sign ×, since the times sign is easily confused with the letter x, a letter that finds frequent use in algebra. Thus,

$3 \times 5 \times 8$

$(3)(5)(8)$

$3 \cdot 5 \cdot 8$

all represent the product of 3, 5, and 8.

The natural numbers, excluding 1, can also be separated into two other important subsets called composite numbers and prime numbers. A natural number is a **composite number** if it can be rewritten as a product of two or more natural numbers other than itself and 1 (8 is a composite number, since $8 = 2 \cdot 4$). Stated in a different but equivalent way, a natural number is a composite number if it can be divided exactly (no remainder) by a natural number other than itself and 1 (9 is a composite number, since it is exactly divisible by 3). A natural number, excluding 1, is a **prime number** if it is not a composite number (11 is a prime number, since it cannot be divided exactly by any natural number other than itself or 1). Equivalently, a number is prime if its only factors are 1 and itself. The number 1 is defined to be neither prime or composite. The natural number 2 is the only even prime number. It can be proved that there are infinitely many prime numbers.

Example 3   Separate the set $\{2, 3, 4, \ldots, 18, 19\}$ into prime and composite numbers.

Solution   The numbers 4, 6, 8, 9, 10, 12, 14, 15, 16, and 18 are composite, since

$$4 = 2 \cdot 2 \qquad 6 = 2 \cdot 3 \qquad 8 = 2 \cdot 4 \qquad 9 = 3 \cdot 3$$

$$10 = 2 \cdot 5 \qquad 12 = 3 \cdot 4 \qquad 14 = 2 \cdot 7 \qquad 15 = 3 \cdot 5$$

$$= 2 \cdot 6$$

The remaining numbers 2, 3, 5, 7, 11, 13, 17, and 19 are prime.

Problem 3   Separate the set $\{6, 9, 11, 21, 23, 25, 27, 29\}$ into prime and composite numbers.

A fundamental theorem of arithmetic states that every composite number has, except for order, a unique (one and only one) set of prime factors. A natural number represented as a product of prime factors is said to be **completely factored**.

Example 4   Write each number in a completely factored form:

(A) 8   **(B)** 36   **(C)** 60

Solution   **(A)** $8 = 2 \cdot 4 = 2 \cdot 2 \cdot 2$ We continue factoring using natural numbers
(B) $36 = 6 \cdot 6 = 2 \cdot 3 \cdot 2 \cdot 3$ until we can go no further.

36 factored   36 completely factored

or

$$36 = 4 \cdot 9 = 2 \cdot 2 \cdot 3 \cdot 3$$

or

$$36 = 3 \cdot 12 = 3 \cdot 4 \cdot 3 = 3 \cdot 2 \cdot 2 \cdot 3$$

or

$$36 = 2 \cdot 18 = 2 \cdot 2 \cdot 9 = 2 \cdot 2 \cdot 3 \cdot 3$$

All four ways in which we factored 36 initially lead to the same set of prime factors: two 2s and two 3s. The order in which the factors are written makes no difference.

(C) $60 = 10 \cdot 6 = 2 \cdot 5 \cdot 2 \cdot 3 = 2 \cdot 2 \cdot 3 \cdot 5$

It may be easier to see the factorization schematically:

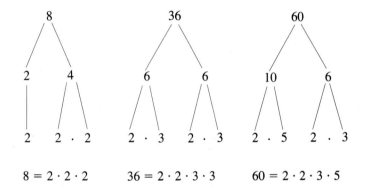

$$8 = 2 \cdot 2 \cdot 2 \qquad 36 = 2 \cdot 2 \cdot 3 \cdot 3 \qquad 60 = 2 \cdot 2 \cdot 3 \cdot 5$$

Problem 4   Write each number in completely factored form:

(A) 12   **(B)** 26   **(C)** 72

In factoring natural numbers it is easiest to look for small prime factors first. Numbers with 2 or 5 as factors are easily recognized, for example, 46 and 65. Also, it is useful to note that a number is exactly divisible by 3 when the sum of its digits is divisible by 3. For example, 51 and 177 are each divisible by 3, since $5 + 1 = 6$ and $1 + 7 + 7 = 15$ are each divisible by 3:

$$51 = 3 \cdot 17 \qquad \text{and} \qquad 177 = 3 \cdot 59$$

LEAST COMMON MULTIPLE

We can use the prime factors of numbers to aid us in finding the least common multiple (LCM) of two or more natural numbers, a process we will need to know later when dealing with fractions and certain types of equations.

The **least common multiple** of two or more natural numbers is defined to be the smallest natural number exactly divisible by each of the numbers. Often one can find the LCM by inspection. For example, the LCM of 3 and 4 is 12, since 12 is the smallest natural number exactly divisible by 3 and 4. But what is the LCM of 15 and 18?

One way to proceed is to list the multiples of 15 and the multiples of 18, and then take the smallest number that occurs on both lists:

Multiples of 15: 15, 30, 45, 60, 75, **90**, 105, 120, . . .

Multiples of 18: 18, 36, 54, 72, **90**, 108, 126, . . .

We see that 90 is the LCM of 15 and 18. For larger numbers, however, this process is impractical. The following method will serve us better and will be more useful in algebraic problems.

To find the LCM of 15 and 18, we start by writing 15 and 18 in completely factored forms:

$$15 = 3 \cdot 5 \qquad 18 = 2 \cdot 9 = 2 \cdot 3 \cdot 3$$

The different prime factors are 2, 3, and 5. The most that 2 appears in any one factorization is once; the most that 3 appears in any one factorization is twice; and the most that 5 appears is once. The LCM will contain one 2, two 3s, and one 5.

$$\text{LCM of 15 and } 18 = 2 \cdot 3 \cdot 3 \cdot 5 = 90$$

and 90 is the smallest natural number exactly divisible by 15 and 18.

The method is summarized as follows:

Finding the LCM

1. Factor each number in the set completely.
2. Identify the different prime factors.
3. The LCM contains each different prime factor as many times as the most number of times it appears in any factorization of the original numbers.

Example 5   Find the LCM for 8, 6, and 9.

Solution   First, write each number as a product of prime factors:

$$8 = 2 \cdot 2 \cdot 2 \qquad 6 = 2 \cdot 3 \qquad 9 = 3 \cdot 3$$

The different prime factors are 2 and 3. The most that 2 appears in any one factorization is three times, and the most that 3 appears in any one factorization is twice; the LCM will contain three 2s and two 3s.

$$LCM = 2 \cdot 2 \cdot 2 \cdot 3 \cdot 3 = 72$$

and 72 is the smallest natural number exactly divisible by 8, 6, and 9.

Problem 5   Find the LCM for 10, 12, and 15.

ANSWERS TO
MATCHED PROBLEMS
1. 4, 19, 305   **2.** Even: 8, 32, 532;   odd: 13, 7, 57, 625
3. Composite: 6, 9, 21, 25, 27;   prime: 11, 23, 29
4. $12 = 2 \cdot 2 \cdot 3$; $26 = 2 \cdot 13$; $72 = 2 \cdot 2 \cdot 2 \cdot 3 \cdot 3$
5. $LCM = 2 \cdot 2 \cdot 3 \cdot 5 = 60$

EXERCISE 1-1   **A**   *Select the natural numbers out of each list.*

  1.   6, 13, 3.5, $\frac{2}{3}$ **2.**   4, $\frac{1}{8}$, 22, 6.5

  3. $3\frac{1}{2}$, 67, 402, 22.35   **4.**   203.17, 63, $\frac{33}{5}$, 999

Separate each list into even and odd numbers.

  5.   9, 14, 28, 33   **6.**   8, 24, 1, 41

  7.   23, 105, 77, 426   **8.**   68, 530, 421, 72

Separate each list into composite and prime numbers.

  9.   2, 6, 9, 11   **10.**   3, 4, 7, 15

11.   12, 17, 23, 27   **12.**   16, 19, 25, 39

B   *Let M be the set of natural numbers from 20 to 30 and N the set of natural numbers from 40 to 50. List the following:*

13.   Even numbers in M **14.**   Even numbers in N

15.   Odd numbers in M **16.**   Odd numbers in N

17.   Composite numbers in M **18.**   Composite numbers in N

19.   Prime numbers in M **20.**   Prime numbers in N

Write each of the following composite numbers as a product of prime factors:

21.   10   **22.**   21   **23.**   30   **24.**   90

25. 84	**26.** 72	**27.** 60	**28.** 120
29. 108	**30.** 112	**31.** 210	**32.** 252

Find the LCM for each group of numbers.

33. 9, 12	**34.** 9, 15	**35.** 6, 16
36. 12, 16	**37.** 3, 8, 12	**38.** 4, 6, 18
39. 4, 10, 15	**40.** 10, 12, 9	**41.** 10, 15, 18
42. 35, 66	**43.** 98, 110	**44.** 20, 33, 75
45. 42, 63, 90	**46.** 16, 40, 130	**47.** 35, 56, 100, 140

C   *Write each of the following numbers as a product of prime factors:*

48. 286	**49.** 560	**50.** 910	**51.** 2,200
51. 1,309	**53.** 1,386	**54.** 1,708	

55. Is every even number a prime number? Is every odd number a prime number? Is every prime number an odd number? Is every prime number except 2 an odd number?

56. Is every even number a composite number? Is every odd number a composite number? Is every even number except 2 a composite number?

Tell whether each of the following sets is finite or infinite:

57. The set of natural numbers between 1 and 1 million

58. The set of even numbers between 1 and 1 million

59. The set of all natural numbers

60. The set of all even numbers

61. The set of all the grains of sand on all the beaches in the world

1-2
ALGEBRAIC EXPRESSIONS—THEIR FORMULATION AND EVALUATION

- Variables and Constants
- Algebraic Expressions
- Evaluating Algebraic Expressions
- From English to Algebra

Consider the statement: "The perimeter of a rectangle is twice its length plus twice its width." If we let

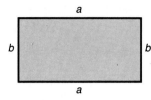

P = Perimeter

a = Length

b = Width

then the familiar formula

$$P = 2 \cdot a + 2 \cdot b \qquad \qquad (1)$$

has the same meaning as the original statement, but with increased clarity and a substantial reduction in the number of symbols used.

VARIABLES AND CONSTANTS

In the perimeter formula (1), the three letters P, a, and b can be replaced with many different numerals, depending on the size of the rectangle; hence, these letters are called variables. The symbol "2" names only one number and is consequently called a constant. In general, a **constant** is defined to be any symbol that names one particular number; a **variable** is a symbol that can be replaced by a number from a set containing more than one number. This latter set is called the **replacement set** for the variable. It is important to remember that the variable represents an unspecified number in the replacement set and as such is manipulated as one of these numbers.

When variables are involved in multiplication, the dot "·" is usually omitted. Thus $2a$ means 2 times a, $2b$ means 2 times b, and the perimeter formula (1) is usually written in the form $P = 2a + 2b$.

Example 6   List the constants and variables in the formula

$$F = \frac{9}{5}C + 32$$

for the conversion of Celsius degrees to Fahrenheit degrees.

Solution   The constants are $\frac{9}{5}$ and 32, the variables C and F.

Problem 6   List the constants and variables in each formula:

(A) $P = 4s$ Perimeter of a square
(B) $A = s^2$ Area of a square [*Note:* $s^2 = s \cdot s$]

Note: A number of useful formulas are listed inside the back cover of the text for convenient reference.

The introduction of variables into mathematics occurred about A.D. 1600.

A French mathematician, François Vieta (1540–1603), is singled out as the one mainly responsible for this new idea. Many mark this point as the beginning of modern mathematics.

ALGEBRAIC EXPRESSIONS

An **algebraic expression** is a symbolic form involving constants; variables; mathematical operations such as addition, subtraction, multiplication, and division (other operations will be added later); and grouping symbols such as parentheses ( ), brackets [ ], and braces { }. For example,

$$8 + 7 \qquad 3 \cdot 5 - 6 \qquad 12 - 2(8 - 5)$$

$$3x - 5y \qquad 8(x - 3y) \qquad 3\{x - 2[x + 4(x + 3)]\}$$

are all algebraic expressions.

Just as with numbers themselves, two or more algebraic expressions joined by plus (+) or minus (−) signs are called **terms**. Two or more algebraic expressions joined by multiplication are called **factors**.

$5 - 2 \cdot 3$ — Two terms: 5 and 2 · 3; second term has two factors: 2 and 3

$10 + 2(6 - 3)$ — Two terms: 10 and 2(6 − 3); second term has two factors: 2 and (6 − 3)

$x + 3$ — Two terms: x and 3

$2x + 3y - 6z$ — Three terms: 2x, 3y, and 6z; each term has two factors

$5[x - 3(x + 5)]$ — One term: the whole thing; two factors: 5 and [x − 3(x + 5)]; second factor has two terms: x and 3(x + 5)

EVALUATING ALGEBRAIC EXPRESSIONS

When evaluating numerical expressions involving various operations and symbols of grouping, we follow this convention:

Order of Operations

1. Simplify inside the innermost symbols of grouping first, then the next innermost, and so on.
2. Unless grouping symbols indicate otherwise, multiplication and division are performed before addition and subtraction. In either case, we proceed from left to right.

For example, to illustrate rule **1**, $2[3 + (5 - 1)]$ means first subtract 1 from 5, then add 3 to the result, and finally multiply this by 2, thus obtaining 14. As an illustration of rule **2**, the expression $2 + 3 \cdot 5$ means first multiply 3 and 5, then add 2 to the result to obtain 17.

$$2 + 3 \cdot 5 \neq 5 \cdot 5 \qquad 2 + 3 \cdot 5 = 2 + 15 = 17$$

Adding parentheses as grouping symbols, however, changes what the expression means:

$$(2 + 3) \cdot 5 = 5 \cdot 5 = 25 \qquad \text{Here the ( ) tell us to do the addition } 2 + 3 \text{ before multiplying.}$$

The grouping symbols [ ] and { } may be used in place of parentheses ( ); they mean the same thing.

Example 7   Evaluate each expression:

(A) $8 - 2 \cdot 3$ **(B)** $9 - 2(5 - 3)$
(C) $(9 - 2)(5 - 3)$ **(D)** $2[12 - 3(8 - 5)]$

Solution   **(A)** $8 - 2 \cdot 3 = 8 - 6$
                   $= 2$

Multiplication precedes addition and subtraction. *Note:* $8 - 2 \cdot 3 \neq 6 \cdot 3$

(B) $9 - 2(5 - 3) = 9 - 2 \cdot 2$
                    $= 9 - 4$
                    $= 5$

Perform operation inside parentheses first, then multiply, then subtract. *Note:* $9 - 2(5 - 3) \neq 7(5 - 3)$

(C) $(9 - 2)(5 - 3) = 7 \cdot 2$
                     $= 14$

Parentheses first, then multiply. Note how parts (B) and (C) differ.

(D) $2[12 - 3(8 - 5)] = 2[12 - 3 \cdot 3]$
                        $= 2(12 - 9)$
                        $= 2 \cdot 3$
                        $= 6$

Parentheses first.

Parentheses ( ) can always replace brackets [ ] and braces { } when the latter are used as symbols of grouping.

Problem 7   Evaluate each expression:

(A) $2 \cdot 10 - 3 \cdot 5$ **(B)** $11 - 3(7 - 5)$
(C) $(11 - 3)(7 - 5)$ **(D)** $6[13 - 2(14 - 8)]$

To evaluate an algebraic expression when number values of the variables are given means to replace the variables by the given values and evaluate the resulting numerical expression. Replacing the variables by numbers is often called **substituting** the numbers for the variables. The same rules for interpreting order of operation given above for numerical expressions apply also to algebraic expressions, since the variables represent numbers.

Example 8   Evaluate each algebraic expression for $x = 10$ and $y = 3$.

  (A) $2x - 3y$ **(B)** $x - 3(2y - 4)$
  (C) $(x - 3)(2y - 4)$ **(D)** $5[32 - x(x - 7)]$

Solution   Substitute $x = 10$ and $y = 3$ into each expression and then evaluate, following the order of operations described above.

  (A) $2x - 3y$
   $2(10) - 3(3) = 20 - 9 = 11$

  (B) $x - 3(2y - 4)$
   $10 - 3(2 \cdot 3 - 4) = 10 - 3(6 - 4) = 10 - 3 \cdot 2 = 10 - 6 = 4$

  (C) $(x - 3)(2y - 4)$
   $(10 - 3)(2 \cdot 3 - 4) = 7(6 - 4) = 7 \cdot 2 = 14$
   Note how parts (B) and (C) differ.

  (D) $5[32 - x(x - 7)]$
   $5[32 - 10(10 - 7)] = 5(32 - 10 \cdot 3) = 5(32 - 30) = 5 \cdot 2 = 10$

Problem 8   Evaluate each algebraic expression for $x = 12$ and $y = 3$:

  (A) $x - 3y$ **(B)** $x - 4(y - 1)$
  (C) $(x - 4)(y - 1)$ **(D)** $3[x - 2(x - 9)]$

Example 9   How far can you travel in 13 hours at 37 kilometers per hour? (Recall the formula "distance equals rate times time," $d = rt$.)

Solution   Here we understand:

   "How far" asks for distance d.
   13 hours gives time t.
   37 kilometers per hour gives the rate (or speed) r.

   We use the formula $d = rt$ with the variable r replaced by 37 and the variable t replaced by 13 to obtain

   $d = 37 \cdot 13 = 481$ kilometers

Problem 9 How many gallons can a water pump pump in 8 minutes if it pumps at a rate of 15 gallons per minute? Use $Q = rt$, where Q represents quantity, r rate, and t time.

FROM ENGLISH TO ALGEBRA

English is a complex language, and it is impossible to summarize briefly all the phrases that translate to algebraic expressions. Table 1 lists some of the more common ones.

TABLE 1

PHRASE	EXAMPLE	ALGEBRAIC EXPRESSION
Addition		
"the sum of"	the sum of 3 and 5	$3 + 5$
"plus"	7 plus 4	$7 + 4$
"added to"	2 added to 6	$6 + 2$
"more than"	8 more than 4	$4 + 8$
Subtraction		
"the difference of"	the difference of 5 and 3	$5 - 3$
"minus"	7 minus 4	$7 - 4$
"subtracted from"	2 subtracted from 6	$6 - 2$
"less than"	4 less than 8	$8 - 4$
Multiplication		
"the product of"	the product of 5 and 3	$5 \cdot 3$
"times"	7 times 4	$7 \cdot 4$
"multiplied by"	2 multiplied by 6	$2 \cdot 6$
"of"	one-half of 10	$\frac{1}{2} \cdot 10$
"times the quantity"	2 times the quantity 3 plus 4	$2(3 + 4)$
Division		
"the quotient of"	the quotient of 6 and 3	$6 \div 3$ or $6/3$ or $\frac{6}{3}$
"over"	8 over 4	$8 \div 4$ or $8/4$ or $\frac{8}{4}$
"divided by"	10 divided by 2	$10 \div 2$ or $10/2$ or $\frac{10}{2}$

Example 10 If x represents a natural number, write an algebraic expression that represents each of the expressed numbers:

(A) A number 3 times as large as x
(B) A number 3 more than x

(C) A number 7 less than the product of 4 and x
(D) A number 3 times the quantity 2 less than x

Solution   **(A)** $3x$ "Times" corresponds to "multiply."
(B) $x + 3$ "More than" corresponds to "added to."
(C) $4x - 7$ (not $7 - 4x$)   "Less than" corresponds to "subtracted from."
(D) $3(x - 2)$ [not $3(2 - x)$ and also not $3x - 2$]

Problem 10   If y represents a natural number, write an algebraic expression that represents each of the expressed numbers:

(A) A number 7 times as large as y
(B) A number 7 less than y
(C) A number 9 more than the product of 4 and y
(D) A number 5 times the quantity 4 less than y

ANSWERS TO   **6. (A)** Constants: 4;   variables: P, s
MATCHED PROBLEMS   **(B)** Constants: 2;   variables: A, s
7. (A) 5   **(B)** 5   **(C)** 16   **(D)** 6
8. (A) 3   **(B)** 4   **(C)** 16   **(D)** 18
9. 120 gallons
10. (A) $7y$ **(B)** $y - 7$ **(C)** $4y + 9$ **(D)** $5(y - 4)$

EXERCISE 1-2   A   *Evaluate each expression.*

1. $7 + 3 \cdot 2$ **2.** $5 + 6 \cdot 3$ **3.** $8 - 2 \cdot 3$

4. $20 - 5 \cdot 3$ **5.** $7 \cdot 6 - 5 \cdot 5$ **6.** $8 \cdot 9 - 6 \cdot 11$

7. $(2 + 9) - (3 + 6)$ **8.** $(8 - 3) + (7 - 2)$ **9.** $8 + 2(7 + 1)$

10. $3 + 8(2 + 5)$ **11.** $(8 + 2)(7 + 1)$ **12.** $(3 + 8)(2 + 5)$

13. $10 - 3(7 - 4)$ **14.** $20 - 5(12 - 9)$ **15.** $(10 - 3)(7 - 4)$

16. $(20 - 5)(12 - 9)$ **17.** $12 - 2(7 - 5)$ **18.** $15 - 3(9 - 5)$

Evaluate each algebraic expression for $x = 8$ and $y = 3$.

19. $x + 2$ **20.** $y + 5$ **21.** $x - y$

22. $22 - x$ **23.** $x - 2y$ **24.** $6y - x$

25. $3x - 2y$ **26.** $9y - xy$ **27.** $y + 3(x - 5)$

28. $5 + y(x - y)$ **29.** $x - 2(y - 1)$ **30.** $x - y(x - 7)$

If x and y represent natural numbers, write an algebraic expression that represents each of the following numbers:

31. A number 5 times as large as x

32. A number 7 times as large as y

33. A number 5 more than x **34.** A number 12 more than y

35. A number 5 less than x **36.** A number 8 less than y

37. A number x less than 5   **38.** A number y less than 8

B   *Identify the constants and variables in each algebraic expression.*

39. $A = \frac{1}{2}bh$ *Area of a triangle*

40. $A = ab$ *Area of a rectangle*

41. $d = rt$ *Distance-rate-time formula*

42. $C = \frac{5}{9}(F - 32)$ *Fahrenheit-Celsius formula*

43. $I = prt$ *Simple interest*

44. $A = P(1 + rt)$ *Simple interest*

45. $y = 2x + 3$ **46.** $3x + 2y = 5$

47. $3(u + v) + 2u$ **48.** $2(x + 1) + 3(w + 5z)$

In Problems 49–52 find the area and perimeter for each rectangle ($A = ab$ and $P = 2a + 2b$). Example: If $a = 5$ meters and $b = 3$ meters, then $A = 5 \cdot 3 = 15$ square meters and $P = 2 \cdot 5 + 2 \cdot 3 = 10 + 6 = 16$ meters.

49. $a = 6$ centimeters, $b = 3$ centimeters

50. $a = 12$ feet, $b = 4$ feet

51. $a = 10$ kilometers, $b = 8$ kilometers

52. $a = 9$ meters, $b = 6$ meters

Evaluate each expression.

53. $4[15 - 10(9 - 8)]$ **54.** $6[22 - 3(13 - 7)]$

55. $7 \cdot 9 - 6(8 - 3)$ **56.** $5(8 - 3) - 3 \cdot 6$

57. $2[(7 + 2) - (5 - 3)]$ **58.** $6[(8 - 3) + (4 - 2)]$

Evaluate each expression for $w = 2$, $x = 5$, $y = 1$, and $z = 3$.

59. $w(y + z)$ **60.** $wy + wx$

61. $wy + z$ **62.** $y + wz$

63. $(z - y) + (z - w)$ **64.** $4(y + w) - 2z$

65. $2[x + 3(z - y)]$ **66.** $6[(x + z) - 3(z - w)]$

67. How far can you travel in 12 hours at 57 kilometers per hour? $(d = rt)$

68. How far can you travel in 9 hours at 43 kilometers per hour? $(d = rt)$

69. How many words can a typist type in 10 minutes if he or she can type 60 words per minute? $(Q = rt)$

70. How many gallons can a pipe fill in 20 minutes if it fills at the rate of 10 gallons per minute? $(Q = rt)$

If x represents a given natural number, write an algebraic expression that represents each of the following numbers:

71. A number 3 more than twice the given number

72. A number 3 more than the product of 12 and the given number

73. A number 3 less than the product of 12 and the given number

74. A number 3 less than twice the given number

75. A number 3 times the quantity 8 less than the given number

76. A number 6 times the quantity 4 less than the given number

C　*Evaluate each expression.*

77. $3[(6 - 4) + 4 \cdot 3 + 3(1 + 6)]$ **78.** $2[(3 + 2) + 2(7 - 4) + 6 \cdot 2]$

79. $2\{26 - 3[12 - 2(8 - 5)]\}$ **80.** $5\{32 - 5[(10 - 2) - 2 \cdot 3]\}$

81. $6 - \{4 - [3 - (7 - 5)]\}$

82. $1 + (4 - 3\{4 - 3[5 - (1 + 3)]\})$

83. $3[14 - 4(5 - 2)] - \{4 - [8 - 2(5 - 2)]\}$

84. $10 + 9\{8 - 7[6 - 5(4 - 3)] + 2\} - 1$

Evaluate for u = 2, v = 3, w = 4, and x = 5.

85. $2\{w + 2[7 - (u + v)]\}$

86. $3\{(u + v) + 3[x - 2(w - u)] + uv\}$

If t represents an even number, write an algebraic expression that represents each of the following:

87. A number 3 times the first even number larger than t

88. A number 5 times the first even number smaller than t

89. The sum of three consecutive natural numbers starting with t

90. The product of three consecutive natural numbers starting with t

91. The sum of three consecutive even numbers starting with t

92. The sum of three consecutive odd numbers following t

1-3
EQUALITY AND INEQUALITY

- Equality Sign
- Algebraic Equations
- Properties of Equality
- Inequality

In the preceding sections the equality sign ($=$) was used in a number of places. You are probably most familiar with its use in formulas such as

$$d = rt \qquad A = ab \qquad I = prt$$

The equal sign is very important in mathematics, and you will be using it frequently. Its mathematical meaning, however, is not as obvious as it first might seem. For this reason we are devoting one section of this chapter to this sign so that you will be able to use it correctly from the beginning.

EQUALITY SIGN

An **equality sign ($=$)** between two expressions asserts that the two expressions are names or descriptions of exactly the same object. The **inequality sign $\neq$** means "is not equal to." Statements involving the use of an equality or inequality sign may be true or they may be false:

$18 - 3 = 5 \cdot 3$ True statement $7 \cdot 8 = 15$ False statement

$11 - 7 = \dfrac{8}{2}$ True statement $7 \cdot 8 \neq 56$ False statement

$11 - 7 \neq \dfrac{8}{2}$ False statement $7 + 8 \neq 16$ True statement

It is interesting to note that the equality sign did not occur until rather late in history—the sixteenth century. It was introduced by the English mathematician Robert Recorde (1510–1558).

ALGEBRAIC EQUATIONS

If two algebraic expressions involving at least one variable are joined with an equal sign, the resulting form is called an **algebraic equation**. The following are algebraic equations in one or more variables:

$$x + 3 = 8 \qquad x + 2 = 2 + x \qquad 2x + 3y = 12$$

Formulas such as

$$P = 2a + 2b \qquad F = \frac{9}{5}C + 32 \qquad P = 4s$$

are also algebraic equations. Since a variable represents unspecified constants, an algebraic equation is neither true nor false as it stands; it does not become true or false until the variable has been replaced by a constant. The set of constants for which an equation becomes true upon replacement of the variables is called the **solution set** of the equation. Formulating algebraic equations is an important step in solving certain types of practical problems using algebraic methods. We address ourselves to this topic now.

Example 11 Translate each statement into an algebraic equation using only one variable:

(A) 15 is 9 more than a certain number.
(B) 3 times a certain number is 7 less than twice the number.

Solution **(A)** 15 $\boxed{\text{is}}$ 9 $\boxed{\text{more than}}$ $\boxed{\text{a certain number}}$

added to

$$15 = 9 \qquad + \qquad\qquad x$$

Thus,

$$15 = 9 + x \qquad \text{or} \qquad 15 = x + 9$$

Note that $9 + x$ and $x + 9$ represent the same number. This property of addition will be discussed further in the next section.

(B) 3 $\boxed{\text{times}}$ $\boxed{\text{a certain number}}$ $\boxed{\text{is}}$ 7 $\boxed{\text{less than}}$ $\boxed{\text{twice the number}}$

$$3 \qquad \cdot \qquad\qquad x \qquad\qquad = 7 \text{ subtracted from} \qquad 2x$$

$$3x = 2x - 7 \qquad (\text{not } 7 - 2x)$$

Compare the symbolic and verbal forms on the right side carefully and note how 7 and $2x$ reverse. Note that $2x - 7$ and $7 - 2x$ in general do not represent the same number.

Problem 11   Repeat Example 11 for

(A) 8 is 5 more than a certain number.
(B) 6 is 4 less than a certain number.
(C) 4 times a certain number is 3 less than twice the number.
(D) If 12 is added to a certain number, the sum is twice a number that is 3 less than the certain number.

Example 12   If x represents an even number, write an algebraic equation that is equivalent to "the sum of three consecutive even numbers is 84."

Solution   The set of even numbers is

$$\{2, 4, 6, \ldots, x, \ldots\}$$

where x is an unspecified even number. We note that even numbers increase two at a time; hence,

$$\left.\begin{array}{l} x \\ x + 2 \\ x + 4 \end{array}\right\}$$ represent three consecutive (one following the other) even numbers, starting with x. Note that $x + 4 = (x + 2) + 2$.

Thus,

$$\left(\begin{array}{c} \text{The sum of three} \\ \text{consecutive even numbers} \end{array}\right) \text{ is 84}$$

$$x + (x + 2) + (x + 4) = 84$$

Problem 12   If x represents an odd number, write an algebraic equation that is equivalent to "the sum of four consecutive odd numbers is 160."

PROPERTIES OF EQUALITY

From the logical meaning of the equality sign, a number of rules or properties can easily be established for its use. We state these properties below for completeness and will return to them later when we discuss equations. They control a great deal of the activity related to the solving of equations.

If a, b, and c are names of objects, then

1. $a = a$ Reflexive property
2.   If $a = b$, then $b = a$.   Symmetric property

3. If $a = b$ and $b = c$, then $a = c$.   Transitive property

4. If $a = b$, then either may replace the other in any expression without changing the truth or falsity of the statement.   Substitution principle

Property 2 allows, for example,

$$5 = x \qquad \text{to become} \qquad x = 5$$

and

$$A = P + Prt \qquad \text{to become} \qquad P + Prt = A$$

Property 3 allows us to conclude, for example, that

$$8 - 3 \cdot 2 = 2$$

since

$$\overset{a}{\overbrace{8 - 3 \cdot 2}} = \overset{b}{\overbrace{8 - 6}} \qquad \text{and} \qquad \overset{b}{\overbrace{8 - 6}} = \overset{c}{\overbrace{2}}$$

Therefore,

$$\overset{a}{\overbrace{8 - 3 \cdot 2}} = \overset{c}{\overbrace{2}}$$

Property 4 allows us to conclude, for example, that

$$8 - 3 \cdot 2 = 8 - 6 \qquad \text{since} \qquad 3 \cdot 2 = 6$$

That is, $3 \cdot 2$ in the first expression is replaced, using the substitution principle, by 6 to obtain the second expression.

The importance of the four properties of equality will not be fully appreciated until we start solving equations and simplifying algebraic expressions.

INEQUALITY

There is a natural order on the set of counting numbers in the sense that if two numbers are not equal, then one of the two is larger than the other. We assume that you know what it means to say that 117 is greater than 68, or that 14 is less than 53. We will use the **inequality symbols** $<$ to represent "is less than" and $>$ to represent "is greater than." The symbol $\leq$ means "is less than or equal to"; similarly, $\geq$ means "is greater than or equal to." The following are all true statements:

$$117 > 68 \qquad 117 \geq 68 \qquad 117 \geq 117$$

$$14 < 53 \qquad 14 \leq 53 \qquad 14 \leq 14$$

The statement $14 \leq 53$ is true, since $14 < 53$: a statement involving $\leq$ is true if either the $<$ part or the $=$ part is true; similarly for $\geq$. The notation is summarized:

$a < b$	a is less than b
$a > b$	a is greater than b
$a \leq b$	a is less than or equal to b
$a \geq b$	a is greater than or equal to b

While it may be clear that $117 > 68$ and $14 < 53$, similar statements in the number systems to be considered in the next chapters will be less obvious. A more careful definition of the ordering of numbers will be necessary. A key idea will be that 117 is greater than 68 because there is a number greater than zero, namely 49, such that $68 + 49 = 117$.

The use of the word "less" can be a source of confusion, so it must be used carefully. It is important to distinguish between the statement "2 is less than 7" and the expression "2 less than 7." The first is a true statement; the second is simply a way of representing the number 5. The mathematical notation avoids the possible confusion:

$2 < 7$ is a statement

$7 - 2$ is a number

ANSWERS TO
MATCHED PROBLEMS

11. **(A)** $8 = 5 + x$ or $8 = x + 5$ **(B)** $6 = x - 4$ (not $6 = 4 - x$)
(C) $4x = 2x - 3$ **(D)** $x + 12 = 2(x - 3)$
12. $x + (x + 2) + (x + 4) + (x + 6) = 160$

EXERCISE 1-3 **A** *Indicate which of the following are true (T) or false (F):*

1. $10 - 6 = 4$ **2.** $12 + 7 = 19$ **3.** $6 \cdot 9 = 56$

4. $8 \cdot 7 = 54$ **5.** $12 - 9 \neq 2$ **6.** $15 - 8 \neq 6$

7. $\text{II} = 2$ **8.** $\text{IX} \neq 11$ **9.** $9 - 2 \cdot 3 \neq 21$

10. $4 + 2 \cdot 5 \neq 30$ **11.** $32 > 19$ **12.** $47 \geq 43$

13. $15 \leq 10$ **14.** $22 < 32$

Translate each statement into an algebraic equation using x as the only variable.

15. 5 is 3 more than a certain number.

16. 10 is 7 more than a certain number.

17. 8 is 3 less than a certain number.

18. 14 is 6 less than a certain number.

19. 18 is 3 times a certain number.

20. 25 is 5 times a certain number.

B   **21.** 49 is 7 more than twice a certain number.

22. 27 is 3 more than 6 times a certain number.

23. 52 is 8 less than 5 times a certain number.

24. 103 is 7 less than 10 times a certain number.

25. 4 times a given number is 3 more than 3 times that number.

26. 8 times a number is 20 more than 4 times the number.

27. 5 more than a certain number is 3 times the quantity that is 4 less than the certain number.

28. 6 less than a certain number is 5 times the quantity that is 7 more than the certain number.

29. The sum of three consecutive natural numbers is 90.

30. The sum of four consecutive natural numbers is 54.

31. The sum of two consecutive even numbers is 54.

32. The sum of three consecutive odd numbers is 105.

APPLICATIONS   C   **33.** Pythagoras found that the octave chord could be produced by placing the movable bridge so that a taut string is divided into two parts with the longer piece twice the length of the shorter piece (see the figure). If the total string is 54 centimeters long and we let x represent the length of the shorter piece, write an equation relating the lengths of the two pieces and the total length of the string.

Monochord

34. A steel rod 7 meters long is cut into two pieces so that the longer piece is 1 meter less than twice the length of the shorter piece. Write an equation relating the lengths of the two pieces with the total length.

35. In a rectangle of area 50 square centimeters the length is 10 centimeters more than the width. Write an equation relating the area with the length and the width.

36. In a rectangle of area 75 square yards the length is 5 more than 3 times the width. Write an equation relating the area with the length and the width.

1-4
PROPERTIES OF ADDITION AND MULTIPLICATION; EXPONENTS

- Commutative Properties
- Associative Properties
- Simplifying Algebraic Expressions
- Exponents: An Introduction

Algebra in many ways can be thought of as a game—a game that requires the manipulation of symbols to change algebraic expressions from one form to another. As is the case in any game, to play, one must know the rules.

In this section we will discuss some of the basic rules in the "game of algebra." These, along with others that we will add later, govern the manipulation of symbols that represent numbers in algebra.

COMMUTATIVE PROPERTIES

We must now discuss a couple of basic properties of natural numbers that you have been using in arithmetic for a long time. Assume we are given the set of natural numbers

$$N = \{1, 2, 3, \ldots\}$$

and the operations

$$+ \quad - \quad \cdot \quad \div$$

Is the result of applying any of these operations on any two natural numbers the same no matter what order the numbers are written in? For example, which of the following are true?

$8 + 4 = 4 + 8$ True

$8 - 4 = 4 - 8$ False ($8 - 4 = 4$; $4 - 8$ hasn't been defined yet, but it is -4, not 4)

$8 \cdot 4 = 4 \cdot 8$ True

$8 \div 4 = 4 \div 8$ False ($8 \div 4 = 2$; $4 \div 8$ has not been defined yet but it is $\frac{1}{2}$, not 2)

We see that the first and third equations are true and the second and fourth are false. In fact, we will not be able to find two natural numbers for which the order in which we add or multiply them will make a difference. We say that the natural numbers are **commutative** relative to addition and multiplication.

By this we simply mean that the order of operation in addition or in multiplication doesn't matter ($2 + 3 = 3 + 2$ and $2 \cdot 3 = 3 \cdot 2$). More formally, we state:

Commutative Properties

For all natural numbers a and b

$$a + b = b + a \qquad 3 + 5 = 5 + 3 \qquad \text{The order in addition doesn't matter.}$$

$$ab = ba \qquad 3 \cdot 5 = 5 \cdot 3 \qquad \text{The order in multiplication doesn't matter.}$$

On the other hand, subtraction and division are not commutative. The order in subtraction and division does matter.

Example 13   If x and y are natural numbers, use the commutative properties for addition and multiplication to write each of the following expressions in an equivalent form:

(A) $x + 7$ **(B)** $y5$ **(C)** yx **(D)** $3 + 5x$

Solution   **(A)** $x + 7 = 7 + x$ Each example illustrates the use of a commutative property.
(B) $y5 = 5y$ Notice that the order is reversed in each case.
(C) $yx = xy$
(D) $3 + 5x = 5x + 3$ and also $3 + 5x = 3 + x5$

Problem 13   If a and b are natural numbers, use the commutative properties for addition and multiplication to write each of the following expressions in an equivalent form:

(A) $a + 3$ **(B)** $b5$ **(C)** ba **(D)** $b + a$

ASSOCIATIVE PROPERTIES

Now we turn to another property of the natural numbers. Suppose you are given the following four problems:

$$8 + 4 + 2 \qquad 8 - 4 - 2 \qquad 8 \cdot 4 \cdot 2 \qquad 8 \div 4 \div 2$$

We notice in the addition problem that if we add 4 to 8 first and then add 2, we get the same result as adding 2 to 4 first and then adding this sum to 8. That is,

$$(8 + 4) + 2 = 8 + (4 + 2) \qquad \begin{cases} (8 + 4) + 2 = 12 + 2 = 14 \\ 8 + (4 + 2) = 8 + 6 = 14 \end{cases}$$

It appears that grouping the terms relative to addition doesn't seem to make a difference. Does grouping make a difference for any of the other three operations? That is,

Does $(8 - 4) - 2 = 8 - (4 - 2)$?

Does $(8 \cdot 4) \cdot 2 = 8 \cdot (4 \cdot 2)$?

Does $(8 \div 4) \div 2 = 8 \div (4 \div 2)$?

Doing the arithmetic on both sides of each equal sign (you should do this), we see that the only equation that is true is the one involving multiplication. Once again we will not be able to find even one case where changing grouping relative to addition or relative to multiplication will make a difference. We say that the natural numbers are **associative** relative to addition and multiplication. By this we simply mean that we may insert or remove parentheses at will relative to addition and insert or remove parentheses at will relative to multiplication. More formally, we state:

Associative Properties

For all natural numbers a, b, and c

$$(a + b) + c = a + (b + c)$$ $(3 + 2) + 5 = 3 + (2 + 5)$ Grouping doesn't matter in addition.

$$(ab)c = a(bc)$$ $(4 \cdot 3)2 = 4(3 \cdot 2)$ Grouping doesn't matter in multiplication.

Because of the associative properties, we can write the sum of three natural numbers, a, b, and c simply as $a + b + c$:

$$a + b + c = a + (b + c) = (a + b) + c$$

Similarly, the product can be written as abc:

$$abc = a(bc) = (ab)c$$

On the other hand, subtraction and division are not associative. Grouping relative to both of these operations does matter $[(8 - 4) - 2 \neq 8 - (4 - 2)$ and $(8 \div 4) \div 2 \neq 8 \div (4 \div 2)]$. The associative properties can be used to transform algebraic expressions into other equivalent forms.

Example 14 If x, y, and z are natural numbers, replace each question mark with an appropriate algebraic expression:

(A) $(x + 3) + 5 = x + (?)$ **(B)** $2(3x) = (?)x$

(C) $(x + y) + z = x + (?)$ **(D)** $(xy)z = x(?)$

Solution   **(A)** $(x + 3) + 5 \boxed{= (x + (3 + 5)}^{\dagger}$

$$= x + (3 + 5) = x + 8$$

(B) $2(3x) \boxed{= (2 \cdot (3)x)} = (2 \cdot 3)x = 6x$

(C) $(x + y) + z \boxed{= (x + (y) + z)} = x + (y + z)$

(D) $(xy)z \boxed{= (x(y)z)} = x(yz)$

> Notice how the parentheses are moved in each case. No order is changed. Each example illustrates the use of an associative property.

Problem 14   If a, b, and c are natural numbers, replace each question mark with an appropriate algebraic expression:

(A) $(a + 5) + 7 = a + (?)$ **(B)** $5(9b) = (?)b$

(C) $(a + b) + c = a + (?)$ **(D)** $(ab)c = a(?)$

SIMPLIFYING ALGEBRAIC EXPRESSIONS

We can use both the associative and commutative properties to simplify

$$(x + 3) + (y + 5) \qquad \text{and} \qquad (3x)(5y)$$

Since only addition is involved in the first example, we can drop the parentheses. Then we can rearrange and regroup the terms to obtain

$$(x + 3) + (y + 5) \boxed{\begin{aligned} &= x + 3 + y + 5 \\ &= x + y + 3 + 5 \end{aligned}}$$
$$= x + y + 8$$

Similarly, since only multiplication is involved in the second example, we can drop the parentheses. Then we can rearrange and regroup the factors to obtain

$$(3x)(5y) \boxed{\begin{aligned} &= 3x5y \\ &= 3 \cdot 5xy \end{aligned}}$$
$$= 15xy$$

It is important to remember that associative and commutative properties are

---

† Dashed boxes are used throughout the text to indicate steps that are usually done mentally.

behind the operations performed in both of these examples. In general, we can state the following:

> **Use of Commutative and Associative Properties— Conclusion**
>
> Relative to addition, commutativity and associativity permit us to change the order of addition at will and insert or remove parentheses as we please. The same thing is true for multiplication, but not for subtraction and division.

Example 15 Remove parentheses and simplify, using commutative and associative properties mentally.

(A) $(a + 5) + (b + 2) + (c + 4)$ (B) $(2x)(3y)(4z)$

Solution (A) $(a + 5) + (b + 2) + (c + 4)$

$= a + 5 + b + 2 + c + 4$

$= a + b + c + 5 + 2 + 4$

$= a + b + c + 11$

Since only addition is involved, we can (mentally) rearrange and regroup the variables and the constants to obtain $a + b + c + 11$.

(B) $(2x)(3y)(4z) = 2x3y4z$

$= (2 \cdot 3 \cdot 4)(xyz)$

$= 24xyz$

Since only multiplication is involved, we can (mentally) rearrange and regroup the variables and the constants to obtain $24xyz$.

Problem 15 Simplify as in Example 15:

(A) $(u + 4) + (v + 5) + (w + 3)$ (B) $(4m)(8n)(2p)$

EXPONENTS: AN INTRODUCTION

Exponent forms play an important role in algebra and we will be using them almost daily. We start by defining

$b^2 = bb$ $2^2 = 2 \cdot 2 = 4$

Thus, $3^2 = 3 \cdot 3 = 9$, $6^2 = 6 \cdot 6 = 36$, and so on. There is obviously no reason to stop here: you no doubt can guess how b^3, 2^3, b^4, and 2^4 should be defined. If you guessed

$b^3 = bbb$ $2^3 = 2 \cdot 2 \cdot 2 = 8$

$b^4 = bbbb$ $2^4 = 2 \cdot 2 \cdot 2 \cdot 2 = 16$

then you have anticipated the following general definition of b^n, where n is any natural number and b is any number:

$$b^n = \underbrace{bbb \cdots \cdot b}_{n \text{ factors of } b} \quad b^n \text{ is read "}b\text{ to the }n\text{th power."}$$

Here b is called the **base** and n the **exponent**. In addition, we define

$$b^1 = b$$

and usually use b in place of b^1. Finally, we emphasize that $3b$ and b^3 are quite different. Compare

$3b = 3 \cdot b$ Three times b

$b^3 = b \cdot b \cdot b$ 3 factors of b

The quantity b^2 is read as ''b squared'' or ''the square of b'' or ''b to the second power.'' Similarly b^3 is read ''b cubed'' or ''the cube of b'' or ''b to the third power.'' Higher powers, such as b^5 and b^{12}, are read ''b to the fifth power'' and ''b to the twelfth power,'' respectively.

Example 16   **(A)** Write in nonexponent form: x^2, t^1, 3^4, $5x^3y^5$
                (B) Write in exponent form: xxx, $2x^2y$, $2 \cdot 2 \cdot 2 \cdot 2$, $3xxxyy$

Solution   **(A)** From exponent to nonexponent form:

$$x^2 = xx \qquad t^1 = t$$

$$3^4 = 3 \cdot 3 \cdot 3 \cdot 3 \qquad 5x^3y^5 = 5xxxyyyyy$$

           (B) From nonexponent to exponent form:

$$xxx = x^3 \qquad 2xxy = 2x^2y$$

$$2 \cdot 2 \cdot 2 \cdot 2 = 2^4 \qquad 3xxxyy = 3x^3y^2$$

Problem 16   **(A)** Write in nonexponent form: y^3, 2^4, $3x^3y^4$
               (B) Write in exponent form: uu, $5 \cdot 5 \cdot 5 \cdot 5$, $7xxxxyyy$

Unless grouping symbols dictate otherwise, exponents are to be applied before multiplication or division. For example, $3 \cdot 2^2$ means first raise 2 to the second power, then multiply by 3 to obtain 12. On the other hand, $(3 \cdot 2)^2$ means first multiply 3 times 2 and then raise the result to the second power to obtain 36. Similarly, we can compare $3x^5$ and $(3x)^5$:

$$3x^5 = 3 \cdot x \cdot x \cdot x \cdot x \cdot x \qquad \text{Right (3 times five factors of } x\text{)}$$

$$3x^5 \neq 3x \cdot 3x \cdot 3x \cdot 3x \cdot 3x \qquad \text{The exponent 5 in } 3x^5 \text{ applies only to the base } x$$

$$(3x)^5 = 3x \cdot 3x \cdot 3x \cdot 3x \cdot 3x \qquad \text{Right (five factors of } 3x\text{)}$$

The order of operations introduced in Sec. 1-2 is thus extended to include exponents:

Order of Operations

1. Simplify inside the innermost symbols of grouping first, then the next innermost, and so on.
2. Unless grouping symbols indicate otherwise, exponents are applied before multiplication or division is performed.
3. Unless grouping symbols indicate otherwise, multiplication and division are performed before addition and subtraction. In either case, proceed from left to right.

Example 17   Evaluate the following expressions for $x = 2$ and $y = 3$:

(A) $(x + y)^2$ (B) $x + y^2$
(C) $(xy)^2$ (D) xy^2

Solution   (A) $(2 + 3)^2 = 5^2 = 25$ (B) $2 + 3^2 = 2 + 9 = 11$
(C) $(2 \cdot 3)^2 = 6^2 = 36$ (D) $2 \cdot 3^2 = 2 \cdot 9 = 18$

Problem 17   Evaluate the following expressions for $x = 12$ and $y = 2$:

(A) $(x - y)^2$ (B) $x - y^2$
(C) $(x/y)^2$ (D) x/y^2

Something interesting happens if we multiply two exponent forms with the same base:

$$x^3 x^5 = (xxx)(xxxxx)$$

$$= xxxxxxxx$$

$$= x^8$$

which we could get by simply adding the exponents in $x^3 x^5$. This example suggests the following general property of exponents:

First Law of Exponents

For any natural numbers m and n and any number b

$$b^m b^n = b^{m+n}$$

$$b^2 b^3 \boxed{= b^{2+3}} = b^5$$

Expressed in words this says: to multiply powers of a common base, write down the base and add the exponents. This **first law of exponents** is one of five very important exponent laws you will get to know well before the end of this book.

Example 18   Apply the first law of exponents to simplify the following expressions:

(A) $x^3 x^4$ (B) $5^{10} \cdot 5^{23}$ (C) $(2y^2)(3y^5)$ (D) $(3x^2 y)(4x^4 y^5)$

Solution   (A) $x^3 x^4 \boxed{= x^{3+4}} = x^7$ Not x^{12}

(B) $5^{10} \cdot 5^{23} \boxed{= 5^{10+23}} = 5^{33}$ Not 25^{33}

(C) $(2y^2)(3y^5) \boxed{= (2 \cdot 3)(y^2 y^5)} = 6y^7$

(D) $(3x^2 y)(4x^4 y^5) \boxed{= (3 \cdot 4)(x^2 x^4)(y y^5)} = 12x^6 y^6$

Note how commutative and associative properties are used in parts (C) and (D) where we rearranged the factors and regrouped them.

Problem 18   Simplify as in Example 18:

(A) $y^5 y^3$ (B) $3^{17} \cdot 3^{20}$ (C) $(3a^6)(5a^3)$ (D) $(2x^2 y^4)(3xy^2)$

ANSWERS TO
MATCHED PROBLEMS

13. (A) $3 + a$ (B) $5b$ (C) ab (D) $a + b$
14. (A) $5 + 7$ (B) $5 \cdot 9$ (C) $b + c$ (D) bc
15. (A) $u + v + w + 12$ (B) $64mnp$
16. (A) $yyy, 2 \cdot 2 \cdot 2 \cdot 2, 3xxxyyyy$ (B) $u^2, 5^4, 7x^4 y^3$
17. (A) 100 (B) 8 (C) 36 (D) 3
18. (A) y^8 (B) 3^{37} (not 9^{37})   (C) $15a^9$ (D) $6x^3 y^6$

EXERCISE 1-4 **A** *Remove parentheses and simplify.*

1. $(7 + x) + 3$
2. $(5 + z) + 12$
3. $(7a)(4b)$
4. $(3x)(4y)$
5. $(7 + a) + (9 + b)$
6. $(x + 7) + (y + 8)$

Write in nonexponent form.

7. x^3
8. y^4
9. $2x^3y^2$
10. $5a^2b^3$
11. $3w^2xy^3$
12. $7ab^3c^2$

Write in exponent form.

13. xxx
14. $yyyy$
15. $2xxxyy$
16. $7uuvvvvv$
17. $3xyyzzz$
18. $9aabccc$

Multiply, using the first law of exponents.

19. $u^{10}u^4$
20. m^8m^7
21. aa^5
22. b^7b
23. $w^{12}w^7$
24. $n^{23}n^{10}$
25. $y^{12}y^4$
26. u^4u^{44}
27. $3^{10} \cdot 3^{20}$
28. $7^8 \cdot 7^5$
29. $9^5 \cdot 9^6$
30. $2^5 \cdot 2^{12}$

B *Remove parentheses and simplify.*

31. $(3a)(5b)(2c)$
32. $(2x)(8y)(3z)$
33. $(4u)(5v)(3w)$
34. $(2x)(3y)(4z)$
35. $(x + 2) + (y + 4) + (z + 8)$
36. $(a + 3) + (b + 5) + (c + 2)$
37. $(u + 5) + (v + 10) + (w + 4)$
38. $(r + 6) + (s + 8) + (t + 10)$

Multiply, using the first law of exponents.

39. x^2xx^4
40. mm^3m^4
41. yyy^6y^2
42. uu^2uu^4
43. $(2x^3)(3x)(4x^5)$
44. $(3u^4)(2u^5)(u^7)$
45. $(a^2b)(ab^2)$
46. $(cd^2)(c^2d^3)$
47. $(4x)(3xy^2)$
48. $(5b)(2a^2b^3)$
49. $(2xy)(3x^3y)$
50. $(3xy^2z^3)(5xyz^2)$

Evaluate the following expressions for $a = 16$ and $b = 2$:

51. $(a + b)^3$
52. $(a - b)^3$

53. $a + b^3$

54. $a - b^3$

55. $(ab)^3$

56. $(a/b)^3$

57. $a \cdot b^3$

58. a/b^3

C **59.** If a statement is not true for all natural numbers a and b, find replacements for a and b that show that the statement is false.
    (A) $a + b = b + a$ **(B)** $ab = ba$
    (C) $a - b = b - a$ **(D)** $a \div b = b \div a$

60. Repeat the preceding problem for
    (A) $(a + b) + c = a + (b + c)$ **(B)** $(ab)c = a(bc)$
    (C) $(a - b) - c = a - (b - c)$ **(D)** $(a \div b) \div c = a \div (b \div c)$

Each statement illustrates either a commutative property or an associative property. State which.

61. $5 + z = z + 5$

62. $bc = cb$

63. $(5x)y = 5(xy)$

64. $(a + 5) + 7 = a + (5 + 7)$

65. $3x + x5 = 3x + 5x$

66. $5(x8) = 5(8x)$

67. $3 + (x + 2) = 3 + (2 + x)$

68. $(5x)y = y(5x)$

69. $5 + (x + 3) = (x + 3) + 5$

70. $(x + 2) + (y + 3) = (x + 2) + (3 + y)$

71. $(x + 3) + (y + 2) = (y + 2) + (x + 3)$

72. $(x + 3) + (y + 2) = x + [3 + (y + 2)]$

73. The distance s in feet that an object falls in t seconds is 16 times the square of the time (see the figure).
    (A) Write a formula that indicates the distance s that the object falls in t seconds.
    (B) Identify the constants and variables.
    (C) How far will the object have fallen at the end of 8 seconds?

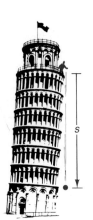

1-5
DISTRIBUTIVE PROPERTIES

- Distributive Property
- Common Factors
- Extended Distributive Property

We now introduce another important property of the natural numbers, a property that involves both multiplication and addition, called the **distributive property**.

DISTRIBUTIVE PROPERTY

To reveal the distributive property, compute $3(5 + 2)$ and $3 \cdot 5 + 3 \cdot 2$:

$$3(5 + 2) = 3 \cdot 7 \qquad 3 \cdot 5 + 3 \cdot 2 = 15 + 6$$
$$= 21 \qquad\qquad\qquad = 21$$

Thus

$$3(5 + 2) = 3 \cdot 5 + 3 \cdot 2$$

Note that the right side of the last equality is obtained from the left by multiplying each term within the parentheses by 3. Is the fact that these are equal just a coincidence? Let us try another set of numbers:

$$7(2 + 6) = 7 \cdot 8 \qquad 7 \cdot 2 + 7 \cdot 6 = 14 + 42$$
$$= 56 \qquad\qquad\qquad = 56$$

Thus

$$7(2 + 6) = 7 \cdot 2 + 7 \cdot 6$$

Again we see that if we multiply each term within the parentheses by 7 first and add, we get the same result as adding the terms first and then multiplying by 7. If we continue testing this apparent relationship for various other sets of natural numbers, we will not be able to find any for which it does not hold. More formally, we state:

Distributive Property

For all natural numbers a, b, and c

$$a(b + c) = ab + ac \quad 5(2 + 3) = 5 \cdot 2 + 5 \cdot 3 \qquad \text{Multiplication distributes over addition.}$$

Notice in the distributive property that one side of the equation is a product $a(b + c)$ and the other side is a sum $ab + ac$. The property allows us to rewrite certain products as sums, and vice versa.

Example 19   Multiply using the distributive property:

(A) $3(x + y)$ **(B)** $4(w + 2)$
(C) $x(x + 1)$ **(D)** $2x^2(3x + 2)$

Solution   **(A)** $3(x + y) = 3x + 3y$

(B) $4(w + 2) \boxed{= 4w + 4 \cdot 2} = 4w + 8$

(C) $x(x + 1) \boxed{= x \cdot x + x \cdot 1} = x^2 + x$

(D) $2x^2(3x + 2y) \boxed{\begin{aligned} &= 2x^2 \cdot 3x + 2x^2 \cdot 2y \\ &= (2 \cdot 3)(x^2 x) + (2 \cdot 2)(x^2 y) \end{aligned}}$
$$= 6x^3 + 4x^2 y$$

Problem 19   Multiply using the distributive property:

(A) $2(a + b)$ **(B)** $5(x + 3)$ **(C)** $u(u^2 + 1)$ **(D)** $3n^2(2m^2 + 3n)$

The symmetric property of equality and the commutative properties of addition and multiplication allow us to write several equivalent forms of the distributive property; the following are true for all natural numbers a, b, and c:

$$a(b + c) = ab + ac \tag{1}$$

$$(b + c)a = ba + ca \tag{2}$$

$$ab + ac = a(b + c) = (b + c)a \tag{3}$$

$$ba + ca = (b + c)a = a(b + c) \tag{4}$$

COMMON FACTORS

The process of changing from $a(b + c)$ to $ab + ac$ or from $(b + c)a$ to $ba + ca$ (Equations 1 and 2) is called **multiplying out** or simply just multiplying. In doing so we are changing a product into a sum. The reverse process of changing from $ab + ac$ to $a(b + c)$ or from $ba + ca$ to $(b + c)a$ (Equations 3 and 4) is called **factoring out** or **taking out the common factor**. In particular, in Equation 3 we are taking out the common factor a:

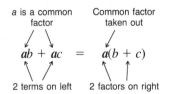

In this case, we are changing a sum to a product.

Example 20   Take out all factors common to all terms:

$\quad$ **(A)** $2x + 2y$ $\quad$ **(B)** $3w + 6$ $\quad$ **(C)** $x^2 + x$ $\quad$ **(D)** $6y + 4y^2$

Solution   **(A)** $2x + 2y = 2(x + y)$

$\quad$ **(B)** $3w + 6 \;\boxed{= 3w + 3 \cdot 2} = 3(w + 2)$

$\quad$ **(C)** $x^2 + x \;\boxed{= x \cdot x + x \cdot 1} = x(x + 1)$ $\quad$ 1 is a factor of every number.

$\quad$ **(D)** $6y + 4y^2 \;\boxed{= 2y \cdot 3 + 2y \cdot 2y} = 2y(3 + 2y)$

Note: Multiplying the expression on the right should take you back where you started on the left.

Problem 20   Take out all factors common to all terms:

$\quad$ **(A)** $5x + 5y$ $\quad$ **(B)** $2w + 8$ $\quad$ **(C)** $u^2 + u$ $\quad$ **(D)** $6y^2 + 4y^3$

$\quad$ Since $a(b + c) = (b + c)a$ (why?), a factor common to two terms may be taken out either on the left or on the right. That is, $ab + ac = (b + c)a$ as well as $a(b + c)$. (See Equations 3 and 4 above.) Consider the following example.

Example 21   Apply the distributive property to simplify:

$\quad$ **(A)** $3x + 5x$ $\quad$ **(B)** $7y + 2y$ $\quad$ **(C)** $3x^2y^2 + 4x^2y^2$

Solution   **(A)** $3x + 5x \;\boxed{= (3 + 5)x} = 8x$

$\quad$ **(B)** $7y + 2y \;\boxed{= (7 + 2)y} = 9y$

$\quad$ **(C)** $3x^2y^2 + 4x^2y^2 \;\boxed{= (3 + 4)x^2y^2} = 7x^2y^2$

Notice the marked simplification that we obtain in each case. This technique is called **combining like terms**. It is significant and will be expanded upon in the next section.

Problem 21   Simplify as in Example 21:

$\quad$ **(A)** $2x + 3x$ $\quad$ **(B)** $8u + 3u$ $\quad$ **(C)** $5uv^2 + 7uv^2$

EXTENDED DISTRIBUTIVE PROPERTY

By repeated use of the distributive property we can show that multiplication distributes over any finite sum. Thus:

Extended Distributive Property

$$a(b + c + d) = ab + ac + ad \qquad 2(x + y + z) = 2x + 2y + 2z$$

$$a(b + c + d + e) = ab + ac + ad + ae \qquad \begin{aligned} 3(w + x + y + z) \\ = 3w + 3x + 3y + 3z \end{aligned}$$

and so on.

Example 22   (A) Multiply: $3(x + y + z)$
(B) Take out factors common to all terms: $ma + mb + mc$
(C) Multiply: $2x(x + 3y + 2)$
(D) Take out factors common to all terms: $4x^2 + 2xy + xz$
(E) Multiply: $3x^2y(2xy^3 + 3xy + x^2y^2)$
(F) Multiply: $(x + 2)(x + 3)$

Solution   (A) $3(x + y + z) = 3x + 3y + 3z$ Multiplication
(B) $ma + mb + mc = m(a + b + c)$ Factoring
(C) $2x(x + 3y + 2) = 2x^2 + 6xy + 4x$ Multiplication
(D) $4x^2 + 2xy + xz = x(4x + 2y + z)$ Factoring
(E) $3x^2y(2xy^3 + 3xy + x^2y^2) = 6x^3y^4 + 9x^3y^2 + 3x^4y^3$ Multiplication
(F) $(x + 2)(x + 3) = (x + 2)x + (x + 2)3 = x^2 + 2x + 3x + 6$
      $= x^2 + 5x + 6$ Multiplication

Problem 22   (A) Multiply: $5(a + b + c)$
(B) Take out factors common to all terms: $ax + ay + az$
(C) Multiply: $3x(2x + 3y + 5)$
(D) Take out factors common to all terms: $4x^3 + 2xy + 6x^2$
(E) Multiply: $2u^2v^3(4u^2v + 2uv + uv^2)$
(F) Multiply: $(y + 1)(y + 5)$

The properties we have considered in this section and the preceding one regulate a considerable amount of activity in algebra. These are, so to speak, some of the rules of the game of algebra. However, as is the case in many games (such as chess), one must practice using the rules to become good at algebra.

ANSWERS TO
MATCHED PROBLEMS

19. (A) $2a + 2b$ (B) $5x + 15$ (C) $u^3 + u$
(D) $6m^2n^2 + 9n^3$
20. (A) $5(x + y)$ (B) $2(w + 4)$ (C) $u(u + 1)$
(D) $2y^2(3 + 2y)$
21. (A) $5x$ (B) $11u$ (C) $12uv^2$
22. (A) $5a + 5b + 5c$ (B) $a(x + y + z)$
(C) $6x^2 + 9xy + 15x$ (D) $2x(2x^2 + y + 3x)$
(E) $8u^4v^4 + 4u^3v^4 + 2u^3v^5$ (F) $y^2 + 6y + 5$

EXERCISE 1-5 A *Compute.*

1. $2(1 + 5)$ and $2 \cdot 1 + 2 \cdot 5$ **2.** $3(4 + 2)$ and $3 \cdot 4 + 3 \cdot 2$

3. $5(2 + 7)$ and $5 \cdot 2 + 5 \cdot 7$ **4.** $7(3 + 2)$ and $7 \cdot 3 + 7 \cdot 2$

Multiply, using the distributive property.

5. $4(x + y)$ **6.** $5(a + b)$ **7.** $7(m + n)$ **8.** $9(u + v)$

9. $6(x + 2)$ **10.** $3(y + 7)$ **11.** $5(2 + m)$ **12.** $8(3 + n)$

Take out factors common to all terms.

13. $3x + 3y$ **14.** $2a + 2b$ **15.** $5m + 5n$

16. $7u + 7v$ **17.** $xa + ya$ **18.** $um + vm$

19. $2x + 4$ **20.** $3y + 9$

Multiply, using the distributive property.

21. $2(x + y + z)$ **22.** $4(a + b + c)$

23. $(x + y + z)3$ **24.** $(a + b + 3)4$

Take out factors common to all terms.

25. $7x + 7y + 7z$ **26.** $9a + 9b + 9c$

27. $2m + 2n + 6$ **28.** $3x + 3y + 12$

B *Multiply, using the distributive property.*

29. $x(1 + x)$ **30.** $y(y + 7)$ **31.** $(1 + y^2)y$

32. $(x^2 + 3)x$ **33.** $3x(2x + 5)$ **34.** $5y(2y + 7)$

35. $(m^2 + 3m)2m^2$ **36.** $(a^3 + 2a^2)3a^2$

37. $3x(2x^2 + 3x + 1)$ **38.** $2y(y^2 + 2y + 3)$

39. $5(2x^3 + 3x^2 + x + 2)$ **40.** $4(y^4 + 2y^3 + y^2 + 3y + 1)$

41. $3x^2(2x^3 + 3x^2 + x + 2)$ **42.** $7m^3(m^3 + 2m^2 + m + 4)$

Write as a single term (see Example 21).

43. $3x + 7x$ **44.** $4y + 5y$ **45.** $2u + 9u$

46. $8m + 5m$ **47.** $2xy + 3xy$ **48.** $5mn + 7mn$

49. $2x^2y + 8x^2y$ **50.** $3uv^2 + 5uv^2$

51. $7x + 2x + 5x$ **52.** $8y + 3y + 4y$

Take out factors common to all terms.

53. $x^2 + 2x$ **54.** $y^2 + 3y$ **55.** $u^2 + u$

56. $m^2 + m$ **57.** $2x^3 + 4x$ **58.** $3u^5 + 6u^3$

59. $x^2 + xy + xz$ **60.** $y^3 + y^2 + y$

61. $3m^3 + 6m^2 + 9m$ **62.** $12x^3 + 9x^2 + 3x$

63. $u^2v + uv^2$ **64.** $2x^3y^2 + 4x^2y^3$

C   *Multiply, using the distributive property.*

65. $4m^2n^3(2m^3n + mn^2)$ **66.** $5uv^2(2u^3v + 3uv^2)$

67. $(2xy^3 + 4x + y^2)3x^2y$ **68.** $(c^2d + 2cd + 4c^3d^2)2cd^3$

69. $4x^2yz^3(3x^2z + yz)$ **70.** $3u^2v^3w(5uw^4 + vw^3)$

71. $(u + v)(c + d) = (u + v)c + (u + v)d = ?$ (finish multiplication)

72. $(m + n)(x + y) = (m + n)x + (m + n)y = ?$ (finish multiplication)

73. $(x + 3)(x + 2)$ **74.** $(m + 5)(m + 3)$

Take out factors common to all terms.

75. $a^2bc + ab^2c + abc^2$ **76.** $m^3n + mn^2 + m^2n^2$

77. $16x^3yz^2 + 4x^2y^2z + 12xy^2z^3$

78. $27u^5v^2w^2 + 9u^2v^3w^4 + 12u^3v^2w^5$

1-6
COMBINING LIKE TERMS

- Coefficient
- Like Terms
- Combining Like Terms
- Multipl ng and Combining Like Terms

In this section, we will use the distributive property to simplify algebraic expressions where the terms involve the same variable. The process, introduced in Example 21 in the last section, is called **combining like terms**.

COEFFICIENT

The factor 3 in $3x^2y$ is called the numerical coefficient. In general, the constant factor in a term is called the **numerical coefficient** (or simply the **coeffi-**

cient) of the term. If no constant factor appears in the term, then the coefficient is understood to be 1. (For example, x^2y has a coefficient of 1, since
$x^2y = 1 \cdot x^2y$.)

Example 23   Given the algebraic expression

$$2x^3 + x^2y + 3xy^2 + y^3$$

what is the coefficient of each term?

Solution   In the expression

$$2x^3 + x^2y + 3xy^2 + y^3$$

the coefficient of the first term is 2, the second 1, the third 3, and the fourth 1.

Problem 23   Given the algebraic expression

$$5x^4 + 2x^3y + x^2y^2 + 4xy^3 + y^4$$

what is the coefficient of each term?

LIKE TERMS

If two or more terms are exactly alike, except for possibly their numerical
coefficients or the order in which the factors are multiplied, then they are
called **like terms**. Thus, like terms must have the same variables to the same
powers, but their coefficients do not have to be the same.

Example 24   List the like terms in

(A) $4x + 2y + 3x$ (B) $9x^2y + 3xy + 2x^2y + x^2y$

Solution   (A) In $4x + 2y + 3x$, $4x$ and $3x$ are like terms.
(B) In $9x^2y + 3xy + 2x^2y + x^2y$, the first, third, and fourth terms are like
terms.

Problem 24   List the like terms in

(A) $5m + 6n + 2n$ (B) $2xy + 3xy^3 + xy + 2xy^3$

COMBINING LIKE TERMS

If an algebraic expression contains two or more like terms, these terms can
always be combined into a single term. The distributive property (as we saw
in the last section) is the principal tool behind the process.

Example 25   Combine like terms:

(A) $3x + 5x$ (B) $5t + 4s + 7t + s$

Solution   (A) $3x + 5x \; \boxed{= (3 + 5)x} \; = 8x$

(B) $5t + 4s + 7t + s \; \boxed{= 5t + 7t + 4s + s = (5 + 7)t + (4 + 1)s}$

$= 12t + 5s$

Problem 25   Combine like terms:

(A) $6y + 5y$ (B) $4x + 7y + x + 2y$

We can mechanize the process of combining like terms as follows:

Mechanical Rule for Combining Like Terms
To combine like terms, add their numerical coefficients.

Example 26   Combine like terms mentally:

(A) $7x + 2y + 3x + y \; \boxed{= 7x + 3x + 2y + 1y}$

$= 10x + 3y$

(B) $2u^2 + 3u + 4u^2 \; \boxed{= 2u^2 + 4u^2 + 3u}$

$= 6u^2 + 3u$

(C) $(3x^2 + x + 2) + (4x^2 + 2x + 1) \; \boxed{\begin{array}{l} = 3x^2 + 1x + 2 + 4x^2 + 2x + 1 \\ = 3x^2 + 4x^2 + 1x + 2x + 2 + 1 \end{array}}$

$= 7x^2 + 3x + 3$

Problem 26   Combine like terms mentally:

(A) $4x + 7y + 9x$ (B) $3x^2 + y^2 + 2x^2 + 3y^2$
(C) $(2m^2 + 3m + 5) + (m^2 + 4m + 2)$

MULTIPLYING AND COMBINING LIKE TERMS

In the next example we will use most of what we have been discussing in this chapter up until now.

Example 27   Multiply as indicated and combine like terms:

(A) $3x(x + 5) + 4x(2x + 3) = 3x^2 + 15x + 8x^2 + 12x$
$$= 11x^2 + 27x$$

(B) $2x(x^2 + 2x + 1) + x(3x^2 + x + 2) = 2x^3 + 4x^2 + 2x + 3x^3 + x^2 + 2x$
$$= 5x^3 + 5x^2 + 4x$$

(C) $3x(2x + 4y) + 2y(3x + y) + 2x^2 + 3y^2$
$$= 6x^2 + 12xy + 6xy + 2y^2 + 2x^2 + 3y^2 \quad \text{Note:} \quad 6yx = 6xy.$$
$$= 8x^2 + 18xy + 5y^2$$

(D) $(4x + 3)(3x + 2) = (4x + 3)3x + (4x + 3)2$
$$= 12x^2 + 9x + 8x + 6$$
$$= 12x^2 + 17x + 6$$

Problem 27   Multiply as indicated and combine like terms:

(A) $4m(m + 3) + m(6m + 1)$
(B) $3x(2x^3 + x + 1) + 2x(x^3 + 3x^2 + 2)$
(C) $4x^2 + 3y(2x + y) + 2x(x + 3y) + y^2$
(D) $(3x + 2)(2x + 1)$

ANSWERS TO
MATCHED PROBLEMS
23.   5, 2, 1, 4, and 1
24.   (A) $6n, 2n$ (B) $2xy, xy; 3xy^3, 2xy^3$
25.   (A) $11y$ (B) $5x + 9y$
26.   (A) $13x + 7y$ (B) $5x^2 + 4y^2$ (C) $3m^2 + 7m + 7$
27.   (A) $10m^2 + 13m$ (B) $8x^4 + 6x^3 + 3x^2 + 7x$
          (C) $6x^2 + 12xy + 4y^2$ (D) $6x^2 + 7x + 2$

EXERCISE 1-6   **A**   *Indicate the numerical coefficient of each term.*

1. $4x$ 2. $7ab$ 3. $8x^2y$ 4. $9uv^2$

5. x^3 6. y^5 7. u^2v^3 8. m^3n^5

Given the algebraic expression $2x^3 + 3x^2 + x + 5$, indicate each of the following:

9.   The coefficient of the second term

10.   The coefficient of the first term

11.   The exponent of the variable in the second term

12.   The exponent of the variable in the first term

13. The coefficient of the third term

14. The exponent of the variable in the third term

Select like terms in each group of terms.

15. $3x, 2y, 4x, 5y$

16. $3m, 2n, 5m, 7n$

17. $6x^2, x^3, 3x^2, x^2, 4x^3$

18. $2y^2, 3y^4, 5y^4, y^2, y^4$

19. $2u^2v, 3uv^2, u^2v, 5uv^2$

20. $5mn^2, m^2n, 2m^2n, 3mn^2$

Combine like terms.

21. $5x + 4x$ **22.** $2m + 3m$ **23.** $3u + u$

24. $x + 7x$ **25.** $7x^2 + 2x^2$ **26.** $4y^3 + 6y^3$

27. $2x + 3x + 5x$ **28.** $4u + 5u + u$

29. $2x + 3y + 5x + y$ **30.** $m + 2n + 3m + 4n$

31. $2x + 3y + 5 + x + 2y + 1$ **32.** $3a + b + 1 + a + 4b + 2$

B   *Select like terms in each group.*

33. $m^2n, 4mn^2, 2mn, 3mn, 5m^2n, mn^2$

34. $3u^2v, 2uv, u^2v, 2uv^2, 4uv, uv^2$

Combine like terms.

35. $2t^2 + t^2 + 3t^2$

36. $6x^3 + 3x^3 + x^3$

37. $3x + 5y + x + 4z + 2y + 3z$

38. $2r + 7t + r + 4s + r + 3t + s$

39. $9x^3 + 4x^2 + 3x + 2x^3 + x$

40. $y^3 + 2y + 3y^2 + 4y^3 + 2y^2 + y + 5$

41. $x^2 + xy + y^2 + 3x^2 + 2xy + y^2$

42. $3x^2 + 2x + 1 + x^2 + 3x + 4$

43. $(2x + 1) + (2x + 3) + (2x + 5)$

44. $(4x + 1) + (3x + 2) + (2x + 5)$

45. $(t^2 + 5t + 3) + (3t^2 + t) + (2t + 7)$

46. $(4x^4 + 2x^2 + 3) + (x^4 + 3x^2 + 1)$

47. $(x^3 + 3x^2y + xy^2 + y^3) + (2x^3 + 3xy^2 + y^3)$

48. $(2u^3 + uv^2 + v^3) + (u^3 + v^3) + (u^3 + 3u^2v)$

Multiply, using the distributive property, and combine like terms.

49. $2(x + 5) + 3(2x + 7)$ **50.** $5(m + 7) + 2(3m + 6)$

51. $x(x + 1) + x(2x + 3)$ **52.** $2t(3t + 5) + 3t(4t + 1)$

53. $5(t^2 + 2t + 1) + 3(2t^2 + t + 4)$

54. $4(u^2 + 3u + 2) + 2(2u^2 + u + 1)$

55. $y(y^2 + 2y + 3) + (y^3 + y) + y^2(y + 1)$

56. $2y(y^2 + 2y + 5) + 7y(3y + 2) + y(y^2 + 1)$

57. $2x(3x + y) + 3y(x + 2y)$

58. $3m(2m + n) + 2n(3m + 2n)$

59. $2x^2(2x^2 + y^2) + y^2(x^2 + 3y^2)$

60. $3u^2(u^2 + 2v^2) + v^2(2u^2 + v^2)$

61. $3m^4(m^2 + 2m + 1) + m^3(m^3 + 3m^2 + m)$

62. $4x^3(x^2 + 3x) + 2x^4(3x + 1)$

63. If x represents a natural number, write an algebraic expression for the sum of four consecutive natural numbers starting with x. Simplify the expression by combining like terms.

64. If t represents an even number, write an algebraic expression for the sum of three consecutive even numbers starting with t. Simplify.

C   *Multiply, using the distributive property, and combine like terms.*

65. $2xy^2(3x + x^2y) + 3x^2y(y + xy^2)$

66. $3s^2t^3(2s^3t + s^2t^2) + 2s^3t^2(3s^2t^2 + st^3)$

67. $3u^2v(2uv^2 + u^2v) + 2uv^2(u^2v + 2u^3)$

68. $4m^3n^2(3mn^2 + n) + 2mn^2(2m^3n^2 + m^2n)$

69. $(2x + 3)(3x + 2) = (2x + 3)3x + (2x + 3)2 = ?$

70. $(x + 2)(2x + 3) = (x + 2)2x + (x + 2)3 = ?$

71. $(x + 2y)(2x + y)$ **72.** $(3x + y)(x + 3y)$

73. $(x + 3)(x^2 + 2x + 5)$ **74.** $(r + s + t)(r + s + t)$

75. If y represents an odd number, write an algebraic expression for the product of y and the next odd number. Write as the sum of two terms.

76. If y represents the first of four consecutive even numbers, write an algebraic expression that would represent the product of the first two added to the product of the last two. Simplify.

77. An even number plus the product of it and the next even number is 180. Introduce a variable and write as an algebraic equation. Simplify the left and right sides of the equation where possible.

78. There exist at least two consecutive odd numbers such that 5 times the first plus twice the second is equal to twice the first plus 3 times the second. Introduce a variable and write as an algebraic equation. Simplify the left and right sides of the equation where possible.

$1\text{-}7$

CHAPTER REVIEW

A set is called **finite** if it can be counted and has an end; otherwise it is **infinite**. The infinite set $\{1, 2, 3, \ldots\}$ is called the set of **counting numbers** or **natural numbers**. The **even numbers**, those natural numbers exactly divisible by 2, and the **odd numbers**, those not divisible by 2, are subsets of the natural numbers. Two or more numbers being added or subtracted are called **terms**; when multiplied they are called **factors**. A **composite number** is a natural number that can be written as the product of two natural numbers, neither being 1. A **prime number** is a natural number, not 1, that is not a composite number. A natural number is **completely factored** when it is represented as a product of primes. The **least common multiple** (LCM) of two or more numbers is the smallest natural number exactly divisible by each; the LCM can be found by taking each prime as a factor as often as it occurs most in the factorizations of the given numbers.   *(1-1)*

A **variable** is a symbol used to represent elements out of a set, called the **replacement set** for the variable. A **constant** is a symbol for one object in a set. An **algebraic expression** is a symbolic form involving constants, variables, mathematical operations (addition, subtraction, multiplication, division), and grouping symbols. Algebraic expressions joined by addition or subtraction are called **terms**; when joined by multiplication they are called **factors**.   *(1-2)*

The **equality sign** ($=$) between two expressions means that they are names or descriptions for the same thing. The symbol $\neq$ means "is not equal to." The symbols $<$ and $>$ mean "less than" and "greater than," respectively. An **algebraic equation** is a form joining two algebraic expressions, involving at least one variable, by an equality sign. The set of replacements for variables that make an algebraic equation true is called the **solution set** of the equation. Equality satisfies these properties:

1.   Reflexive: $a = a.$

2. **Symmetric:** If $a = b$, then $b = a$.
3. **Transitive:** If $a = b$ and $b = c$, then $a = c$.
4. **Substitution principle:** If $a = b$, then either may be substituted for the other. *(1-3)*

Addition and multiplication are **commutative** ($a + b = b + a$, $ab = ba$) and **associative** [$(a + b) + c = a + (b + c)$, $(ab)c = a(bc)$]. The product $bbb \cdots \cdot b$ with n factors of b can be written as b^n; b is called the **base**, n the **exponent**. For any natural numbers m and n, $b^m b^n = b^{m+n}$; this is the **first law of exponents**. The **order of operations** for arithmetic operations, unless grouping symbols indicate otherwise, is first to apply exponents, then do multiplications and divisions left to right, and then additions and subtractions left to right. *(1-4)*

The **distributive property** states that $a(b + c) = ab + ac$; that is, multiplication distributes over addition. *(1-5)*

The constant factor in a term is called the **coefficient**. Two terms identical except possibly for their coefficients are called **like terms** and may be combined using the distributive property. *(1-6)*

REVIEW EXERCISE 1-7

Work through all the problems in this chapter review and check answers in the back of the book. (Answers to all review problems are there, and following each answer is a number in italics indicating the section in which that type of problem is discussed.) Where weaknesses show up, review appropriate sections in the text.

All variables represent natural numbers.

A   **1.** Given $G = \{10, 11, 12, 13, 14, 15\}$:
    (A) Write the set of odd numbers in G.
    (B) Write the set of prime numbers in G.

Evaluate.

2. $12 - 5 \cdot 2$ **3.** $5 + 3(7 - 5)$

4. $x - 4(x - 7)$ for $x = 9$ **5.** $(x + 4)(x - 4)$ for $x = 6$

Multiply.

6. $x^{12}x^{13}$ **7.** $(2x^3)(3x^5)$ **8.** $2^5 \cdot 2^{20}$

9. $x(x + 1)$ **10.** $5(2x + 3y + z)$ **11.** $3u(2u^2 + u)$

Combine like terms.

12. $3y + 6y$ **13.** $2m + 5n + 3m$

14. $3x^2 + 2x + 4x^2 + x$ **15.** $3x^2y + 2xy^2 + 5x^2y$

Write in a factored form by taking out factors common to all terms.

16. $3m + 3n$ **17.** $8u + 8v + 8w$

18. $xy + xw$ **19.** $4x + 8w$

If x represents a natural number, write an algebraic expression that represents each of the following:

20. A number 12 times as large as x

21. A number 3 more than 3 times x

22. A number 5 less than twice x

B   **23.** Let A be the set of natural numbers starting at 21 and ending at 31:
      (A) List the elements in the set A which are primes.
      (B) Is A finite or infinite?

24. Given $5x^3 + 3x^2 + x + 7$:
      (A) What is the coefficient of the second term?
      (B) What is the coefficient of the third term?
      (C) What is the exponent of the variable in the third term?

25. Write 120 as a product of prime factors.

Find the LCM.

26. 3, 4, 9   **27.** 6, 5, 9

28. 15, 18   **29.** 12, 18, 10

Evaluate.

30. $(8 + 10) - 3(7 - 3)$ **31.** $2 \cdot 9 - 6(8 - 2 \cdot 3)$

32. $2[12 - 2(6 - 3)]$ **33.** $2[(8 + 4) - (7 - 5)]$

34. $2[x + 3(x - 4)]$ for $x = 6$

35. $6[(x + y) - 3(x - y)]$ for $x = 7$ and $y = 5$

Multiply as indicated and combine like terms where possible.

36. $(2x^3)(3x)(3x^4)$ **37.** $(3xy^2z)(4x^2y^3z^3)$

38. $3y^3(2y^2 + y + 5)$

39. $2(5u^2 + 2u + 1) + 3(3u^2 + u + 5)$

40. $3x(x + 5) + 2x(2x + 3) + x(x + 1)$

41. $(x + 2y)3x + (x + 2y)y$

Write in a factored form by taking out factors common to all terms.

42. $u^3 + u^2 + u$ **43.** $6x^2y + 3xy^2$

44. $3m^5 + 6m^4 + 15m^2$

Translate each statement into an algebraic equation using only the variable x.

45. 24 is 6 less than twice a certain number.

46. 3 times a given number is 12 more than that number.

47. The sum of four consecutive natural numbers is 138. (Let x be the first of the four consecutive natural numbers.)

48. The sum of three consecutive even numbers is 78. (Let x be the first of the three consecutive even numbers.)

C   *Given the set $M = \{27, 51, 61\}$, write as a set.*

49. The odd numbers in M **50.** The prime numbers in M

Evaluate.

51. $4\{20 - 4[(11 - 3) - 3 \cdot 2]\}$

52. $3\{x + 2[8 - 2(x - y)]\}$ for $x = 5$ and $y = 3$

Multiply and combine the terms where possible.

53. $5u^3v^2(2u^2v^2 + uv + 2)$

54. $2x^3(2x^2 + 1) + 3x^2(x^3 + 3x + 2)$

55. $(4x + 3)(2x + 1)$

Write in factored form by taking out factors common to all terms.

56. $12x^3yz^2 + 9x^2yz$ **57.** $20x^3y^2 + 5x^2y^3 + 15x^2y^2$

Each statement is justified by either the commutative or associative property. State which.

58. $x3 = 3x$ **59.** $(x + 3) + 2 = x + (3 + 2)$

60. $(3 + x) + 5 = (x + 3) + 5$

61. $(x + 3) + (x + 5) = x + [3 + (x + 5)]$

62. If x represents the first of three consecutive odd numbers, write an algebraic equation that represents the fact that 4 times the first is equal to the sum of the second and third.

2

INTEGERS

By limiting ourselves in the first chapter to the simplest number system within your experience, the natural numbers, we were able to develop many basic algebraic processes without the distracting influence of more complicated numbers such as decimals, fractions, and radicals. We will find that most of these processes carry on without change to the more involved number systems to be presented in this and the next chapter. In this chapter, we will extend basic algebraic ideas to the set of integers.

2-1

THE SET OF INTEGERS

- Natural Numbers and Positive Integers
- Integers and a Number Line

The set of natural numbers has restrictions. For example, neither

$$3 \div 5 \qquad \text{nor} \qquad 3 - 5$$

have answers that are natural numbers. As a step toward remedying these deficiencies and at the same time increasing our manipulative power, we now extend the natural numbers to the integers.

NATURAL NUMBERS AND POSITIVE INTEGERS

We start by giving the natural numbers another name. From now on they will also be called **positive integers**. To help us emphasize the difference between the positive integers (natural numbers) and the negative integers that are to be introduced shortly, we will often place a plus sign in front of a numeral used to name a natural number. Thus, we may use either

$$+3 \text{ or } 3 \qquad +25 \text{ or } 25 \qquad +372 \text{ or } 372$$

and so on.

INTEGERS AND A NUMBER LINE

If we form a **number line** (a line with numbers associated with points on the line) using the positive integers, and divide the line to the left into line segments equal to those used on the right, how should the points on the left be labeled?

```
  ?   ?   ?   ?   ?   ?   ?   ?   ?  +1  +2  +3  +4  +5  +6  +7  +8
```

As you might guess, we label the first point to the left of +1 with *zero*

$$0$$

and the other points in succession with

$$-1, -2, -3, \ldots$$

These last numbers are called **negative integers**.

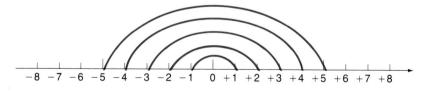

In general, to each positive integer there corresponds a unique (one and only one) number called a negative integer: -1 to $+1$, -2 to $+2$, -3 to $+3$, and so on. The minus sign is part of the number symbol. The elements in the integer pairs -1 and $+1$, -2 and $+2$, and so on are often referred to as **opposites** of each other. Zero has no sign attached.

Zero and the negative integers are relatively recent concepts, historically speaking. Both concepts were introduced as numbers in their own right between A.D. 600 and 700. Hindu mathematicians in India are given credit for their invention. The growing importance of commercial activities seemed to be the stimulus. Since business transactions involve decreases as well as increases, it was found that both transactions could be treated at once if the positive integers represented amounts received and the negative integers represented amounts paid out. Of course, since then negative numbers have been put to many other uses such as recording temperatures below 0, indicating altitudes below sea level, and representing deficits in financial statements, to name a few that you are probably already aware of.

By collecting the positive integers, 0, and the negative integers into one set we obtain the set of **integers**, J, the subject of this chapter.

The Set of Integers J

$$\{\ldots, -4, -3, -2, -1, 0, +1, +2, +3, +4, \ldots\}$$

We do not attempt to give a precise definition of each integer. We do, however, assume the existence of this set of numbers, and we will learn to manipulate the symbols that name them according to certain rules.

Example 1 What numbers are associated with the points a, b, c, and d on the following number line?

Solution The points a, b, c, and d on the number line are associated with -8, -6, 0, and $+7$, respectively.

Problem 1 What numbers are associated with the points a, b, c, and d on the following number line?

Example 2   Locate the set of numbers $\{-8, -3, 0, +5, +9\}$ on a number line.

Solution   Draw a number line and locate each number with a solid dot:

Problem 2   Locate the set of numbers $\{-12, -6, +2, +10\}$ on a number line.

Example 3   Express each of the following by means of an appropriate integer:

(A) A bank deposit of $37   (B) A bank withdrawal of $52

Solution   (A) $+37$ (B) -52

Problem 3   Express each of the following by means of an appropriate integer:

(A) A 36-yard gain in football   (B) A 5-yard loss in football

Without negative numbers it is not possible to perform the operation

$$7 - 12$$

or to solve the equation

$$8 + x = 2$$

Before this course is over, many more uses of negative numbers will be considered. In the next several sections we will learn how to add, subtract, multiply, and divide integers—an essential step to their many uses.

ANSWERS TO   **1.** $a = -13; b = -6; c = -1; d = +9$
MATCHED PROBLEMS
2.

3.   (A) $+36$ (B) -5

EXERCISE 2-1   A   **1.**   What numbers are associated with points a, b, c, and d?

2.   What numbers are associated with points a, b, c, d, and e?

Locate each set of numbers on a number line.

3. {−4, −2, 0, +2, +4}   **4.** {−7, −4, 0, +4, +8}

5. {−25, −20, −15, +5, +15}   **6.** {−30, −20, −5, +10, +15}

Using the figure for Problem 2, write down the number associated with the point.

7.   3 units to the left of *d*   **8.**   4 units to the right of *e*

9.   4 units to the right of *a*   **10.** 2 units to the left of *b*

11. 10 units to the left of *d*   **12.** 20 units to the right of *a*

B   *Let A be the set $\{-2, 4, -\frac{3}{5}, 3.14, 17, 6035, -21, 0, \sqrt{13}, \frac{2}{9}, 1\}$ and B be the set $\{23, 0, -5, 1.4142, \frac{1}{3}, -\sqrt{2}, 6, -1, 33, 712, -8\}$.*

13. List the positive integers in *A*.

14. List the positive integers in *B*.

15. List the negative integers in *A*.

16. List the negative integers in *B*.

17. List the integers in *A*.

18. List the integers in *B*.

19. List the nonintegers in *A*.

20. List the nonintegers in *B*.

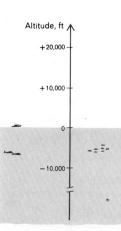

Referring to the figure, express each of the following quantities by means of an appropriate integer.

21. A mountain height of 20,270 feet (Mount McKinley, highest mountain in the United States)

22. A mountain peak 29,141 feet high (Mount Everest, highest point on earth)

23. A valley depth of 280 feet below sea level (Death Valley, the lowest point below sea level in the Western Hemisphere)

24. An ocean depth of 35,800 feet (Marianas Trench in the Western Pacific, greatest known depth in the world)

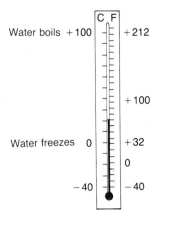

Water boils +100

Water freezes 0

−40

C F

+212

+100

+32

0

−40

Referring to the figure, express each of the following quantities by means of an appropriate integer.

25. 5° below freezing on the Celsius scale

26. 35° below freezing on the Celsius scale

27. 5° below freezing on the Fahrenheit scale

28. 100° below boiling on the Fahrenheit scale

29. 35° below freezing on the Fahrenheit scale

30. 220° below boiling on the Fahrenheit scale

Express each of the following quantities by means of an appropriate integer.

31. A bank deposit of $25

32. A bank balance of $237

33. A bank withdrawal of $10

34. An overdrawn checking account of $17

35. A 9-yard loss in football

36. A 23-yard gain in football

37. Enter each of the following numbers in your calculator.† If necessary, read the instruction book to find how negative numbers are entered and displayed.
  (A) +23   **(B)** −6   **(C)** −78   **(D)** +31   **(E)** −103

38. Enter each of the following numbers in your calculator:
  (A) −38   **(B)** +9   **(C)** −110   **(D)** +234   **(E)** −87

C   *In each problem start at 0 on a number line and give the number associated with the final position.*

39. Move 7 units in the positive direction, 4 units in the negative direction, 5 more units in the negative direction, and finally 3 units in the positive direction.

40. Move 4 units in the negative direction, 7 units in the positive direction, and 13 units in the negative direction.

† Most problems in this text do not *require* the use of a calculator. However, many of the problems, especially those in subsequent chapters that involve decimals, are made easier by using one. It is assumed that students have access to basic calculators.

Express the net gain or loss by means of an appropriate integer.

41.   In banking: a $23 deposit, a $20 withdrawal, a $14 deposit

42.   In banking: a $32 deposit, a $15 withdrawal, an $18 withdrawal

43.   In football: a 5-yard gain, a 3-yard loss, a 4-yard loss, an 8-yard gain, a 9-yard loss

44.   In an elevator: up 2 floors, down 7 floors, up 3 floors, down 5 floors, down 2 floors

2-2
THE OPPOSITE OF AND ABSOLUTE VALUE OF A NUMBER

- The Opposite of a Number
- The Absolute Value of a Number
- Combined Operations

An algebraic expression is like a recipe in that it contains instructions on how to proceed in its evaluation. For example, if we were to evaluate

$$5(x + 2y)$$

for $x = 10$ and $y = 3$, we would write

$$5(10 + 2 \cdot 3)$$

Then we would multiply 2 and 3, add the product to 10, and then multiply the sum by 5. Thus, the instructions expressed symbolically involve the operations "multiply" and "add."

In this section we are going to define two more operations on numbers called "the opposite of" and "the absolute value of," and you will get further practice in following symbolic instructions. These two new operations are widely used in mathematics and its applications. We will use them in the following sections to help us define addition, subtraction, multiplication, and division for integers. We start by defining the opposite of a number.

THE OPPOSITE OF A NUMBER

By the **opposite of a number** x, we mean an operation on x, symbolized by

$-x$ Opposite of x

that produces another number. What number? It changes the sign of x if x is not 0, and if x is 0 it leaves it alone.

Example 4   Find:

(A) $-(+3)$ (B) $-(-5)$ (C) $-(0)$ (D) $-[-(+3)]$

Solution   (A) $-(+3) = -3$ (B) $-(-5) = +5$
(C) $-(0) = 0$ (D) $-[-(+3)] = -(-3) = +3$

Problem 4   Find:

(A) $-(+7)$ (B) $-(-6)$ (C) $-(0)$ (D) $-[-(-4)]$

Graphically, the opposite of a number is its "mirror image" relative to 0 (see Figure 1).

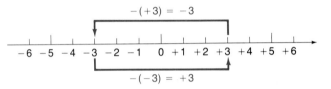

FIGURE 1   Number
opposites

As a consequence of the definition of the opposite of a number, we note the following important properties:

1.   The opposite of a positive number is a negative number.
2.   The opposite of a negative number is a positive number.
3.   The opposite of 0 is 0.

Thus, we see that $-x$ is not necessarily a negative number: **$-x$ represents a positive number if x is negative and a negative number if x is positive** (see Figure 1: if x is -3, then $-x$ is 3; if x is 3, then $-x$ is -3).
You should be aware by now that the negative sign $(-)$ is used in three distinct ways:

1. As the operation "subtract": $7 \overset{\downarrow}{-} 5 = 2$ 7 minus 5

2. As the operation "the opposite of": $\overset{\downarrow}{-}(-6) = +6$ Opposite of negative 6
   $\overset{\downarrow}{-}(+3) = -3$ Opposite of 3

3. As part of a number symbol: $\overset{\downarrow}{-} 8$ Negative 8

Note: The opposite of a number x, $-x$, is sometimes referred to as "the negative of x." Since this terminology often causes confusion at this stage, we will avoid its use until later.

THE ABSOLUTE VALUE OF A NUMBER

The **absolute value of a number** x is an operation on x, denoted symbolically by

$|x|$ Absolute value of x

that produces another number. What number? If x is positive or 0, it leaves it alone; if x is negative, it makes it positive. That is, the absolute value of a number may be thought of as the number "without the sign." (Don't confuse square brackets $[x]$ with the absolute value symbol $|x|$.)

Symbolically, and more formally,

$$|x| = \begin{cases} x & \text{if } x \text{ is a positive number or 0} \\ -x & \text{if } x \text{ is a negative number} \end{cases}$$

Do not be afraid of this symbolic form of the definition. It represents a first exposure to more precise mathematical representations and it will take on more meaning with repeated exposure.

Example 5   Evaluate:

(A) $|+7|$ **(B)** $|-7|$ **(C)** $|0|$

Solution   **(A)** $|+7| = +7$ **(B)** $|-7| = +7$ **(C)** $|0| = 0$

Problem 5   Evaluate:

(A) $|+5|$ **(B)** $|-5|$ **(C)** $|0|$

We see that:

1. The absolute value of a positive number is a positive number.
2. The absolute value of a negative number is a positive number.
3. The absolute value of 0 is 0.

We therefore conclude that:

The absolute value of a number is never negative.

Geometrically, $|x|$ represents the distance—a positive quantity—that x is from 0 (see Figure 2).

FIGURE 2 Absolute value

COMBINED OPERATIONS

"The absolute value of" and "the opposite of" operations are often used in combination, and it is important to perform the operations in the right order— generally, from the inside out.

Example 6   Evaluate:

(A) $|-(-3)|$ (B) $-|-3|$ (C) $\{-(|-5| - |-2|)\}$

Solution   (A) $|-(-3)| = |+3| = +3$
(B) $-|-3| = -(+3) = -3$
(C) $\{-(|-5| - |-2|)\} = -(5 - 2) = -(+3) = -3$

Problem 6   Evaluate:

(A) $|-(+5)|$ (B) $-|+5|$ (C) $-(|-7| + |-3|)$

Example 7   Replace each question mark with an appropriate integer:

(A) $-(?) = +7$ (B) $-(?) = -7$ (C) $|?| = +3$ (D) $|?| = -3$

Solution   (A) -7 since $-(-7) = +7$
(B) $+7$ since $-(+7) = -7$
(C) $+3$ or -3 since $|+3| = +3$ and $|-3| = +3$
(D) No integer will work, since the absolute value of a number is never negative.

Problem 7   Replace each question mark with an appropriate integer:

(A) $-(?) = -6$ (B) $-(?) = +6$ (C) $|?| = -1$ (D) $|?| = +5$

Example 8   Evaluate for $x = -3$ and $y = +2$:

(A) $-x$ (B) $|x|$ (C) $-(-y)$ (D) $-|-y|$

Solution   (A) $-x \;\boxed{= -(\;\;)} = -(-3) = +3$ Remember that the dashed boxes are "think" steps and usually are not written down as a separate step.

(B) $|x| \;\boxed{= |\;\;|} = |-3| = +3$

(C) $-(-y) \;\boxed{= -[-(\;\;)]} = -[-(+2)] = -(-2) = +2$

(D) $-|-y| \;\boxed{= -|-(\;\;)|} = -|-(+2)| = -|-2| = -(+2) = -2$

Problem 8   Evaluate for $x = +3$ and $y = -2$:

(A) $-y$ (B) $|y|$ (C) $-(-x)$ (D) $-|-x|$

4. (A) -7 (B) $+6$ (C) 0 (D) -4
5. (A) $+5$ (B) $+5$ (C) 0
6. (A) $+5$ (B) -5 (C) -10

7. **(A)** 6 **(B)** −6 **(C)** No value **(D)** +5 or −5

8. **(A)** +2 **(B)** +2 **(C)** +3 **(D)** −3

EXERCISE 2-2 A *Evaluate.*

1. $-(+9)$ **2.** $-(+14)$ **3.** $-(-2)$ **4.** $-(-3)$

5. $|+4|$ **6.** $|+10|$ **7.** $|-6|$ **8.** $|-7|$

9. $-(0)$ **10.** $|0|$

11. The opposite of a number is *(always, sometimes, never)* a negative number.

12. The opposite of a number is *(always, sometimes, never)* a positive number.

13. The absolute value of a number is *(always, sometimes, never)* a negative number.

14. The absolute value of a number is *(always, sometimes, never)* a positive number.

Replace each question mark with an appropriate integer.

15. $-(+11) = ?$ **16.** $-(-15) = ?$ **17.** $-(?) = +5$

18. $+(?) = -8$ **19.** $|-13| = ?$ **20.** $|+17| = ?$

21. $|?| = +2$ **22.** $|?| = +8$ **23.** $|?| = -4$ **24.** $|?| = 0$

B *Evaluate.*

25. $-[-(+6)]$ **26.** $-[-(-11)]$ **27.** $|-(-5)|$

28. $|-(+7)|$ **29.** $-|-5|$ **30.** $-|+7|$

31. $(|-3| + |-2|)$ **32.** $(|-7| - |+3|)$

33. $-(|-12| - |-4|)$ **34.** $-(|-6| + |-2|)$

Evaluate for $x = +7$ and $y = -5$.

35. $-x$ **36.** $|x|$ **37.** $|y|$

38. $-y$ **39.** $-|x|$ **40.** $-|y|$

41. $-(-y)$ **42.** $-(-x)$ **43.** $|-y|$

44. $|-x|$ **45.** $|x| - |y|$ **46.** $-(|x| + |y|)$

Find the solution set of each equation from the set of integers.

47. $|+5| = x$

48. $|-7| = x$

49. $-x = -3$

50. $-x = +8$

51. $|x| = +6$

52. $|x| = +9$

53. $|x| = -4$

54. $-|x| = +4$

C   *Solve each equation by describing the set of integers for which the equation is true.*

55. $|x| = 0$

56. $-x = 0$

57. $-x = |x|$

58. $x = |x|$

59. $-(-x) = x$

60. $|-x| = |x|$

61. $|-x| = x$

62. $-x = x$

63. $-|x| = |x|$

64. $|-x| = -|x|$

2-3

ADDITION OF INTEGERS

■ Definition of Addition
■ Adding Several Integers

How should addition in the integers be defined so that we can assign numbers to each of the following sums?

$$(+2) + (+5) = ? \qquad (-2) + (+5) = ? \qquad (+7) + 0 = ?$$
$$(+2) + (-5) = ? \qquad (-2) + (-5) = ? \qquad 0 + (-3) = ?$$

To give us an idea, let us think of addition of integers in terms of deposits and withdrawals in a checking account, starting with a 0 balance. If we do this, then a deposit of $2 followed by another deposit of $5 would provide us with a balance of $7. Thus, as we would expect from addition in the natural numbers,

$$(+2) + (+5) = +7$$

Similarly, a deposit of $2 followed by a withdrawal of $5 would yield an overdrawn account of $3, and we would write

$$(+2) + (-5) = -3$$

Continuing in the same way, we can assign to each sum the value that indicates the final status of our account after the two transactions have been completed. Hence,

$$(-2) + (+5) = +3 \qquad (+7) + 0 = +7$$
$$(-2) + (-5) = -7 \qquad 0 + (-3) = -3$$

DEFINITION OF ADDITION

We now define addition of integers so that we get the same results as above, as well as satisfy the rearrangement (commutative) and grouping (associative) properties we had with the natural numbers. Before we state the definition of addition, we point out that **two numbers of like sign** are either two positive numbers or two negative numbers and that **two numbers of unlike sign** are numbers such that one is positive and the other is negative. Now we are ready to define addition.

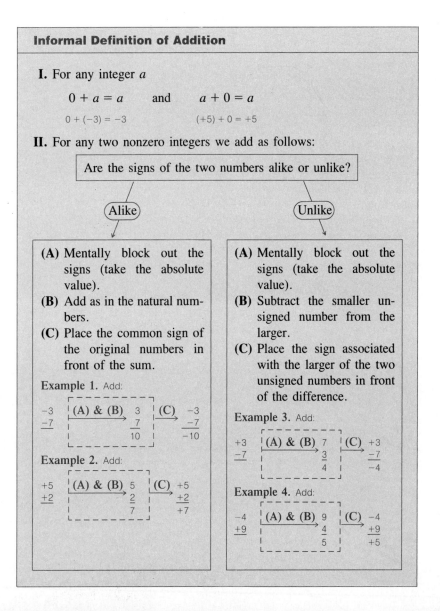

Informal Definition of Addition

I. For any integer a

$$0 + a = a \qquad \text{and} \qquad a + 0 = a$$

$$0 + (-3) = -3 \qquad\qquad (+5) + 0 = +5$$

II. For any two nonzero integers we add as follows:

Are the signs of the two numbers alike or unlike?

Alike

Unlike

(A) Mentally block out the signs (take the absolute value).
(B) Add as in the natural numbers.
(C) Place the common sign of the original numbers in front of the sum.

Example 1. Add:

$$\begin{matrix} -3 \\ -7 \end{matrix} \xrightarrow{\text{(A) \& (B)}} \begin{matrix} 3 \\ 7 \\ \hline 10 \end{matrix} \xrightarrow{\text{(C)}} \begin{matrix} -3 \\ -7 \\ \hline -10 \end{matrix}$$

Example 2. Add:

$$\begin{matrix} +5 \\ +2 \end{matrix} \xrightarrow{\text{(A) \& (B)}} \begin{matrix} 5 \\ 2 \\ \hline 7 \end{matrix} \xrightarrow{\text{(C)}} \begin{matrix} +5 \\ +2 \\ \hline +7 \end{matrix}$$

(A) Mentally block out the signs (take the absolute value).
(B) Subtract the smaller unsigned number from the larger.
(C) Place the sign associated with the larger of the two unsigned numbers in front of the difference.

Example 3. Add:

$$\begin{matrix} +3 \\ -7 \end{matrix} \xrightarrow{\text{(A) \& (B)}} \begin{matrix} 7 \\ 3 \\ \hline 4 \end{matrix} \xrightarrow{\text{(C)}} \begin{matrix} +3 \\ -7 \\ \hline -4 \end{matrix}$$

Example 4. Add:

$$\begin{matrix} -4 \\ +9 \end{matrix} \xrightarrow{\text{(A) \& (B)}} \begin{matrix} 9 \\ 4 \\ \hline 5 \end{matrix} \xrightarrow{\text{(C)}} \begin{matrix} -4 \\ +9 \\ \hline +5 \end{matrix}$$

If you think of each example in the definition in terms of deposits and withdrawals in a bank account, then the processes and results will seem more reasonable. Of course, we want to be able to do addition of integers mentally as in Example 9 below. It is important that you practice integer addition sufficiently so that you can perform the operation with speed and accuracy.

Example 9   **(A)** Add:

$$
\begin{array}{ccccc}
-8 & +8 & -8 & +4 & 0 \\
\underline{-3} & \underline{-3} & \underline{+3} & \underline{\ 0} & \underline{-6}
\end{array}
$$

(B) Add:

$$(+4) + (+6) \qquad (-4) + (-6) \qquad (-4) + (+6)$$
$$(+4) + (-6) \qquad 0 + (-1)$$

Solution   **(A)**
$$
\begin{array}{ccccc}
-8 & +8 & -8 & +4 & 0 \\
\underline{-3} & \underline{-3} & \underline{+3} & \underline{\ 0} & \underline{-6} \\
-11 & +5 & -5 & +4 & -6
\end{array}
$$

(B) $(+4) + (+6) \; \boxed{= +(4 + 6)} \; = +10$

$\qquad (-4) + (-6) \; \boxed{= -(4 + 6)} \; = -10$

$\qquad (-4) + (+6) \; \boxed{= +(6 - 4)} \; = +2$

$\qquad (+4) + (-6) \; \boxed{= -(6 - 4)} \; = -2$

$\qquad\quad 0 + (-1) \quad = -1$

Problem 9   **(A)** Add:

$$
\begin{array}{cccc}
-4 & +4 & -4 & -9 \\
\underline{-5} & \underline{-5} & \underline{+5} & \underline{\ 0}
\end{array}
$$

(B) Add:

$$(-2) + (+7) \qquad (+2) + (-7) \qquad (-2) + (-7) \qquad 0 + (-5)$$

Two important properties of addition follow directly from the definition of addition.

Addition Properties

For all integers a, b, and c:

(A) $a + b = b + a$ COMMUTATIVE PROPERTY

$\qquad (-2) + (+3) = (+3) + (-2)$

(B) $(a + b) + c = a + (b + c)$ ASSOCIATIVE PROPERTY

$\qquad [(-1) + (+3)] + (-2) = (-1) + [(+3) + (-2)]$

As a consequence of these properties we will have essentially the same kind of freedom that we had with the natural numbers in rearranging terms and inserting or removing parentheses relative to addition.

ADDING SEVERAL INTEGERS

Now let us turn to the problem of adding three or more integers. The commutative and associative properties of the integers are behind this procedure:

Steps in Adding Several Integers
1. Add all positive integers.   2. Add all negative integers.   3. Add the two resulting sums.

Example 10   Add: $(+3) + (-6) + (+8) + (-4) + (-5)$.

Solution

$$(+3) + (-6) + (+8) + (-4) + (-5)$$
$$= [(+3) + (+8)] + [(-6) + (-4) + (-5)]$$
$$= (+11) + (-15)$$
$$= -4$$

List the positive integers first.
Add the positive integers; add the negative integers.
Add the resulting sums.

Or vertically,

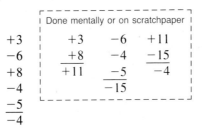

$$+3$$
$$-6$$
$$+8$$
$$-4$$
$$\underline{-5}$$
$$-4$$

Problem 10   Add: $(-8) + (-4) + (+6) + (-3) + (+10) + (+1)$.

We conclude this section with a less obvious property of addition that follows from the definition:

Addition of Opposites
1. For each integer a, the sum of a and its opposite is 0; that is, $a + (-a) = 0$. $5 + (-5) = 0$ 2. If the sum of two numbers is 0, then each must be the opposite of the other; that is, if $a + b = 0$, then $a = -b$ and $b = -a$.   If $a + 5 = 0$, then $a = -5$ and $5 = -a$

Example 11   Replace the question marks with appropriate integers:

(**A**) $(+5) + (-5) = ?$ (**B**) $(-y) + y = ?$
(**C**) $(+7) + (?) = 0$ (**D**) $m + (?) = 0$

Solution   (**A**) $(+5) + (-5) = \mathbf{0}$ (**B**) $(-y) + y = \mathbf{0}$
(**C**) $(+7) + (\mathbf{-7}) = 0$ (**D**) $m + (\mathbf{-m}) = 0$

Problem 11   Repeat Example 11 for

(**A**) $(-3) + (+3) = ?$ (**B**) $d + (-d) = ?$
(**C**) $(-4) + (?) = 0$ (**D**) $(-w) + (?) = 0$

ANSWERS TO
MATCHED PROBLEMS

9. (**A**) $-9, -1, +1, -9$ (**B**) $+5, -5, -9, -5$ **10.** $+2$
11. (**A**) 0 (**B**) 0 (**C**) $+4$ (**D**) w

EXERCISE 2-3   A   *Add.*

1. $+5$ $\underline{+6}$	**2.** $+7$ $\underline{-4}$	**3.** -9 $\underline{+6}$	**4.** -6 $\underline{+8}$	**5.** $+6$ $\underline{-8}$
6. -3 $\underline{-4}$	**7.** -7 $\underline{-1}$	**8.** $+8$ $\underline{+2}$	**9.** 0 $\underline{+3}$	**10.** -4 $\underline{0}$

11. $(+5) + (+4)$ **12.** $(-7) + (-3)$ **13.** $(-8) + (+2)$

14. $(+3) + (-7)$ **15.** $(-6) + (-3)$ **16.** $(+2) + (+3)$

17. $0 + (-9)$ **18.** $(+2) + 0$

19. $+4$ -3 -5 -7 $\underline{+9}$	**20.** -6 -4 $+8$ $+3$ $\underline{-5}$	**21.** -7 $+2$ -3 -1 $\underline{+5}$	**22.** $+6$ -4 -8 -2 $\underline{+9}$

23. $(+5) + (-8) + (-9) + (+7)$

24. $(-8) + (-7) + (+3) + (+9)$

25. $(-6) + 0 + (+5) + (-2) + (-1)$

26. $(+9) + (-3) + 0 + (-8)$

B   *Add.*

27. $+11$ $\underline{-23}$	**28.** -12 $\underline{-21}$	**29.** -403 $\underline{-219}$	**30.** -307 $\underline{+231}$

31. $(-63) + (+25)$ **32.** $(-45) + (-73)$

33. $(-237) + (-431)$

34. $(-197) + (+364)$

35. $+12$
$\quad\ \ -18$
$\quad\ \ -23$
$\quad\ \ \ +4$
$\quad\underline{\ -11}$

36. -63
$\quad\ \ +45$
$\quad\ \ \ -3$
$\quad\ \ +17$
$\quad\underline{+12}$

37. $(+12) + (+7) + (-37) + (+14)$

38. $(-23) + (-35) + (+43) + (-33)$

Replace each question mark with an appropriate integer.

39. $(-3) + ? = -7$

40. $? + (-9) = -13$

41. $(+8) + ? = +3$

42. $(-12) + ? = +4$

43. $? + (-12) = -7$

44. $(+54) + ? = -33$

45. $(+33) + ? = -44$

46. $? + (-14) = +20$

Add.

47. $(+3,462) + (-5,237) + (-1,304) + (-7,064)$

48. $(+2,062) + (-3,896) + (+6,438) + (-7,064)$

Evaluate.

49. $|-8| + |+6|$

50. $|(-8) + (+6)|$

51. $(-|-3|) + (-|+3|)$

52. $|-5| + [-(-8)]$

Evaluate for $x = -5$, $y = +3$, and $z = -2$.

53. $x + y$

54. $y + z$

55. $|(-x) + z|$

56. $-(|x| + |z|)$

57. You own a stock that is traded on a stock exchange. On Monday it closed at $23 per share, it fell $3 on Tuesday and another $6 on Wednesday, it rose $2 on Thursday, and finished strongly on Friday by rising $7. Use addition of signed numbers to determine the closing price of the stock on Friday.

58. Your football team is on the opponent's 10-yard line and in four downs gains 8 yards, loses 4 yards, loses another 8 yards, and gains 13 yards. Use addition of signed numbers to determine whether a touchdown was made.

59. A spelunker (cave explorer) descended 2,340 (vertical) feet into the 3,300-foot Gouffre Berger, the world's deepest pothole cave, located in the Isere province of France. On his ascent he climbed 732 feet, slipped back 25 feet and then another 60 feet, climbed 232 feet, and finally slipped back 32 feet. Use addition of signed numbers, starting with −2,340, to find his final position.

60. In a card game (such as rummy, where cards held in your hand after someone goes out are counted against you) the following scores were recorded after four hands of play. Who was ahead at this time and what was his or her score?

RUSS	JAN	PAUL	MEG
+35	+80	−5	+15
+45	+5	+40	−10
−15	−35	+25	+105
−5	+15	+35	−5

C   *Replace each question mark with an appropriate symbol (variables represent integers).*

61. $a + (-a) = ?$ **62.** $(-x) + x = ?$

63. $m + ? = 0$ **64.** $(-x) + ? = 0$

65. Give a reason for each step:

$$[a + b] + (-a) = (-a) + [a + b]$$
$$= [(-a) + a] + b$$
$$= 0 + b$$
$$= b$$

2-4
SUBTRACTION OF INTEGERS

- Definition of Subtraction
- Order in the Integers

From subtraction of natural numbers we know that

$$(+8) - (+5) = +3$$

But what can we write for the differences

$$(+8) - (-5) = ?   \quad (-8) - (+5) = ?   \quad (-5) - (-8) = ?$$
$$(+5) - (+8) = ?   \quad (-8) - (-5) = ?   \quad 0 - (-5) = ?$$

We are going to define subtraction for the integers in such a way that not only will the definition be consistent with what we learned in arithmetic (we will still get $+3$ for the first answer above), but we will also be able to write answers for the difference between *any* two integers.

DEFINITION OF SUBTRACTION

Informal Definition of Subtraction†

To subtract S from M, add the opposite of S to M; that is, **change the sign of S and add**. Symbolically,

$$M - S = M + (-S)$$

Change sign.

$$(-3) - (-4) = (-3) + (+4) = +1$$

Subtraction becomes addition.

Thus, any subtraction problem can be changed to an equivalent addition problem. Applying the definition to the problems stated at the beginning of this section, we obtain:

Change sign.

$$(+8) - (+5) = (+8) + (-5) = +3$$
$$(+8) - (-5) = (+8) + (+5) = 13$$
$$(-8) - (+5) = (-8) + (-5) = -13$$
$$(-8) - (-5) = (-8) + (+5) = -3$$
$$(-5) - (-8) = (-5) + (+8) = +3$$
$$0 - (-5) = \quad 0 + (+5) = +5$$

We first convert each subtraction problem to an equivalent addition problem, and then use the definition of addition of integers to complete the process.

Subtraction becomes addition.

Hence, subtracting $(+5)$ is the same as adding (-5), subtracting (-5) is the same as adding $(+5)$, and so on.

Example 12   Subtract:

(A) $\begin{array}{r} (+7) \\ -(-8) \\ \hline \end{array}$ **(B)** $\begin{array}{r} (-4) \\ -(+5) \\ \hline \end{array}$ **(C)** $(-9) - (-4)$ **(D)** $0 - (+8)$

---

† In a more advanced treatment of the subject, subtraction is usually defined formally as follows: We write $M - S = D$ if and only if $S + D = M$; that is, D is the number that must be added to S to produce M. The informal definition given above is based on this formal definition.

Solution   **(A)** $(+7)$ $(+7)$
$-(-8)$ $-\big[$ Change the sign of (-8) and add. $\big]\!\rightarrow$ $\underline{+(+8)}$
$+15$

(B) (-4) (-4)
$-(+5)$ $-\big[$ Change the sign of $(+5)$ and add. $\big]\!\rightarrow$ $\underline{+(-5)}$
-9

(C) $(-9) - (-4) = (-9) + (+4) = -5$ Change the sign of (-4) and add.
(D) $0 - (+8) = 0 + (-8) = -8$ Change the sign of $(+8)$ and add.

Problem 12   Subtract:

(A) $(+6)$ **(B)** (-3) **(C)** $(-7) - (-2)$ **(D)** $(-3) - (+8)$
$\underline{-(-9)}$ $\underline{-(-5)}$

Example 13   Evaluate:

(A) $[(-3) - (+2)] - [(+2) - (+5)]$
(B) $(-x) - y$ for $x = -3$ and $y = +5$

Solution   **(A)** $[(-3) - (+2)] - [(+2) - (+5)]$ Evaluate inside
brackets first.

$= [(-3) + (-2)] - [(+2) + (-5)]$

$= (-5) - (-3)$ Now subtract.

$= (-5) + (+3)$

$= -2$

(B) $(-x) - y$ Substitute $x = -3$ and $y = +5$.
$[-(-3)] - (+5)$ Evaluate inside brackets first.
$= (+3) - (+5)$ Subtract.

$= (+3) + (-5)$

$= -2$

Problem 13   Evaluate:

(A) $[(+3) + (-8)] - [(-2) - (+3)]$
(B) $x - (-y)$ for $x = -3$ and $y = +8$

ORDER IN THE INTEGERS

In Chapter 1, we introduced the inequality symbols $<$, $>$, $\leq$, and $\geq$ to deal with the natural order on the positive integers and assumed that it was obvious to you that 3 is less than 7, that is, that

$$3 < 7$$

is a true statement. But does it seem equally obvious that

$$-8 < -1 \qquad -15 < 1 \qquad -2 > -10{,}000$$

are also true statements? To make the inequality relation precise so that we can interpret it relative to *all* integers, we need a careful definition of the concept.

Intuitively, one integer is greater than a second if it is located to the right of the second on the number line. Thus, from their location on the line, $7 > 3$:

```
 ┼──┼──┼──┼──┼──┼──┼──┼──┼──
-1  0  1  2  3  4  5  6  7
```

Addition and subtraction of integers are related to moving back and forth on the number line. To add a positive integer to a given one, start at the given integer and move to the *right* the number of units being added; to add a negative integer, move to the *left:*

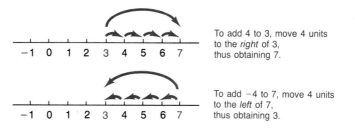

To add 4 to 3, move 4 units to the *right* of 3, thus obtaining 7.

To add −4 to 7, move 4 units to the *left* of 7, thus obtaining 3.

Since we subtract by changing the sign and adding, these rules are reversed for subtraction. To subtract a positive integer we move that many units to the *left;* to subtract a negative integer we move to the *right:*

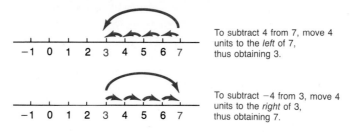

To subtract 4 from 7, move 4 units to the *left* of 7, thus obtaining 3.

To subtract −4 from 3, move 4 units to the *right* of 3, thus obtaining 7.

Since moving to the right means adding a positive integer and moving to the left means subtracting a positive integer, we are led to a formal definition of $<$ and $>$:

Definition of $<$ and $>$

If a and b are integers, then we write $a < b$ if there exists a positive integer p such that $a + p = b$. We write $c > d$ if there exists a positive integer q such that $c - q = d$.

> $3 < 7$ because there is a positive integer,
> namely 4, such that $3 + 4 = 7$.

The definition is not as complicated as it might seem and will prove useful in establishing properties of inequalities later. Certainly, one would expect that if a positive number were added to *any* integer it would make it larger and if it were subtracted from *any* integer it would make it smaller. That is essentially what the definition states. Note that if $a > b$, then it follows that $b < a$ and vice versa. That is, $a > b$ and $b < a$ mean the same thing.

Example 14   Replace each question mark with $<$ or $>$:

(A) 2 ? 3   (B) -8 ? -1 (C) 0 ? -5 (D) -2 ? $-10,000$

Solution   (A) $2 < 3$ Since $2 + 1 = 3$
(B) $-8 < -1$ Since $-8 + 7 = -1$
(C) $0 > -5$ Since $0 - 5 = -5$
(D) $-2 > -10,000$ Since $-2 - 9,998 = -10,000$

Problem 14   Replace each question mark with $<$ or $>$:

(A) 4 ? 6   (B) 6 ? 4   (C) -6 ? -4
(D) -9 ? 9   (E) 3 ? -9 (F) 0 ? -14

As in Chapter 1, the inequality symbols $<$ and $>$ are often combined with the equality symbol $=$ to form statements such as $a \le b$ or $c \ge d$:

$a \le b$ means a is less than or equal to b

$c \ge d$ means c is greater than or equal to d

ANSWERS TO
MATCHED PROBLEMS
12. (A) $+15$ (B) $+2$ (C) -5 (D) -11
13. (A) 0   (B) $+5$
14. (A) $<$ (B) $>$ (C) $<$ (D) $<$ (E) $>$
(F) $>$

EXERCISE 2-4 A   *Subtract as indicated.*

1. $(+9)$	**2.** $(+10)$	**3.** $(+9)$	**4.** $(+10)$
$-(+4)$	$-(+7)$	$-(-4)$	$-(-7)$

5. $(+4)$	**6.** $(+7)$	**7.** (-9)	**8.** (-10)
$-(+9)$	$-(+10)$	$-(-4)$	$-(-7)$

9. (-4)	**10.** (-7)
$-(-9)$	$-(-10)$

Replace each question mark with $<$ or $>$.

11. 7 ? 5   **12.** 3 ? 6   **13.** 5 ? 7

14. 6 ? 3   **15.** -7 ? -5 **16.** -3 ? -6

17. -5 ? -7 **18.** -6 ? -3 **19.** 0 ? 8

20. 5 ? 0   **21.** 0 ? -8 **22.** -5 ? 0

23. -7 ? 5   **24.** -6 ? 3   **25.** -842 ? 0

26. -905 ? -10 **27.** 900 ? $-1,000$ **28.** 505 ? -55

Subtract as indicated.

29. $(+6) - (-8)$ **30.** $(-4) - (+7)$

31. $(+6) - (+10)$ **32.** $(+6) - (-10)$

33. $(-9) - (-3)$ **34.** $0 - (-7)$

35. $0 - (+5)$ **36.** $(-1) - (+6)$

B **37.** $(-12) - (-27)$ **38.** $(+57) - (+92)$

39. $0 - (-87)$ **40.** $0 - (+101)$

41. $(-271) - (+44)$ **42.** $(+327) - (-73)$

43. $(-245) - 0$ **44.** $(+732) - 0$

45. $(+8,063) - (-9,810)$ **46.** $(-6,024) - (-5,321)$

47. $(-1,203) - (+4,027)$ **48.** $(+2,539) - (+7,681)$

49. $(-984) - (-1,803)$ **50.** $(+4,398) - (-1,661)$

51. $(+3,899) - (+5,604)$ **52.** $(-609) - (+4,477)$

Perform the indicated operations.

53. $[(-2) - (+4)] - (-7)$ **54.** $(-2) - [(+4) - (-7)]$

55. $(-23) - [(-7) + (-13)]$ **56.** $[(-23) - (-7)] + (-13)$

57. $[(+6) - (-8)] + [(-8) - (+6)]$

58. $[(+3) - (+5)] - [(-5) - (-8)]$

59. $\big||3 - 5| - 2\big|$ **60.** $\big||5 - 9| + 1\big|$

61. $\big|(3 - 8) - |8 - 11|\big|$ **62.** $\big|-4 - |1 - 6|\big|$

63. $\big||1 - 5| - |4 - 9|\big|$ **64.** $\big||3 - 6| - |1 - 8|\big|$

C *Evaluate for* $x = +2$, $y = -5$, *and* $z = -3$.

65. $x - y$ **66.** $y - z$

67. $(x + z) - y$ **68.** $x - (y - z)$

69. $(-y) - (-z)$ **70.** $(-z) - y$

71. $-(|x| - |y|)$ **72.** $|(x - y) - (y - z)|$

73. $\big|x - |y - z|\big|$ **74.** $\big||x - y| - z\big|$

75. $\big|x - |x - |x - y|\,|\big|$ **76.** $\big|z - |x - |y - z|\,|\big|$

Use the figure and subtraction of integers, subtracting the one lower on the scale from the higher one, to find each of the following:

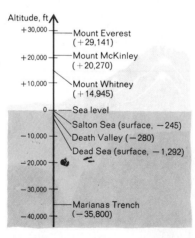

77. The difference in altitude between the highest point on earth, Mount Everest, and the deepest point in the ocean, the Marianas Trench

78. The difference in altitude between the highest point in the United States, Mount McKinley, and the lowest point in the United States, Death Valley

79. The difference in altitude between the Salton Sea and Death Valley (both in California)

80. The difference in altitude between the Dead Sea, the deepest fault in the earth's crust, and Death Valley

Which of the following statements hold for all integers a, b, and c? Illustrate each false statement with an example showing that it is false.

81. $a + b = b + a$

82. $a + (-a) = 0$

83. $a - b = b - a$

84. $a - b = a + (-b)$

85. $(a + b) + c = a + (b + c)$

86. $(a - b) - c = a - (b - c)$

87. $|a + b| = |a| + |b|$

88. $|a - b| = |a| - |b|$

2-5

MULTIPLICATION AND
DIVISION OF INTEGERS

- Definition of Multiplication
- Properties of Multiplication
- Definition of Division
- Combined Operations

Having discussed addition and subtraction of integers, we now turn to multiplication and division.

DEFINITION OF MULTIPLICATION

We already know from natural numbers that

$$(+3)(+2) = +6$$

But how should we define

$$(-3)(-2) = ? \qquad (-3)(+2) = ?$$
$$(+3)(-2) = ? \qquad (0)(-4) = ?$$

We would like to define multiplication of integers in such a way that each of these problems has an answer and so that the rearrangement (commutative), grouping (associative), and distributive properties we had with the natural numbers will still hold. To achieve these ends it turns out we have little choice but to define integer multiplication as follows.

Informal Definition of Multiplication†

I. We multiply 0 and any integer a as follows:

$$a \cdot 0 = 0 \qquad \text{and} \qquad 0 \cdot a = 0$$

$(-3)(0) = 0 \qquad (0)(+5) = 0 \qquad 0 \cdot 0 = 0$

II. We multiply any two nonzero integers as follows:

Are the signs of the two numbers alike or unlike?

(Alike)   (Unlike)

(A) Mentally block out the signs.	**(A)** Mentally block out the signs.
(B) Multiply as in the natural numbers.	**(B)** Multiply as in the natural numbers.
(C) Place a $+$ sign in front of the product.	**(C)** Place a $-$ sign in front of the product.

$(+3)(+2) = +(3 \cdot 2) = +6$ $(-3)(+2) = -(3 \cdot 2) = -6$

$(-3)(-2) = +(3 \cdot 2) = +6$ $(+3)(-2) = -(3 \cdot 2) = -6$

We see that:

The product of two integers with like signs is positive. The product of two integers with unlike signs is negative.

Example 15   Multiply:

    (A) $(+5)(+3)$ **(B)** $(-8)(-6)$ **(C)** $(-7)(+3)$ **(D)** $(+9)(-4)$

Solution   **(A)** $(+5)(+3) = +15$ ⎱
            (B) $(-8)(-6) = +48$ ⎰   Product of two numbers with like signs is positive.

            (C) $(-7)(+3) = -21$ ⎱
            (D) $(+9)(-4) = -36$ ⎰   Product of two numbers with unlike signs is negative.

† In a more advanced treatment of the subject, multiplication of integers is more formally defined as follows: The product of two integers with like signs is a positive number and is found by multiplying the absolute values of the two numbers. The product of two integers with unlike signs is a negative integer and is found by taking the opposite of the product of the absolute values of the two integers. The product of any integer and 0 is 0. The informal definition given above is based on this formal definition.

Problem 15 Multiply:

(A) $(+6)(+5)$ (B) $(+7)(-6)$ (C) $(-4)(-10)$ (D) $(-9)(+8)$

PROPERTIES OF MULTIPLICATION

Two important sets of properties follow from the definition of multiplication.

Multiplication Properties

For all integers a, b, and c:

(A) $ab = ba$ COMMUTATIVE PROPERTY

$(-3)(+2) = (+2)(-3)$

(B) $(ab)c = a(bc)$ ASSOCIATIVE PROPERTY

$[(-4)(+2)](-1) = (-4)[(+2)(-1)]$

(C) $a(b + c) = ab + ac$ DISTRIBUTIVE PROPERTY

$(-4)[(+2) + (-3)] = (-4)(+2) + (-4)(-3)$

Because of these properties we will have the same kind of freedom we had with the natural numbers to rearrange and regroup factors as well as to distribute a product over a sum.

Now let us consider the second set of important properties.

Additional Multiplication Properties

For all integers a and b:

(A) $(+1)a = a$
(B) $(-1)a = -a$
(C) $(-a)b = a(-b) = -(ab)$
(D) $(-a)(-b) = ab$

In words, part (B) states that multiplying a number by -1 is the same as taking the opposite of the number. Part (D) states that the product of the opposites of two numbers is the same as the product of the original numbers. Similar interpretations are given to parts (A) and (C). It is also worth observing that parts (A) and (B) provide the justification for saying that a has a coefficient of $+1$ and $-a$ has a coefficient of -1, since a is the same as $(+1)a$ and $-a$ is the same as $(-1)a$.

Example 16   Evaluate for $a = -5$ and $b = +4$:

     (A) $(+1)a$ and a **(B)** $(-1)a$ and $-a$
     (C) $(-a)b$, $a(-b)$, and $-(ab)$ **(D)** $(-a)(-b)$ and ab

Solution   **(A)** $(+1)a = (+1)(-5) = -5$ **(B)** $(-1)a = (-1)(-5) = +5$
               $a = -5$ $-a = -(-5) = +5$

     (C) $(-a)b = [-(-5)](+4) = (+5)(+4) = +20$
           $a(-b) = (-5)[-(+4)] = (-5)(-4) = +20$
         $-(ab) = -[(-5)(+4)] = -(-20) = +20$

     (D) $(-a)(-b) = [-(-5)][-(+4)] = (+5)(-4) = -20$
              $ab = (-5)(+4) = -20$

Problem 16   Repeat Example 16 for $a = +3$ and $b = -2$.

Expressions of the form

$$-ab$$

occur frequently and at first glance can be confusing. If you were asked to evaluate $-ab$ for $a = -3$ and $b = +2$, how would you proceed? Would you take the opposite of a and then multiply it by b, or multiply a and b first and then take the opposite of the product? Actually it does not matter! Because of the multiplication properties we get the same result either way since $(-a)b = -(ab)$. If, in addition, we consider other material in this section, we find that

$$-ab = \begin{cases} (-a)b \\ a(-b) \\ -(ab) \\ (-1)ab \end{cases}$$

and we are at liberty to replace any one of these five forms with another from the same group.

◇ CAUTION ◇   It is not correct to say that in $-ab$ the minus sign applies to both a and b to yield $(-a)(-b)$. The latter is equal to ab and not $-ab$.

DEFINITION OF DIVISION

We now consider division of integers when the quotient is an integer. Because of our knowledge of natural numbers, we know that

$(+8) \div (+4) = +2$

Recall that for this example, 2 would be called the **quotient** of 8 divided by the **divisor** 4.

But what can we write for the following quotients:

$(+8) \div (-4) = ?$ $(0) \div (-4) = ?$

$(-8) \div (+4) = ?$ $(-8) \div (0) = ?$

$(-8) \div (-4) = ?$

We are going to define division for integers in such a way that not only will the definition be consistent with what we learned in arithmetic [we will still get $+2$ for $(+8) \div (+4)$], but we will also be able to write answers for the quotient of any two integers whose quotient is an integer.

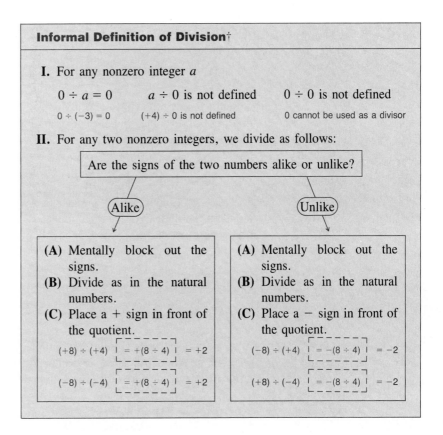

Informal Definition of Division†

I. For any nonzero integer a

$0 \div a = 0$ $a \div 0$ is not defined $0 \div 0$ is not defined

$0 \div (-3) = 0$ $(+4) \div 0$ is not defined   0 cannot be used as a divisor

II. For any two nonzero integers, we divide as follows:

Are the signs of the two numbers alike or unlike?

(Alike)   (Unlike)

(A) Mentally block out the signs.

(B) Divide as in the natural numbers.

(C) Place a + sign in front of the quotient.

$(+8) \div (+4) = +(8 \div 4) = +2$

$(-8) \div (-4) = +(8 \div 4) = +2$

(A) Mentally block out the signs.

(B) Divide as in the natural numbers.

(C) Place a − sign in front of the quotient.

$(-8) \div (+4) = -(8 \div 4) = -2$

$(+8) \div (-4) = -(8 \div 4) = -2$

† In a more advanced treatment of the subject, division is usually defined as follows: we write $a \div b = Q$ if and only if $Qb = a$ and Q is unique; that is, Q is the number that when multiplied times b and produces a. The informal definition given above is based on this formal definition.

We see that the rule of signs for division and multiplication are the same.

The quotient of two integers with like signs is positive. The quotient of two integers with unlike signs is negative.

Of course, quotients of some integers are not integers. For example, $(+2) \div (-3)$ is not an integer. We will consider quotients of this type in detail in Chapter 3.

Applying the definition to the problems stated above, we obtain

$$(+8) \div (+4) \;\; \boxed{= +(8 \div 4)} \;\; = +2$$

$$(+8) \div (-4) \;\; \boxed{= -(8 \div 4)} \;\; = -2$$

$$(-8) \div (+4) \;\; \boxed{= -(8 \div 4)} \;\; = -2$$

$$(-8) \div (-4) \;\; \boxed{= +(8 \div 4)} \;\; = +2$$

$$(0) \div (-4) = 0$$

$$(-8) \div (0) \;\; = \text{Not defined (does not name any number)}$$

Let us look a little closer at 0 in division to see why 0 cannot be used as a divisor. Consider the simple division problem

$$\overset{Q}{3\overline{)12}}$$

The quotient Q must be the number that when multiplied by the divisor 3 produces the dividend 12. The quotient is, of course, 4. Now consider the following three division problems involving 0.

$$\overset{?}{3\overline{)0}} \qquad \overset{?}{0\overline{)3}} \qquad \overset{?}{0\overline{)0}}$$

The first quotient is 0, since $0 \cdot 3 = 0$. The second quotient is not defined, since no number times 0 can be 3. In the third case any number would seem to fit as a quotient, since 0 times any number is 0. However, there should be only one quotient, and since we cannot choose a unique (one and only one) result, it is agreed to choose no result at all. In conclusion:

Zero cannot be used as a divisor—ever!

The two division symbols $\div$ and $\overline{)}$ from arithmetic are not used a great deal in algebra and higher mathematics. The horizontal bar (—) and slash mark (/) are the symbols most frequently used. Thus,

$$a/b \qquad \frac{a}{b} \qquad a \div b \qquad \text{and} \qquad b\overline{)a} \quad \text{In all cases } b \text{ is the divisor.}$$

all name the same number (assuming the quotient is defined), and we can write

$$a/b = \frac{a}{b} = a \div b = b\overline{)a}$$

Example 17 Divide:

(A) $\dfrac{+27}{+9}$ (B) $\dfrac{-27}{-9}$ (C) $\dfrac{-27}{+9}$ (D) $\dfrac{+27}{-9}$

(E) $\dfrac{0}{-4}$ (F) $\dfrac{+7}{0}$ (G) $\dfrac{0}{0}$

Solution

(A) $\dfrac{+27}{+9} = +3$ ⎫

(B) $\dfrac{-27}{-9} = +3$ ⎬ Quotients of numbers with like signs are positive.

(C) $\dfrac{-27}{+9} = -3$ ⎫

(D) $(+27)/(-9) = -3$ ⎬ Quotients of numbers with unlike signs are negative.

(E) $0/(-4) = 0$ } 0 divided by a nonzero number is 0.

(F) $(+7)/0$ ⎫

(G) $0/0$ ⎬ Not defined, since 0 cannot be a divisor.

Problem 17 Divide:

(A) $\dfrac{+18}{+6}$ (B) $\dfrac{-18}{-6}$ (C) $\dfrac{+18}{-6}$

(D) $(-18)/(+6)$ (E) $0/(-6)$ (F) $(-18)/0$

(G) $\dfrac{0}{0}$

COMBINED OPERATIONS

Let us finish this section by considering examples involving all four arithmetic operations $(+, -, \cdot, \div)$. Recall that:

Multiplication and division precede addition and subtraction, unless grouping symbols indicate otherwise. Also, all the operations are performed from left to right.

Example 18   Evaluate:

$$\textbf{(A)} \ \frac{-18}{-3} + (-2)(+3) \qquad \textbf{(B)} \ (+6)(-3) - \frac{-20}{4}$$

$$\textbf{(C)} \ (-1)(-2)(-3) - \left[(-4) - \frac{-6}{+2}\right]$$

Solution $\textbf{(A)} \ \dfrac{-18}{-3} + (-2)(+3) = (+6) + (-6) = 0$

$\textbf{(B)} \ (+6)(-3) - \dfrac{-20}{+4} = (-18) - (-5) = -13$

$\textbf{(C)} \ (-1)(-2)(-3) - \left[(-4) - \dfrac{-6}{+2}\right] = (-6) - [(-4) - (-3)]$

$$= (-6) - (-1)$$
$$= -5$$

Problem 18   Evaluate:

$$\textbf{(A)} \ (-4)(-3) + \frac{-16}{+2} \qquad \textbf{(B)} \ \frac{(+2)(-9)}{-3} + \frac{(+4) - (-6)}{-5}$$

$$\textbf{(C)} \ (-3)[(-4) - (-2)] - \frac{-24}{-3}$$

Example 19   Evaluate each for $x = -24$, $y = +6$, $z = -3$:

$$\textbf{(A)} \ \frac{xz}{y} \qquad \textbf{(B)} \ yz + \frac{x}{y} \qquad \textbf{(C)} \ \frac{y}{z} - \frac{x}{y}$$

Solution $\textbf{(A)} \ \dfrac{xz}{y} = \dfrac{(-24)(-3)}{+6} = \dfrac{+72}{+6} = +12$

$\textbf{(B)} \ yz + \dfrac{x}{y} = (+6)(-3) + \dfrac{-24}{+6} = (-18) + (-4) = -22$

$\textbf{(C)} \ \dfrac{y}{z} - \dfrac{x}{y} = \dfrac{+6}{-3} - \dfrac{-24}{+6} = (-2) - (-4) = (-2) + (+4) = +2$

Problem 19   Evaluate each algebraic expression in Example 19 for $x = +18$, $y = -9$, $z = -3$.

15. **(A)** $+30$ **(B)** -42 **(C)** $+40$ **(D)** -72
16. **(A)** $+3$ **(B)** -3 **(C)** $+6$ **(D)** -6
17. **(A)** $+3$ **(B)** $+3$ **(C)** -3 **(D)** -3 **(E)** 0
(F) Not defined **(G)** Not defined
18. **(A)** $+4$ **(B)** $+4$ **(C)** -2
19. **(A)** $+6$ **(B)** $+25$ **(C)** $+5$

EXERCISE 2-5 *All variables represent integers.*

A *Multiply or divide as indicated.*

1. $(-8)(-4)$ **2.** $(+8)(+4)$ **3.** $(+8)(-4)$

4. $(-8)(+4)$ **5.** $(0)(-7)$ **6.** $(-5)(0)$

7. $\dfrac{-4}{-2}$ **8.** $\dfrac{+14}{+7}$ **9.** $\dfrac{-6}{+2}$

10. $\dfrac{+8}{-4}$ **11.** $\dfrac{-6}{0}$ **12.** $\dfrac{0}{0}$

13. $(+2)(-7)$ **14.** $(-2)(-7)$ **15.** $(-2)(+7)$

16. $(+2)(+7)$ **17.** $(+1)(0)$ **18.** $(0)(+6)$

19. $(-9)/(-3)$ **20.** $(+9)/(+3)$ **21.** $(-9)/(+3)$

22. $(+9)/(-3)$ **23.** $0/(+3)$ **24.** $(-9)/0$

B *Evaluate.*

25. $(-2) + (-1)(+3)$ **26.** $(-3)(-2) + (+4)$

27. $\dfrac{-9}{+3} + (-4)$ **28.** $(-8) + \dfrac{-12}{-2}$

29. $(+2)[(+3) + (-2)]$ **30.** $(+5)[(-4) + (+6)]$

31. $\dfrac{(-10) + (-6)}{-4}$ **32.** $\dfrac{(-12) + (+4)}{+2}$

33. $(+4) - (-2)(-4)$ **34.** $(-7) - (+4)(-3)$

35. $(-6)[(+3) - (+8)]$ **36.** $(-3)[(-2) - (-4)]$

37. $(-7)(+2) - \dfrac{-20}{+5}$ **38.** $\dfrac{+36}{-12} - (-4)(-8)$

39. $(-6)(+2) + (-2)^2$ **40.** $(-3)^2 + (-2)(+1)$

41. $(-6)(+7) - (-3)^2$ **42.** $(-6) - (-2)^2$

43. $(-4)(-3) - \left[(-8) - \dfrac{-6}{+2}\right]$ **44.** $(+7)(-2) - \left[(+10) - \dfrac{+9}{-3}\right]$

Evaluate for $w = +2$, $x = -3$, $y = 0$, and $z = -24$.

45. wx **46.** wz **47.** z/x **48.** z/w **49.** xyz

50. wyz **51.** y/x **52.** y/z **53.** w/y **54.** z/y

55. $z/(wx)$ **56.** xy/z **57.** $wx - \dfrac{z}{w}$ **58.** $\dfrac{z}{x} - wz$

59. $\dfrac{z}{w} - \dfrac{z}{x}$ **60.** $\dfrac{+15}{x} - \dfrac{-12}{w}$

61. $wxy - \dfrac{y}{z}$ **62.** $\dfrac{xy}{w} - xyz$

C **63.** Evaluate for $x = -4$ and $y = +3$:
     (A) $(-x)y$ **(B)** $x(-y)$ **(C)** $-(xy)$

64. Repeat Problem 63 for $x = -2$ and $y = -5$.

65. Evaluate for $x = -3$:
     (A) $(-1)x$ **(B)** $-x$

66. Repeat Problem 65 for $x = +8$.

67. Evaluate for $x = +5$ and $y = -7$:
     (A) $(-x)(-y)$ **(B)** xy

68. Repeat Problem 67 for $x = -3$ and $y = -4$.

What integer replacements for x will make each equation true?

69. $(-3)x = -24$ **70.** $(+5)x = -20$

71. $\dfrac{-24}{x} = -3$ **72.** $\dfrac{x}{-4} = +12$

73. $(-3)x = 0$ **74.** $\dfrac{x}{+32} = 0$

75. $\dfrac{x}{0} = +4$ **76.** $\dfrac{0}{x} = 0$

Evaluate.

77. $(-271)(-196)$ **79.** $(-37)(+166)$

79. $(+304)(-32)$ **80.** $(-831)(-104)$

81. $\dfrac{-10,881}{+403}$ **82.** $\dfrac{+22,977}{-621}$

83. $\dfrac{-12,276}{-1,023}$ **84.** $\dfrac{-7,854}{-462}$

85. $\dfrac{-2,808}{+12} - (+131)(-13)$ **86.** $(+17)(-29) - \dfrac{-7,000}{-14}$

2-6 SIMPLIFYING ALGEBRAIC EXPRESSIONS

- Addition and Subtraction without Grouping Symbols
- Removing Grouping Symbols
- Multiplying by +1 or by −1
- Order of Removing Grouping Symbols
- Inserting Grouping Symbols

We are close to where we can use algebra to solve practical problems. First, however, we need to streamline our methods of representing algebraic expressions. For ease of reading and faster manipulation, it is desirable to reduce the number of grouping symbols and plus signs to a minimum. Thus, **we drop the plus sign from numerals that name positive integers unless a particular emphasis is desired**, so we will usually write

1, 2, 3, . . .   instead of   +1, +2, +3, . . .

ADDITION AND SUBTRACTION WITHOUT GROUPING SYMBOLS

When three or more terms are combined by addition or subtraction and symbols of grouping are omitted, we convert (mentally) any subtraction to addition (Sec. 2-4) and add. Thus,

$$8 - 5 + 3 \boxed{= 8 + (-5) + 3} = 6$$
$$\text{Think}$$

Example 20 Evaluate:

(A) $2 - 3 - 7 + 4$ **(B)** $-4 - 8 + 2 + 9$
(C) $-3 - 8$

Solution   **(A)** $2 - 3 - 7 + 4 \boxed{= 2 + (-3) + (-7) + 4} = -4$
$$\text{Think}$$

(B) $-4 - 8 + 2 + 9$ | $= (-4) + (-8) + 2 + 9$ | $= -1$

Think

(C) $-3 - 8$ | $= (-3) + (-8)$ | $= -11$ Note that $-3 - 8$ is not the same as $(-3)(-8)$ nor is it $(-3) - (-8)$.

Think

Problem 20   Evaluate:

(A) $5 - 8 + 2 - 6$ **(B)** $-6 + 12 - 2 - 1$ **(C)** $-5 - 9$

From the preceding discussion comes the following general process for rearranging terms:

> **Rearranging Terms**
>
> The terms in an algebraic expression may be rearranged without restriction so long as the sign preceding each term accompanies it in the process. For example,
>
> $$a - b + c = a + c - b \qquad x^2 + y^2 - 2xy = x^2 - 2xy + y^2$$

We now modify the earlier definition of a numerical coefficient and state a simple mechanical rule for combining like terms in more involved algebraic expressions. The **(numerical) coefficient** of a given term in an algebraic expression includes the sign that precedes it.

Example 21   In $3x^3 - 2x^2 - x + 3$, what is the coefficient of

(A) The first term?   **(B)** The second term?   **(C)** The third term?

Solution   Since $3x^3 - 2x^2 - x + 3$ | $= 3x^3 + (-2x^2) + (-1x) + 3$

Think

the coefficient of

(A) The first term is 3   **(B)** The second term is -2
(C) The third term is -1

Problem 21   In $2y^3 - y^2 - 2y + 4$, what is the coefficient of

(A) The first term?   **(B)** The second term?   **(C)** The third term?

Using distributive and commutative properties, we can write an expression such as

$$3x - 2y - 5x + 7y$$

in the form

$$3x + (-2y) + (-5x) + 7y$$

or

$$3x + (-5x) + (-2y) + 7y$$ Using the commutative and associative properties mentally

or

$$[3 + (-5)]x + [(-2) + 7]y$$ Using the distributive property

or

$$-2x + 5y$$

which leads to the same mechanical rule we had before for combining like terms. That is:

Combining Like Terms
Like terms are combined by adding their numerical coefficients.

Using this process, we would work the preceding example as follows:

$$3x - 2y - 5x + 7y \; = 3x - 5x - 2y + 7y \; = -2x + 5y$$

Example 22   Combine like terms:

(A) $2x - 3x$ (B) $-4x - 7x$
(C) $3x - 5y + 6x + 2y$ (D) $2x^2 - 3x - 5 + 5x^2 - 2x + 3$

Solution   (A) $2x - 3x = -x$ (B) $-4x - 7x = -11x$
(C) $3x - 5y + 6x + 2y = 9x - 3y$
(D) $2x^2 - 3x - 5 + 5x^2 - 2x + 3 = 7x^2 - 5x - 2$

Problem 22   Combine like terms:

(A) $4x - 5x$ (B) $-8x - 2x$
(C) $7x + 8y - 5x - 10y$ (D) $4x^2 + 5x - 8 - 3x^2 - 7x - 2$

REMOVING GROUPING SYMBOLS

How can we simplify expressions such as

$$2(3x - 5y) - 2(x + 3y)$$

We would like to multiply and combine like terms as we did when only plus signs were involved. Since any subtraction can be converted to addition, we can proceed as follows:

$$
\begin{aligned}
2(3x - 5y) - 2(x + 3y) \ &= 2[3x + (-5)y] + (-2)(x + 3y) \\
&= 6x + (-10)y + (-2)x + (-6)y \\
&= 6x - 10y - 2x - 6y \\
&= 4x - 16y
\end{aligned}
$$

Mechanically, we usually leave out the justifying steps in the dashed box and use the following process, which is simply an application of the distributive property.

Mechanics of Removing Grouping Symbols

Parentheses (and other symbols of grouping) can be cleared by multiplying each term within the parentheses by the coefficient of the parentheses.

$$
\begin{aligned}
2(3 + 5) &= 2 \cdot 3 + 2 \cdot 5 = 6 + 10 = 16 \\
-2(3 + 5) &= (-2) \cdot 3 + (-2) \cdot 5 = (-6) + (-10) = -16 \\
2(3 - 5) &= 2 \cdot 3 - 2 \cdot 5 = 6 - 10 = -4 \\
-2(3 - 5) &= (-2) \cdot 3 - (-2) \cdot 5 = -6 - (-10) = -6 + 10 = 4
\end{aligned}
$$

Example 23   Remove parentheses and simplify:

(A) $2(x - 3y) + 3(2x - y)$
(B) $4x(2x + y) - 3x(x - 3y)$

Solution   (A) $2(x - 3y) + 3(2x - y) = 2x - 6y + 6x - 3y$
$$= 8x - 9y$$

(B) $4x(2x + y) - 3x(x - 3y) = 8x^2 + 4xy - 3x^2 + 9xy$
$$= 5x^2 + 13xy$$

Problem 23 Remove parentheses and simplify:

(A) $3(2x - 3y) + 2(x - 2y)$ **(B)** $5x(x - 2y) - 3x(2x + y)$

MULTIPLYING BY +1 OR BY −1

If parentheses do not have a coefficient, we can treat them as if the coefficient were $+1$ or -1. Since for any number a, $a = 1 \cdot a$, we can think of an expression like $(x + 5y)$ as $+1 \cdot (x + 5y)$. The distributive property then allows us to rewrite the expression without parentheses:

$$(x + 5y) = +1 \cdot (x + 5y) = +1 \cdot x + 1 \cdot 5y = x + 5y$$

Similarly, since $-1 \cdot a = -a$, we can rewrite an expression like $-(2x - 3y)$ as $-1 \cdot (2x - 3y)$ and thus remove parentheses:

$$-(2x - 3y) = -1 \cdot (2x - 3y) = -1 \cdot 2x - (-1) \cdot 3y$$
$$= -2x - (-3y) = -2x + (+3y)$$
$$= -2x + 3y$$

This leads to simple rules for removing parentheses when they are not preceded by a coefficient:

1. If parentheses are preceded by a minus sign, the sign of each term within the parentheses is changed when the parentheses are removed.

Minus sign   Both signs are changed
$$-(a - b) = -a + b$$

2. If parentheses are preceded by a plus sign, the signs of the terms within the parentheses remain unchanged when the parentheses are removed.

Plus sign   No sign change
$$+(a - b) = a - b$$

No sign   No sign change
$$(a - b) = a - b$$

Using statements 1 and 2, we see that

$$(x + 7) - (x - 3) = x + 7 - x + 3 = 10$$

The first rule is particularly important. You can either apply the rule directly or remember that it is a result of thinking of parentheses preceded by a minus sign as being multiplied by -1.

Example 24   Remove parentheses and simplify:

(A) $(x + 5y) + (x - 3y)$
(B) $(x + 5y) - (2x - 3y)$

Solution   **(A)** $(x + 5y) + (x - 3y)$ $= 1(x + 5y) + 1(x - 3y)$ Think of the coefficient of $(x + 5y)$ and $(x - 3y)$ as 1. Then use the rule given above.

Think

$$= x + 5y + x - 3y$$

$$= 2x + 2y$$

(B) $(x + 5y) - (2x - 3y)$ $= 1(x + 5y) - 1(2x - 3y)$ Think of the coefficient of $-(2x - 3y)$ as -1. Then distribute -1 over $(2x - 3y)$.

Think

$$= x + 5y - 2x + 3y$$

$$= -x + 8y$$

Problem 24   Remove parentheses and simplify:

(A) $(3x + 2y) + (2x - 4y)$ **(B)** $(3x + 2y) - (2x - 4y)$

ORDER OF REMOVING GROUPING SYMBOLS

When grouping symbols exist within grouping symbols, we will follow the following rule to simplify the expression:

Order of Removing Grouping Symbols
Generally, when removing grouping symbols we work from the inside out, removing the innermost grouping symbols first.

Schematically, with the size of the grouping symbols exaggerated to clarify the pairing of the symbols, the rules says this:

1.   Remove these inner symbols first.

2. Remove these symbols next.
3. Remove these outer symbols last.

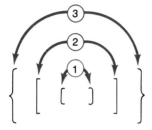   or, using just
parentheses,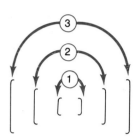

Example 25   Remove grouping symbols and combine like terms:

(A) $4x - 3[x - 2(x + 3)]$ (B) $u - \{u - [u - 2(u - 1)]\}$

Solution   We work from the "inside out," removing the innermost grouping symbols first.

(A) $4x - 3[x - 2(x + 3)] = 4x - 3[x - 2x - 6]$ Remove ( ) first; combine like terms.

$= 4x - 3[-x - 6]$ Remove [ ].

$= 4x + 3x + 18$ Combine like terms.

$= 7x + 18$

(B) $u - \{u - [u - 2(u - 1)]\}$ Work from inside out.

$= u - \{u - [u - 2u + 2]\}$ We can collect like terms as we go or wait until the end. Here we wait until the end.

$= u - \{u - u + 2u - 2\}$

$= u - u + u - 2u + 2$

$= -u + 2$

Collecting like terms as we go, we obtain the same result:

$u - \{u - [u - 2(u - 1)]\}$

$= u - \{u - [u - 2u + 2]\} = u - \{u - [-u + 2]\}$

$= u - \{u + u - 2\} = u - \{2u - 2\}$

$= u - 2u + 2 = -u + 2$

In expressions such as those in Example 25, we could use only parentheses for grouping and write

$4x - 3(x - 2(x + 3))$ in place of $4x - 3[x - 2(x + 3)]$

and

$$u - (u - (u - 2(u - 1))) \quad \text{in place of} \quad u - \{u - [u - 2(u - 1)]\}$$

but the use of brackets [   ] and braces {   } makes it easier to see the group-ings.

Problem 25 Remove grouping symbols and combine like terms:

(A) $3y + 2[y - 3(y - 5)]$ (B) $3m - \{m - [2m - (m - 1)]\}$

INSERTING GROUPING SYMBOLS

Later we will find it useful to reverse the process described above and insert grouping symbols. In Example 26 we are to replace each question mark with an appropriate algebraic expression (so that if the parentheses are removed we will obtain the expression to the left of the equal sign).

Example 26 Replace each question mark with an appropriate algebraic expression:

(A) $3x + 4a - 6b = 3x + 2(?)$ (B) $6a - 3x + 9y = 6a - 3(?)$
(C) $5 + 2x - 3y = 5 + (?)$ (D) $5 + 2x - 3y = 5 - (?)$

Solution (A) $3x + 4a - 6b = 3x + 2(2a - 3b)$ We note again that if parentheses are to
(B) $6a - 3x + 9y = 6a - 3(x - 3y)$ be preceded by a plus sign, the terms
(C) $5 + 2x - 3y = 5 + (2x - 3y)$ placed within the parentheses remain
(D) $5 + 2x - 3y = 5 - (-2x + 3y)$ unchanged. If parentheses are to be
   preceded by a minus sign, then each
   term placed inside the parentheses
   undergoes a sign change.

Problem 26 Repeat Example 26 for

(A) $2y + 3z - 4w = 2y + (?)$ (B) $2y + 3z - 4w = 2y - (?)$
(C) $a + 4b - 12c = a + 4(?)$ (D) $u - 6v - 9w = u - 3(?)$

ANSWERS TO
MATCHED PROBLEMS **20.** (A) -7 (B) 3 (C) -14
21. (A) 2 (B) -1 (C) -2
22. (A) $-x$ (B) $-10x$ (C) $2x - 2y$ (D) $x^2 - 2x - 10$
23. (A) $8x - 13y$ (B) $-x^2 - 13xy$
24. (A) $5x - 2y$ (B) $x + 6y$
25. (A) $-y + 30$ (B) $3m + 1$
26. (A) $3z - 4w$ (B) $-3z + 4w$ (C) $b - 3c$
    (D) $2v + 3w$

EXERCISE 2-6 A *Evaluate.*

1. $3 - 2 + 4$
2. $3 + 4 - 2$
3. $4 - 8 - 9$
4. $-8 + 4 - 9$
5. $-4 + 7 - 6$
6. $7 - 6 - 4$
7. $2 - 3 - 6 + 5$
8. $5 + 2 - 6 - 3$
9. $-3 - 2 + 6 - 4$
10. $-8 + 9 - 4 - 3$
11. $-7 + 1 + 6 + 2 - 1$
12. $9 - 5 - 4 + 7 - 6 + 10$
13. $-5 - 3 - 8 + 15 - 1$
14. $1 - 12 + 5 + 7 - 1 + 6 - 8$

Remove symbols of grouping where present and combine like terms.

15. $7x - 3x$
16. $9x - 4x$
17. $2x - 5x - x$
18. $4t - 8t - 9t$
19. $-3y + 2y - 5y - 6y$
20. $2y - 3y - 6y + 5y$
21. $2x - 3y - 5x$
22. $4y - 3x - y$
23. $2x + 8y - 7x - 5y$
24. $5m + 3n - m - 9n$
25. $2(m + 3n) + 4(m - 2n)$
26. $3(u - 2v) + 2(3u + v)$
27. $2(x - y) - 3(x - 2y)$
28. $4(m - 3n) - 3(2m + 4n)$
29. $(x + 3y) + (2x - 5y)$
30. $(2u - v) + (3u - 5v)$
31. $x - (2x - y)$
32. $m - (3m + n)$
33. $(x + 3y) - (2x - 5y)$
34. $(2u - v) - (3u - 5v)$
35. $3(2x - 3y) - (2x - y)$
36. $2(3m - n) - (4m + 2n)$

B 37. $3xy + 4xy - xy$
38. $3xy - xy + 4xy$
39. $-x^2y + 3x^2y - 5x^2y$
40. $-4r^3t^3 - 7r^3t^3 + 9r^3t^3$
41. $3x^2 - 2x + 5 - x^2 + 4x - 8$
42. $y^3 + 4y^2 - 10 + 2y^3 - y + 7$
43. $2x^2y + 3xy^2 - 5xy + 2xy^2 - xy$
44. $a^2 - 3ab + b^2 + 2a^2 + 3ab - 2b^2$
45. $x - 3(x + 2y) + 5y$
46. $y - 2(x - y) - 3x$
47. $-3(-t + 7) - (t - 1)$
48. $-2(-3x + 1) - (2x + 4)$

49. $-2(y - 7) - 3(2y + 1) - (-5y + 7)$

50. $2(x - 1) - 3(2x - 3) - (4x - 5)$

51. $3x(2x^2 - 4) - 2(3x^3 - x)$ **52.** $5y(2y - 3) + 3y(-2y + 4)$

53. $3x - 2[2x - (x - 7)]$ **54.** $y - [5 - 3(y - 2)]$

55. $2t - 3t[4 - 2(t - 1)]$ **56.** $2u - 3u[4 - (u - 3)]$

Combine like terms.

57. $23{,}041 - 2{,}315 - 43{,}201 + 12{,}792$

58. $-623 + 328 - 34 - 512 + 402$

59. $312x + 203y - 278x - 461y$

60. $2{,}530u - 1{,}462v - 187u - 239v$

61. $89u - 106v - 137u + 47v$

62. $4{,}881x - 783y - 6{,}008x - 608y$

Replace each question mark with an appropriate algebraic expression.

63. $2 + 3x - y = 2 + (?)$ **64.** $5 + m - 2n = 5 + (?)$

65. $2 + 3x - y = 2 - (?)$ **66.** $5 + m - 2n = 5 - (?)$

67. $x - 4y - 8z = x - 4(?)$ **68.** $2x - 3a + 12b = 2x - 3(?)$

69. $w^2 - x + y - z = w^2 - (?)$ **70.** $w^2 - x + y - z = w^2 + (?)$

71. The width of a rectangle is 5 meters less than its length. If x is the length of the rectangle, write an algebraic expression that represents the perimeter of the rectangle. Then multiply and combine like terms.

72. The length of a rectangle is 8 feet more than its width. If y is the width of the rectangle, write an algebraic expression that represents its area. Change the expression to a form without parentheses.

C   *Remove symbols of grouping and combine like terms.*

73. $x - \{x - [x - (x - 1)]\}$

74. $2t - 3\{t + 2[t - (t + 5)] + 1\}$

75. $2x[3x - 2(2x + 1)] - 3x[8 + (2x - 4)]$

76. $-2t\{-2t(-t - 3) - [t^2 - t(2t + 3)]\}$

77. $3x^2 - 2\{x - x[x + 4(x - 3)] - 5\}$

78. $w - \{x - [z - (w - x) - z] - (x - w)\} + x$

79.   A coin purse contains dimes and quarters only. There are four more dimes than quarters. If x represents the number of quarters, write an algebraic expression that represents the value of the money in the purse in cents. Clear grouping symbols and combine like terms.

80.   A pile of coins consists of nickels, dimes, and quarters. There are twice as many dimes as nickels and four fewer quarters than dimes. If x represents the number of nickels, write an algebraic expression that represents the value of the pile of coins in cents. Remove grouping symbols and combine like terms.

2-7
EQUATIONS INVOLVING INTEGERS

- Solutions to Equations
- Solving Equations
- Equations with No Solution or with Infinitely Many Solutions
- Formulas and Literal Equations

We have reached the point where we can discuss methods of solving equations other than by guessing. For example, you would not be likely to guess the solution of

$$2(2x + 5) + 2x = 52$$

an equation related to a practical problem that we will consider later.

Up to now we have mainly been dealing with algebraic *expressions* such as $2(2x + 5) + 2x$, the left side of the above *equation*. The inclusion of the equal sign in the statement changes our emphasis: We are now interested in what values of the variable x will make the statement true. You can substitute 7 for x and find that the expression on the left side of the equation is, in fact, 52. In this section we will develop a systematic procedure for finding that $x = 7$.

SOLUTIONS TO EQUATIONS

A **solution** or **root** of an equation in one variable is a replacement of the variable by a number that makes the left side equal to the right. For example, -2 is a solution of

$$4 + x = 2$$

since

$$4 + (-2) = 2$$

To **solve an equation** is to find all its solutions.

Knowing what we mean by a solution of an equation is one thing; finding it is another. Our objective now is to develop a systematic method of solving equations that is free from guesswork. We start by introducing the idea of equivalent equations. We say that **two equations are equivalent** if they both have exactly the same solutions.

The basic idea in solving equations is to perform operations on equations that produce simpler equivalent equations and to continue the process until we reach an equation whose solution is obvious—generally, an equation such as

$$x = -3$$

With a little practice you will find the methods that we are going to develop very easy to use and very powerful. The following properties of equality produce equivalent equations when applied.

Properties of Equality

(A) ADDITION PROPERTY   The same quantity may be added to each side of an equation.
$$a = b$$
$$a + c = b + c$$

(B) SUBTRACTION PROPERTY   The same quantity may be subtracted from each side of an equation.
$$a = b$$
$$a - c = b - c$$

(C) MULTIPLICATION PROPERTY   Each side of an equation may be multiplied by the same nonzero quantity.
$$a = b$$
$$ca = cb$$

(D) DIVISION PROPERTY   Each side of an equation may be divided by the same nonzero quantity.
$$a = b$$
$$\frac{a}{c} = \frac{b}{c}$$

We can also think of the process of solving equations as a game. The objective of the game is to isolate the variable (with a coefficient of 1) on one side of the equation (usually the left), leaving a constant on the other side. The rules of the game include the equality properties given above as well as the simplifying processes discussed in Sec. 2-6.

SOLVING EQUATIONS

We are now ready to solve equations. Several examples will illustrate the process.

Example 27   Solve $x - 5 = -2$ and check.

Solution
$$x - 5 = -2$$ How can we isolate x on the left side?

$$x - 5 + 5 = -2 + 5$$ Add 5 to each side (addition property of equality).

$$x = 3$$ Solution.

Check $x - 5 = -2$ Replace x with 3.

$3 - 5 \overset{?}{=} -2$ Evaluate both sides.

$-2 \overset{\checkmark}{=} -2$ We have a check since both sides are equal.

Note: After some practice the steps in the dashed boxes should be done mentally. If in doubt, include them.

Problem 27   Solve $x + 8 = -6$ and check.

Example 28   Solve $-3x = 15$ and check.

Solution
$$-3x = 15$$ How can we make the coefficient of x positive 1 (that is, how can we isolate x on the left side)?

$$\frac{-3x}{-3} = \frac{15}{-3}$$ Divide each side by -3 (division property of equality). Note that adding 3 to each side (a common mistake) will not isolate x.

$$x = -5$$ Solution.

Problem 28   Solve $5x = -20$ and check.

CAUTION

Do not confuse the following two types of equations:

(A) $x + 2 = 8$ **(B)** $2x = 8$

Right method of solution for each:

(A) $x + 2 = 8$ **(B)** $2x = 8$

$\quad\quad x + 2 - 2 = 8 - 2 \quad\quad\quad\quad \dfrac{2x}{2} = \dfrac{8}{2}$

$\quad\quad\quad\quad\quad x = 6 \quad\quad\quad\quad\quad\quad\quad x = 4$

To remove the 2 from the left side in either equation, we perform the operation opposite of that in which the 2 is involved—for the first equation the opposite of addition is subtraction; for the second equation the opposite of multiplication is division.

The equations we are solving here involve no power of the variable higher than 1. For reasons that will be apparent in Chapters 4 and 5, such equations are called **linear** or **first-degree equations**. We can state a strategy for solving such equations.

Strategy for Solving Linear Equations

Objective: Isolate the variable (with a coefficient of 1) on one side of the equation (usually the left), leaving a constant on the other side. To do this:

1. Simplify each side of the equation separately by removing any grouping symbols and combining any like terms.
2. Use addition or subtraction properties of equality to get all variable terms on one side (usually the left) and all constant terms on the other side (usually the right). Simplify both sides again.
3. Finally, if the variable has a coefficient other than 1, use the multiplication or division property of equality to make the coefficient of the variable 1.
4. Check your answer by substituting it into the original equation.

The following examples are a little more difficult, but not a lot. The above strategy should help you sort out the details.

Example 29   Solve $2x - 8 = 5x + 4$ and check.

Solution

$$2x - 8 = 5x + 4$$

To remove -8 from the left side, add 8 to both sides (addition property of equality).

$$2x - 8 + 8 = 5x + 4 + 8$$
$$2x = 5x + 12$$

$$2x - 5x = 5x + 12 - 5x$$

To remove $5x$ from the right side, subtract $5x$ from both sides (subtraction property of equality).

$$-3x = 12$$

$$\frac{-3x}{-3} = \frac{12}{-3}$$

To isolate x on the left side with a coefficient of $+1$, divide both sides by -3 (division property of equality).

$$x = -4$$

We have solved the equation!

Check

$$2x - 8 = 5x + 4$$
$$2(-4) - 8 \stackrel{?}{=} 5(-4) + 4$$
$$-8 - 8 \stackrel{?}{=} -20 + 4$$
$$-16 \stackrel{\checkmark}{=} -16$$

Replace x with -4 and proceed as in Examples 27 and 28.

Problem 29   Solve $3x - 9 = 7x + 3$ and check.

Example 30   Solve and check:

(A) $3x - 2(2x - 5) = 2(x + 3) - 8$

(B) $3x^2 + 5(x - 1) = 3x(x + 2) - 3$

Solution **(A)** This equation is not as difficult as it might at first appear. Simplify the expressions on each side of the equal sign first, and then proceed as in the preceding example. (Note that some steps in the following solution are done mentally.)

$$3x - 2(2x - 5 = 2(x + 3) - 8 \qquad \text{Remove grouping symbols.}$$
$$3x - 4x + 10 = 2x + 6 - 8 \qquad \text{Combine like terms.}$$
$$-x + 10 = 2x - 2 \qquad \text{Subtract 10 from each side.}$$
$$-x = 2x - 12 \qquad \text{Subtract } 2x \text{ from each side.}$$
$$-3x = -12 \qquad \text{Divide each side by } -3.$$
$$x = 4 \qquad \text{We now have the solution.}$$

Check
$$3x - 2(2x - 5) = 2(x + 3) - 8 \qquad \text{Replace } x \text{ with 4.}$$
$$3(4) - 2[2(4) - 5] \overset{?}{=} 2[(4) + 3] - 8$$
$$12 - 2(8 - 5) \overset{?}{=} 2(7) - 8$$
$$12 - 2(3) \overset{?}{=} 14 - 8$$
$$12 - 6 \overset{?}{=} 6$$
$$6 \overset{\checkmark}{=} 6$$

(B)
$$3x^2 + 5(x - 1) = 3x(x + 2) - 3 \qquad \text{Clear parentheses.}$$
$$3x^2 + 5x - 5 = 3x^2 + 6x - 3 \qquad \begin{array}{l}\text{Note how } 3x^2 \text{ drops}\\ \text{out by subtracting it}\end{array}$$
$$\boxed{3x^2 + 5x - 5 - 3x^2 = 3x^2 + 6x - 3 - 3x^2} \quad \text{from each side.†}$$
$$5x - 5 = 6x - 3 \qquad \text{Add 5 to each side.}$$
$$5x = 6x + 2 \qquad \begin{array}{l}\text{Subtract } 6x \text{ from each}\\ \text{side.}\end{array}$$
$$-x = 2 \qquad \begin{array}{l}\text{Multiply each side by}\\ -1.\end{array}$$
$$x = -2$$

Check
$$3x^2 + 5(x - 1) = 3x(x + 2) - 3$$
$$3(-2)^2 + 5[(-2) - 1] \overset{?}{=} 3(-2)[(-2) + 2] - 3$$
$$12 + (-15) \overset{?}{=} (-6)(0) - 3$$
$$-3 \overset{\checkmark}{=} -3$$

Problem 30 Solve and check:

(A) $8x - 3(x - 4) = 3(x - 4) + 6$ **(B)** $x(x + 3) + 3 = x^2 + 4(x + 1)$

† If the square terms did not drop out, we would be stuck at this time.

EQUATIONS WITH NO SOLUTION OR INFINITELY MANY SOLUTIONS

The equations studied so far all had exactly one solution. It is possible that equations such as these have no solution. This will be true if the equation can be changed into an equivalent form that is never true, for example $0 = 1$. It is also possible that every number—that is, every number in the replacement set—is a solution. This will be true if the equation can be changed into an equivalent form that is always true, for example, $x = x$ or $3 = 3$.

Example 31   Solve:

(A) $2(x - 3) = 2(x + 1) - 5$ (B) $2(x - 3) = 2(x + 1) - 8$

Solution   (A) $2(x - 3) = 2(x + 1) - 5$ Remove grouping symbols.
$2x - 6 = 2x + 2 - 5$ Combine like terms.
$2x - 6 = 2x - 3$ Subtract 2x from each side.
$-6 = -3$ Impossible!

Therefore, the equation has no solution.

(B) $2(x - 3) = 2(x + 1) - 8$
$2x - 6 = 2x + 2 - 8$
$2x - 6 = 2x - 6$ This is always true.

Therefore, every number in the replacement set is a solution to the equation.

Problem 31   Solve:

(A) $7 + 3(x - 5) = 4x - (x + 5)$ (B) $7 + 3(x - 5) = 4x - (x + 8)$

FORMULAS AND LITERAL EQUATIONS

The familiar formula for the perimeter of a rectangle, $P = 2l + 2w$, contains three variables: P, l, and w. As written, the formula expresses the perimeter P in terms of the length l and width w. We can also think of this formula as an equation in any of the three variables, and since none of the variables occurs with power higher than 1, it is a linear equation in each variable. We can solve such an equation for any of the variables by treating the other variables as if they were constant. Since we are manipulating letters (variables) and letters remain in the solution, such equations are also called **literal equations**.

Example 32 Solve these equations, the perimeter and area formulas for rectangles, for w:

(A) $A = lw$ (B) $P = 2l + 2w$

Solution (A) $A = lw$ The variable w is isolated on the
                          right side in a single term; we solve
                          by dividing by its coefficient, l

$$\frac{A}{l} = w$$

(B) $P = 2l + 2w$

$P - 2l = 2l + 2w - 2l$ Subtract $2l$ from both sides. The quantity $2l$
                         will be treated like a number.

$P - 2l = 2w$ On the right-hand side, $2l + 2w - 2l = 2l - 2l + 2w$
                         $= 0 + 2w = 2w$

$$\frac{P - 2l}{2} = w$$ Divide both sides by 2.

Notice that the solutions must be left in fraction form, since we cannot actually perform the division. Fractional forms will be investigated in detail in the next chapter.

Problem 32 Solve the equations in Example 32 for l.

ANSWERS TO
MATCHED PROBLEMS

27. $x = -14$ **28.** $x = -4$ **29.** $x = -3$
30. (A) -9 (B) -1
31. (A) No solution   (B) All numbers
32. (A) $l = \dfrac{A}{w}$ (B) $l = \dfrac{P - 2w}{2}$

EXERCISE 2-7 A *Solve and check.*

1. $x + 5 = 8$ **2.** $x + 2 = 7$ **3.** $x + 8 = 5$

4. $x + 7 = 2$ **5.** $x + 9 = -3$ **6.** $x + 4 = -6$

7. $x - 3 = 2$ **8.** $x - 4 = 3$ **9.** $x - 5 = -8$

10. $x - 7 = -9$ **11.** $y + 13 = 0$ **12.** $x - 5 = 0$

13. $4x = 32$ **14.** $9x = 36$ **15.** $6x = -24$

16. $7x = -21$ **17.** $-3x = 12$ **18.** $-2x = 18$

19. $-8x = -24$ **20.** $-9x = -27$ **21.** $3y = 0$

22. $-5m = 0$ **23.** $4x - 7 = 5$ **24.** $3y - 8 = 4$

25. $2y + 5 = 9$ **26.** $4x + 3 = 19$ **27.** $2y + 5 = -1$

28. $2w + 18 = -2$ **29.** $-3t + 8 = -13$

30. $-4m + 3 = -9$ **31.** $4m = 2m + 8$

32. $3x = x + 6$ **33.** $2x = 8 - 2x$

34. $3x = 10 - 7x$ **35.** $2n = 5n + 12$

36. $3y = 7y + 8$ **37.** $2x - 7 = x + 1$

38. $4x - 9 = 3x + 2$ **39.** $3x - 8 = x + 6$

40. $4y + 8 = 2y - 6$ **41.** $2t + 9 = 5t - 6$

42. $3x - 4 = 6x - 19$

B   **43.** $x - 3 = x + 7$ **44.** $2y + 8 = 2y - 6$

45. $2x + 2(x - 6) = 52$ **46.** $5x + 10(x + 7) = 100$

47. $x + (x + 2) + (x + 4) = 54$ **48.** $10x + 25(x - 3) = 275$

49. $2(x + 7) - 2 = x - 3$ **50.** $5 + 4(t - 2) = 2(t - 7) + 1$

51. $-3(4 - t) = 5 - (t + 1)$

52. $5x - (7x - 4) - 2 = 5 - (3x + 2)$

53. $x(x + 2) = x(x + 4) - 12$

54. $x(x - 1) + 5 = x^2 + x - 3$

55. $t(t - 6) + 8 = t^2 - 6t - 3$

56. $x(x - 4) - 2 = x^2 - 4(x + 3)$

57. $3 + 2(x - 4) = x - (5 - x)$

58. $x + 7 = 2x - (5 - x)$

59. $3x - (x + 1) = 2x + 1$

60. $3x - (1 - x) = x + 3(x - 1)$

61. $x^2 + 3x + 5 = x^2 + 3(x + 1) - 1$

62. $2(x - 5) + 8 = -2(1 - x)$

63. $2 - x = x - 2(x - 1)$

64. $x = x - (1 - x) - (x - 1)$

C   *Solve each equation for the indicated variable.*

65. $A = bh$; b **66.** $A = bh$; h

67. $d = rt; r$ **68.** $d = rt; t$

69. $I = prt; r$ **70.** $I = prt; t$

71. $A = P(1 + rt); P$ **72.** $A = P(1 + rt); t$

Solve and check:

73. $-307x + 2{,}132 = 4{,}281$

74. $642x - 1{,}304 = -8{,}366$

75. $391x + 2{,}312 = 161x + 1{,}162$

76. $31x - 420 = 73x - 714$

77. $u - [u - 3(u - 1)] = u - (1 - u)$

78. $3[t - (1 + t)] = t + 4$

79. $1 - [x - (2 - x)] = x - (1 - x)$

80. $1 - w = 1 - [w - (1 - w)]$

81. $3 + z - 5(z + 3) = 6 - z$

82. $7 + x - (3 - 2x) = 6 - \{1 - [2x - (1 - x)]\}$

83. Which of the following are equivalent to $3x - 6 = 6$; $3x = 12$, $3x = 0$, $x = 4$, $x = 0$?

84. Which of the following are equivalent to $2x + 5 = x - 3$; $2x = x - 8$, $2x = x + 2$, $3x = -8$, $x = -8$?

2-8
WORD PROBLEMS AND APPLICATIONS

- Solving Word Problems
- Strategy

In preceding sections we considered the problem of translating words into algebraic expressions and equations. We are now ready to consider the more general problem of solving word problems and real-world applications using algebra. We will consider a number of examples in detail and will state a strategy (method of attack) that will be useful in many problems. Word problems will be considered again in Chapter 3 in more detail and with fewer restrictions.

SOLVING WORD PROBLEMS

Let us start by solving a fairly simple problem dealing with numbers. Through this problem you will learn some basic ideas about setting up and solving word problems in general.

Example 33   Find three consecutive integers whose sum is 66.

Solution   Let

$$x = \text{the first integer}$$

Identify one of the unknowns with a variable, say x, then write other unknowns in terms of this variable. In this case, x, $x + 1$, and $x + 2$ represent three consecutive integers starting with the integer x.

Then

$$x + 1 = \text{the next integer}$$

and

$$x + 2 = \text{the third integer}$$

$$x + (x + 1) + (x + 2) = 66$$

Write an equation that relates the unknown quantities with other facts in the problem (sum of three consecutive integers is 66).

$$x + x + 1 + x + 2 = 66$$

Solve the equation.

$$3x + 3 = 66$$

$$3x = 63$$

$$\left.\begin{array}{r} x = 21 \\ x + 1 = 22 \\ x + 2 = 23 \end{array}\right\}$$

Write all answers requested.

Check $\left.\begin{array}{r} 21 \\ 22 \\ 23 \\ \hline 66 \end{array}\right\}$ Three consecutive integers

Checking your answer in the original equation is not enough, since you might have made a mistake in setting up the equation. A final check is provided only if the conditions in the original problem are satisfied.

Thus we have found three consecutive integers whose sum is 66.

Problem 33   Find three consecutive integers whose sum is 54.

Example 34   Find three consecutive even numbers such that twice the second plus 3 times the third is 7 times the first.

Solution   Let

$$x = \text{the first even number}$$

Then

$$x + 2 = \text{the second even number}$$

and

$$x + 4 = \text{the third even number}$$

$$\begin{pmatrix} \text{Twice the second} \\ \text{even number} \end{pmatrix} + \begin{pmatrix} \text{Three times the} \\ \text{third even number} \end{pmatrix} = \begin{pmatrix} \text{Seven times the} \\ \text{first even number} \end{pmatrix}$$

$$2(x + 2) \quad + \quad 3(x + 4) \quad = \quad 7x$$
$$2x + 4 + 3x + 12 = 7x$$
$$5x + 16 = 7x$$
$$-2x = -16$$
$$x = 8 \qquad \text{First even number}$$
$$x + 2 = 10 \qquad \text{Second even number}$$
$$x + 4 = 12 \qquad \text{Third even number}$$

Check First, it is true that 8, 10, and 12 are three consecutive even numbers.

$$2 \cdot 10 + 3 \cdot 12 \overset{?}{=} 7 \cdot 8$$
$$20 + 36 \overset{?}{=} 56$$
$$56 \overset{\checkmark}{=} 56$$

Problem 34 Find three consecutive even numbers such that the second plus twice the third is 4 times the first.

Example 35 Find the dimensions of a rectangle with a perimeter of 52 centimeters if its length is 5 centimeters more than twice its width.

Solution First draw a figure, then label parts using an appropriate variable. In this case, since the length is given in terms of the width, we let x represent the width; then the length will be given by $2x + 5$.

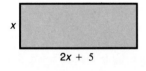

$$2(\text{Length}) + 2(\text{width}) = \text{perimeter}$$
$$2(2x + 5) + 2x = 52$$
$$4x + 10 + 2x = 52$$
$$6x = 42$$
$$x = 7 \text{ centimeters} \qquad \text{Width}$$
$$2x + 5 = 19 \text{ centimeters} \qquad \text{Length}$$

Check First, 19 is 5 more than twice 7.

$$2 \cdot 19 + 2 \cdot 7 \overset{?}{=} 52$$
$$38 + 14 \overset{?}{=} 52$$
$$52 \overset{\checkmark}{=} 52$$

Problem 35 Find the dimensions of a rectangle, given that the perimeter of the rectangle is 30 meters and the length of the rectangle is 7 meters more than its width.

Example 36   In a pile of coins that is composed of only dimes and nickels, there are 7 more dimes than nickels. If the total value of all the coins in the pile is $1, how many of each type of coin are in the pile?

Solution   Let

x = the number of nickels in the pile

Do not confuse the number of nickels with the value of the nickels or the number of dimes with the value of the dimes.

Then

$x + 7$ = the number of dimes in the pile

$$\left(\begin{array}{c}\text{Value of nickels}\\ \text{in cents}\end{array}\right) + \left(\begin{array}{c}\text{Value of dimes}\\ \text{in cents}\end{array}\right) = \left(\begin{array}{c}\text{Value of pile}\\ \text{in cents}\end{array}\right)$$

$$5x \quad + \quad 10(x + 7) \quad = \quad 100$$

The value of the nickels in cents is 5 cents times the number of nickels. Similarly, for the value of dimes.

$$5x + 10x + 70 = 100$$

$$15x = 30$$

$$x = 2 \qquad \text{Nickels}$$

$$x + 7 = 9 \qquad \text{Dimes}$$

Check   First, 9 dimes is 7 more than 2 nickels.

$$\begin{array}{rl}\text{Value of nickels in cents} = & 10\\ \text{Value of dimes in cents} = & \underline{90}\\ \text{Total value} = & 100\end{array}$$

Problem 36   A boy has dimes and quarters worth $1.80 in his pocket. If there are twice as many dimes as quarters, how many of each does he have?

Example 37   A car leaves town A and travels at 55 miles per hour toward town B at the same time a car leaves town B and travels 45 miles per hour toward town A. If the towns are 600 miles apart, how long will it take the two cars to meet? Set up an equation and solve.

Solution   Let t = number of hours until both cars meet. Then draw a diagram and label known and unknown parts:

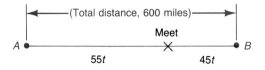

$$\left(\begin{array}{c}\text{Distance car}\\\text{from } A \text{ travels}\end{array}\right) + \left(\begin{array}{c}\text{Distance car}\\\text{from } B \text{ travels}\end{array}\right) = \left(\begin{array}{c}\text{Total}\\\text{distance}\end{array}\right)$$

$$55t \quad + \quad 45t \quad = \quad 600$$

$$100t = 600$$

$$t = \frac{600}{100}$$

$$t = 6 \text{ hours}$$

Problem 37   If an older printing press can print 50 handbills per minute and a newer press can print 75, how long will it take both together to print 1,500 handbills? Set up an equation and solve.

STRATEGY

You are now beginning to see the power of algebra. It was a historic occasion when it was realized that a solution to a problem that was difficult to obtain by arithmetical computation could be obtained instead by a deductive process involving a symbol that represented the solution.

There are many different types of algebraic applications—so many, in fact, that no single approach will apply to all. The following suggestions, however, may be of help to you:

Strategy for Solving Word Problems

1. Read the problem very carefully—several times if necessary.
2. Write down important facts and relationships on a piece of scratch paper. Draw figures if it is helpful. Write down any formulas that might be relevant.
3. Identify the unknown quantities in terms of a single variable if possible.
4. Look for key words and relationships in a problem that will lead to an equation involving the variables introduced in step 3.
5. Solve the equation. Write down all the solutions asked for in the original problem.
6. Check the solutions in the original problem.

The key step, and usually the most difficult one, in the above strategy is the fourth: finding the equation. There is no set procedure for carrying out this step. A variety of techniques will be illustrated in examples throughout the text. A more general approach, which some students find helpful, is suggested in Appendix B.

Remember, mathematics is not a spectator sport! Just reading examples is not enough; you must set up and solve problems yourself.

33. 17, 18, 19   **34.** 10, 12, 14
35. 4 meters by 11 meters   **36.** 4 quarters and 8 dimes
37. 12 minutes

EXERCISE 2-8   A

1. Find three consecutive integers whose sum is 78.

2. Find three consecutive integers whose sum is 96.

3. Find three consecutive even numbers whose sum is 54.

4. Find three consecutive even numbers whose sum is 42.

5. How long would it take you to drive from San Francisco to Los Angeles, a distance of about 424 miles, if you could average 53 miles per hour? (Use $d = rt$.)

6. If you drove from Berkeley to Lake Tahoe, a distance of 200 miles, in 4 hours, what was your average speed?

7. About 8 times the height of an iceberg of uniform cross section is under water as is above the water. If the total height of an iceberg from bottom to top is 117 feet, how much is above and how much is below the surface?

8. A chord called an octave can be produced by dividing a stretched string into two parts so that one part is twice as long as the other part. How long will each part of the string be if the total length of the string is 57 inches?

9. The sun is about 390 times as far from the earth as the moon. If the sun is approximately 93,210,000 miles from the earth, how far is the moon from the earth?

10. You are asked to construct a triangle with two equal angles so that the third angle is twice the size of either of the two equal ones. How large should each angle be? [*Note:* The sum of the three angles in any triangle is 180°.]

B   11. Find three consecutive odd numbers such that the sum of the first and second is 5 more than the third.

12. Find three consecutive odd numbers such that the sum of the second and third is 1 more than 3 times the first.

13. Find the dimensions of a rectangle with perimeter 66 feet if its length is 3 feet more than twice the width.

14. Find the dimensions of a rectangle with perimeter 128 inches if its length is 6 inches less than 4 times the width.

15. In a pile of coins containing only quarters and dimes, there are 3 fewer quarters than dimes. If the total value of the pile is $2.75, how many of each type of coin is in the pile?

16. If you have 20 dimes and nickels in your pocket worth $1.40, how many of each do you have?

17. A toy rocket shot vertically upward with an initial velocity of 160 feet per second (fps) has at time t a velocity given by the equation $v = 160 - 32t$, where air resistance is neglected. In how many seconds will the rocket reach its highest point? [*Hint:* Find t when $v = 0$.]

18. In the preceding problem, when will the rocket's velocity be 32 feet per second?

19. Air temperature drops approximately 5°F per 1,000 feet in altitude above the surface of the earth up to 30,000 feet. If T represents temperature and A represents altitude in thousands of feet, and if the temperature on the ground is 60°F, then we can write

$$T = 60 - 5A \qquad 0 \leq A \leq 30$$

If you were in a balloon, how high would you be if the thermometer registered $-50°F$?

20. A mechanic charges $15 per hour for his labor and $12 per hour for his assistant. On a repair job the bill was $344 with $246 for labor and $98 for parts. If the assistant worked 2 hours less than the mechanic, how many hours did each work?

C 21. A mother and son in a kayak went up a river and back in 6 hours. If their rate up the river was 2 miles per hour and back 4 miles per hour, how far did they go up the river?

22. You are at a river resort and rent a motor boat for 5 hours at 7 A.M. You are told that the boat will travel at 8 miles per hour upstream and 12 miles per hour returning. You decide that you would like to go as far up the river as you can and still be back at noon. At what time should you turn back, and how far from the resort will you be at that time?

23. One ship leaves England and another leaves the United States at the same time. The distance between the two ports is 3,150 miles. The ship from the United States averages 25 miles per hour and the one from England 20 miles per hour. If they both travel the same route, how long will it take the ships to reach a rendezvous point, and how far from the United States will they be at that time?

24. At 8 A.M. your father left by car on a long trip. An hour later you find that he has left his wallet behind. You decide to take another car to try to catch up with him. From past experience you know that he averages about 42 miles per hour. If you can average 54 miles per hour, how long will it take you to catch him?

25. In a computer center two electronic card sorters are used to sort 52,000 IBM cards. If the first sorter operates at 225 cards per minute and the second sorter operates at 175 cards per minute, how long will it take both sorters together to sort all the cards?

26. Find four consecutive even numbers so the sum of the first and last is the same as the sum of the second and third. (Be careful!)

2-9 CHAPTER REVIEW

The natural numbers are also called **positive integers**. For each positive integer there is a corresponding **negative integer**. The positive integers and negative integers together with 0 make up the set of **integers** $J = \{ \ldots, -2, -1, 0, +1, +2, \ldots \}$. The integers can be represented on a **number line**:

$$\begin{array}{ccccccccccccc} & | & | & | & | & | & | & | & | & | & | & | & | \\ \hline -6 & -5 & -4 & -3 & -2 & -1 & 0 & 1 & 2 & 3 & 4 & 5 & 6 \end{array} \longrightarrow \qquad (2\text{-}1)$$

The **opposite** of a nonzero integer is produced by changing its sign; 0 is its own opposite. The **absolute value** of a number is given by

$$|x| = \begin{cases} x & \text{if } x \text{ is positive or } 0 \\ -x & \text{if } x \text{ is negative} \end{cases} \qquad (2\text{-}2)$$

For any integer a, $a + 0 = 0 + a = a$. To **add** two nonzero integers:

1. If they are of like sign, add the numerical parts and attach the common sign.
2. If they are of opposite sign, take the difference of the numerical parts and attach the sign of the larger numerical part.

Addition is **commutative** $[a + b = b + a]$ and **associative** $[a + (b + c) = (a + b) + c]$. $(2\text{-}3)$

To **subtract** two integers, change the sign of the number being subtracted and add: $a - b = a + (-b)$. For integers a and b, $a < b$ if there is a positive integer p such that $a + p = b$. $(2\text{-}4)$

For any integer a, $a \cdot 0 = 0 \cdot a = 0$. To **multiply** two nonzero integers:

1. If they are of like sign, multiply the numerical parts and attach a plus sign.

2. If they are of opposite sign, multiply the numerical parts and attach a minus sign.

Multiplication is **commutative** $[ab = ba]$, **associative** $[a(bc) = (ab)c]$, and **distributive** over addition $[a(b + c) = ab + ac]$. Moreover, $(+1)a = a$, $(-1)a = -a$, $(-a)b = a(-b) = -(ab)$, and $(-a)(-b) = ab$ for all integers a and b.

For any nonzero integer a, $0 \div a = 0$ and $a \div 0$ is not defined; $0 \div 0$ is not defined. To **divide** two nonzero integers:

1. If they are of like sign, divide the numerical parts and attach a plus sign.
2. If they are of opposite sign, divide the numerical parts and attach a minus sign. *(2-5)*

The plus sign may be omitted in denoting positive integers. Terms in algebraic expressions may be rearranged as long as the sign preceding each term accompanies it in the process. A grouping symbol can be removed from an expression by multiplying each term within the symbol by the coefficient of the symbol. *(2-6)*

The **solution** of an equation in one variable is a replacement of the variable that makes the equation true. To **solve** an equation means to find all its solutions. Two equations are **equivalent** if they have exactly the same solutions. These **properties of equality** produce equivalent equations: if $a = b$, then

$a + c = b + c$	**Addition property**
$a - c = b - c$	**Subtraction property**
$a \cdot c = b \cdot c$ $(c \neq 0)$	**Multiplication property**
$a/c = b/c$ $(c \neq 0)$	**Division property**

The basic strategy for solving equations is to

1. Simplify each side.
2. Get all variable terms on one side and constant terms on the other by using the addition and subtraction properties. Simplify each side.
3. Use the multiplication or division property to make the coefficient of the variable 1.

The same strategy can be applied to solving **literal equations**, that is, equations involving more than one variable that are to be solved for one of the variables, and no variable is raised to a power other than 1. *(2-7)*

A general strategy for solving word problems is, in brief:

1. Read the problem very carefully.
2. Write down the important facts and relationships.

3. Identify the unknown quantities in terms of one variable.
4. Find the equation.
5. Solve the equation and write down all solutions asked for.
6. Check the solutions. *(2-8)*

REVIEW EXERCISE 2-9

Work through all the problems in this chapter review and check answers in the back of the book. (Answers to all review problems are there, and following each answer is a number in italics indicating the section in which that type of problem is discussed.) Where weaknesses show up, review appropriate sections in the text.

A *Evaluate as indicated.*

1. $-(+4)$

2. $|-(+3)|$

3. $(-8) + (+3)$

4. $(-9) + (-4)$

5. $(-3) - (-9)$

6. $(+4) - (+7)$

7. $(-7)(-4)$

8. $(+3)(-6)$

9. $(-16)/(+4)$

10. $(-12)/(-2)$

11. $0/(+2)$

12. $(-6)/0$

13. $-6 + 8 - 5 + 1$

14. $(-2)(+5) + (-6)$

15. $(-4)(-3) - (+20)$

16. $\dfrac{-8}{-2} - (-4)$

17. $(-6)(0) + \dfrac{0}{-3}$

18. $\dfrac{-9}{+3} - \dfrac{-12}{-4}$

Remove symbols of grouping, if present, and combine like terms.

19. $4x - 3 - 2x - 5$

20. $(2x - 3) + (3x + 1)$

21. $3(m + 2n) - (m - 3n)$

22. $2(x - 3y) - 4(2x + 3y)$

Solve and check.

23. $4x - 9 = x - 15$

24. $2x - 5 = 3x + 2$

25. Express each quantity by means of an appropriate integer:
    (A) Salton Sea's surface at 245 feet below sea level
    (B) Mount Whitney's height of 14,495 feet

26. Find three consecutive integers whose sum is 159.

B *Evaluate for $x = -12$, $y = -2$, and $z = +3$.*

27. $-x$

28. $-(-z)$

29. $-|-y|$

30. $x - y$

31. $|x + z|$

32. $(z - y) - x$

33. $(3y + x)/z$ **34.** $(x/y) - yz$ **35.** $(4z + x)/y$

36. $\left(yz - \dfrac{x}{z}\right) - xz$ **37.** $\dfrac{0}{x} + x(0)y$

Remove grouping symbols and combine like terms.

38. $(3x^2y^2 - xy) - (5x^2y^2 + 4xy)$

39. $3y(2y^2 - y + 4) - 2y(y^2 + 2y - 3)$

40. $7x - 3[(x + 7y) - (2x - y)]$

41. $2x^2y(3xy - 5) - 3xy^2(4x^2 - 1)$

Replace each question mark with an appropriate algebraic expression.

42. $3x - 6y + 9 = 3x - 3(?)$

43. $3(x - 2y) - x + 2y = 3(x - 2y) - (?)$

Solve and check.

44. $3(m - 2) - (m + 4) = 8$ **45.** $2x + 3(x - 1) = 8 - (x - 1)$

46. If the sum of four consecutive even numbers is 188, find the numbers.

47. A pile of coins consists of nickels and quarters. How many of each kind are there if the whole pile is worth $1.45 and there are 3 fewer quarters than twice the number of nickels?

48. Express the net gain by means of an appropriate integer: a 15° rise in temperature followed by a 30° drop, another 15° drop, a 25° rise, and, finally, a 40° drop.

C **49.** Show that subtraction is not associative by evaluating the following expressions for $x = +7$, $y = -3$, and $z = -5$:
(A) $(x - y) - z$ (B) $x - (y - z)$

50. Show that division is not associative by evaluating the following expressions for $x = +16$, $y = -8$, and $z = -2$:
(A) $(x \div y) \div z$ (B) $x \div (y \div z)$

51. Simplify: $3x - 2\{x - 2[x - (4x + 2)]\}$.

52. Find all integers x such that $2(x - 5) = 4x + 8$.

53. A space shuttle passes over Vandenberg Air Force Base at 8 A.M. traveling at 17,000 miles per hour. Another shuttle, attempting a rendezvous, passes over the same spot at 9 A.M. traveling at 18,000 miles per hour. How long will it take the second shuttle to catch up with the first?

3

RATIONAL NUMBERS

In the last chapter we formed the set of integers by extending the natural numbers to include 0 and the negative integers. With this extension came added power to perform more operations on more numbers and to solve more equations. But even with the integers we are not able to find

$$2 \div 5$$

or to solve

$$2x = 3$$

We need fractions! You will recall that in the last chapter we said we would use

$$a \div b \qquad a/b \qquad \frac{a}{b} \qquad b\overline{)a}$$

interchangeably; hence,

$$4 \div 2 \qquad 4/2 \qquad \frac{4}{2} \qquad 2\overline{)4}$$

are different names for the number 2. However, what does

$$\frac{3}{2}$$

name? Certainly not an integer. We are going to extend the set of integers so that $\frac{3}{2}$ will name a number and division will always be defined (except by 0). The extended number system will be called the set of *rational* numbers because the numbers are related to *ratios* of integers. Section 3-1 reviews the arithmetic of fractions and decimals and may be omitted unless a thorough review of these topics is needed. Section 3-2 introduces the rational number system.

3-1
FRACTIONS AND DECIMALS (OPTIONAL REVIEW)

- Multiplication of Fractions
- Reducing to Lowest Terms
- Division of Fractions
- Addition and Subtraction of Fractions
- Decimals
- Decimal Arithmetic

In this section we will review the arithmetic of fractions and decimals. Students with a clear understanding of these topics can omit this review and proceed directly to Section 3-2.

A **fraction** is most easily thought of as a number representing parts of a whole, as illustrated in the following diagram:

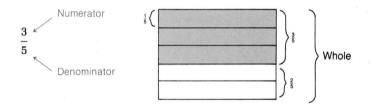

Thus, if a whole is divided into five equal parts, $\frac{3}{5}$ represents 3 of the 5 parts. An **improper fraction**, in which the numerator is larger than the denominator, such as $\frac{7}{5}$, represents 7 of these 5 parts, and thus more than the whole.

MULTIPLICATION OF FRACTIONS

> To multiply two fractions, multiply their numerators and place the product over the product of the denominators:
>
> $$\frac{a}{b} \cdot \frac{c}{d} = \frac{a \cdot c}{b \cdot d}$$

Example 1 $\dfrac{3}{5} \cdot \dfrac{2}{7} = \dfrac{3 \cdot 2}{5 \cdot 7} = \dfrac{6}{35}$

Problem 1   Multiply: **(A)** $\dfrac{7}{4} \cdot \dfrac{5}{6}$ **(B)** $\dfrac{3}{8} \cdot \dfrac{5}{7}$

REDUCING TO LOWEST TERMS

> A common factor can be removed from a numerator and denominator:
>
> $$\frac{ka}{kb} = \frac{a}{b}$$

Example 2 $\dfrac{9}{12} \left[= \dfrac{3 \cdot 3}{3 \cdot 4} = \dfrac{3}{3} \cdot \dfrac{3}{4} = 1 \cdot \dfrac{3}{4} \right] = \dfrac{3}{4}$

or

$\dfrac{9}{12} \left[= \dfrac{9 \div 3}{12 \div 3} \right] = \dfrac{3}{4}$

Removing *all* common factors from a numerator and denominator is called **reducing a fraction to lowest terms**.

Problem 2   Reduce to lowest terms: **(A)** $\dfrac{12}{15}$ **(B)** $\dfrac{17}{51}$

Example 3   Multiply and reduce to lowest terms: $\dfrac{8}{9} \cdot \dfrac{3}{4}$

Solution $\dfrac{8}{9} \cdot \dfrac{3}{4} = \dfrac{\overset{2}{\cancel{8}}}{\underset{3}{\cancel{9}}} \cdot \dfrac{\overset{1}{\cancel{3}}}{\underset{1}{\cancel{4}}}$ Any factor in a numerator can be removed with a like factor in a denominator.

$= \dfrac{2}{3}$

Problem 3   Multiply and reduce to lowest terms: **(A)** $\dfrac{2}{15} \cdot \dfrac{3}{8}$ **(B)** $\dfrac{9}{7} \cdot \dfrac{14}{24}$

DIVISION OF FRACTIONS

> To divide two fractions, invert the divisor and multiply:
>
> $$\frac{a}{b} \div \frac{c}{d} = \frac{a}{b} \cdot \frac{d}{c}$$
>
> Invert divisor

Example 4 $\dfrac{5}{8} \div \dfrac{3}{4} = \dfrac{5}{8} \cdot \dfrac{4}{3}$ Invert divisor and multiply. Do not remove common factors before inverting divisor.

$$= \dfrac{5}{\underset{2}{\cancel{8}}} \cdot \dfrac{\overset{1}{\cancel{4}}}{3}$$

$$= \dfrac{5}{6}$$

Problem 4 Divide and reduce to lowest terms:

(A) $\dfrac{7}{16} \div \dfrac{14}{10}$ **(B)** $\dfrac{4}{7} \div \dfrac{14}{49}$

ADDITION AND SUBTRACTION OF FRACTIONS

> If two fractions have the same denominator, we add or subtract them by adding or subtracting their numerators and placing the result over the common denominator:
>
> $$\dfrac{a}{b} + \dfrac{c}{b} = \dfrac{a+c}{b} \qquad \dfrac{a}{b} - \dfrac{c}{b} = \dfrac{a-c}{b}$$

Example 5 **(A)** $\dfrac{5}{6} + \dfrac{4}{6} = \dfrac{5+4}{6} = \dfrac{9}{6} = \dfrac{3}{2}$

(B) $\dfrac{5}{8} - \dfrac{3}{8} = \dfrac{5-3}{8} = \dfrac{2}{8} = \dfrac{1}{4}$

Problem 5 Perform the indicated operation and reduce to lowest terms:

(A) $\dfrac{11}{24} + \dfrac{4}{24}$ **(B)** $\dfrac{17}{12} - \dfrac{9}{12}$

If two fractions do not have a common denominator, then we must change them so that they do before we can add or subtract. The following important property of fractions is behind this process.

Fundamental Principle of Fractions

We can multiply the numerator and denominator by the same nonzero number:

$$\frac{a}{b} = \frac{ka}{kb} \qquad k \neq 0$$

The most convenient common denominator to use is the least common multiple (LCM) of the denominators. The **LCM** is the smallest number exactly divisible by each denominator. The least common multiple of the denominators is also called the **least common denominator (LCD)**.

Example 6   **(A)** $\dfrac{3}{4} + \dfrac{2}{3}$ $\boxed{= \dfrac{3 \cdot 3}{3 \cdot 4} + \dfrac{4 \cdot 2}{4 \cdot 3}}$ The LCD is 12 (the smallest number divisible by 4 and 3). Use the fundamental principle of fractions to make each denominator 12.

$$= \frac{9}{12} + \frac{8}{12}$$

$$\boxed{= \frac{9 + 8}{12}}$$

$$= \frac{17}{12}$$

(B) $\dfrac{5}{6} - \dfrac{11}{15}$ $\boxed{= \dfrac{5 \cdot 5}{5 \cdot 6} - \dfrac{2 \cdot 11}{2 \cdot 15}}$ LCD = 30

$$= \frac{25}{30} - \frac{22}{30}$$

$$\boxed{= \frac{25 - 22}{30}}$$

$$= \frac{3}{30} = \frac{1}{10}$$

Problem 6   Perform the indicated operations and reduce to lowest terms:

(A) $\dfrac{5}{6} + \dfrac{4}{9}$ **(B)** $\dfrac{7}{10} - \dfrac{3}{25}$

DECIMALS

A decimal fraction is a way of representing numbers in decimal form. The base 10 is central to the process. Recall:

$$3\ 4\ 6\ .\ 2\ 3\ 5 = 300 + 40 + 6 + \frac{2}{10} + \frac{3}{100} + \frac{5}{1,000}$$

(Hundreds, Tens, Units, Tenths, Hundredths, Thousandths)

Thus,

$$0.2 = \frac{2}{10} \qquad 0.03 = \frac{3}{100} \qquad 0.005 = \frac{5}{1,000} \qquad 0.235 = \frac{235}{1,000}$$

Fractions to Decimal Fractions

To convert a fraction into a decimal fraction, divide the denominator into the numerator.

Example 7 Convert $\frac{12}{23}$ to a decimal fraction rounded to three decimal places.

Solution

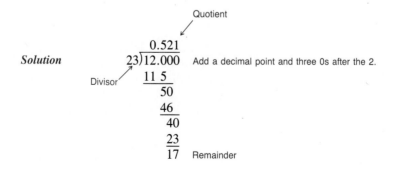

In order to round to three decimal places, we do the following. If the remainder after carrying out the division to three decimal places is greater than or equal to one-half the divisor, we add 1 to the last decimal place in the quotient. If the remainder is less than one-half the divisor, we leave the last decimal place alone. In this case the remainder 17 is more than one-half the divisor 23, so we add 1 to the third decimal place to obtain

$$\frac{12}{23} \approx 0.522$$ $\approx$ means approximately equal to

We write 0.522 instead of .522 because the latter might be mistaken for the whole number 522. Placing the 0 to the left of the decimal point keeps the decimal point from getting lost.

Problem 7   Convert $\frac{26}{35}$ to a decimal fraction rounded to two decimal places.

DECIMAL ARITHMETIC

We will briefly review the arithmetic operations on decimal fractions.

> To add two or more decimal fractions, line up decimal points and add as in whole-number arithmetic. The decimal point is carried straight down to the sum.

Example 8   Add: 325.2, 62.25, 3.012

Solution
$$\begin{array}{r} \downarrow \\ 325.2 \\ 62.25 \\ \underline{3.012} \\ 390.462 \\ \uparrow \end{array}$$
Line up decimal points.

Problem 8   Add: 22.06, 204.135, 3.4

> To subtract one decimal fraction from another, line up decimals and subtract as in whole-number arithmetic. The decimal point is carried straight down to the difference.

Example 9   Subtract 23.427 from 125.8.

Solution

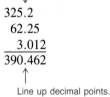
Add two 0s.
$$\begin{array}{r} 125.800 \\ \underline{23.427} \\ 102.373 \\ \uparrow \end{array}$$ Difference

Line up decimal points.

Problem 9   Subtract 325.63 from 407.5.

To multiply two decimal fractions, multiply as in whole-number arithmetic. The product has as many decimal places as the sum of the number of decimal places used in the two original decimal fractions.

Example 10   Multiply 36.24 and 13.6.

Solution

$$
\begin{array}{r}
3\,6.2\,4 \quad \text{2 decimal places} \\
1\,3.6 \quad \text{1 decimal place} \\
\hline
2\,1\,7\,4\,4 \quad \text{3 decimal places} \\
1\,0\,8\,7\,2 \\
3\,6\,2\,4 \\
\hline
4\,9\,2.8\,6\,4
\end{array}
$$

Add

Problem 10   Multiply 103.2 and 26.72.

To divide one decimal fraction by another, divide as in whole-number arithmetic. To locate the decimal in the quotient, move the decimal point in the dividend and divisor as many places to the right as there are decimal places in the divisor. Then move the decimal point straight up from the dividend to the quotient.

Example 11   Divide 425.3 by 2.43, and round your answer to two decimal places.

Solution

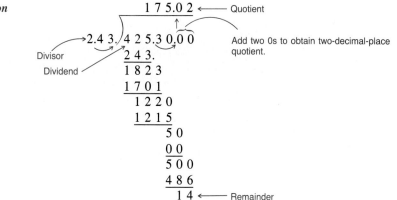

Quotient
Divisor
Dividend
Add two 0s to obtain two-decimal-place quotient.
Remainder

The remainder 14 is less than half the divisor 243, so we do not add 1 to the second decimal place. The quotient rounded to two decimal places is 175.02.

Problem 11   Divide 3.74 by 2.4, and round your answer to two decimal places.

ANSWERS TO
MATCHED PROBLEMS

1. (A) $\frac{35}{24}$ (B) $\frac{15}{56}$ 2. (A) $\frac{4}{5}$ (B) $\frac{1}{3}$
3. (A) $\frac{1}{20}$ (B) $\frac{3}{4}$ 4. (A) $\frac{5}{16}$ (B) 2
5. (A) $\frac{5}{8}$ (B) $\frac{2}{3}$ 6. (A) $\frac{23}{18}$ (B) $\frac{29}{50}$
7. 0.74   8. 229.595
9. 81.87   10. 2,757.504
11. 1.56

EXERCISE 3-1   *Since this section is included to provide a brief review of arithmetic operations on fractions and decimals, the designations A, B, and C for level of difficulty are omitted.*

Perform the indicated operations and reduce to lowest terms.

1. $\dfrac{2}{3} \cdot \dfrac{4}{5}$ 2. $\dfrac{3}{4} \cdot \dfrac{2}{7}$ 3. $\dfrac{1}{2} \div \dfrac{2}{3}$

4. $\dfrac{3}{4} \div \dfrac{4}{3}$ 5. $\dfrac{4}{9} \cdot \dfrac{3}{12}$ 6. $\dfrac{5}{12} \cdot \dfrac{9}{10}$

7. $\dfrac{10}{12} \div \dfrac{6}{18}$ 8. $\dfrac{18}{24} \div \dfrac{12}{9}$ 9. $\dfrac{5}{12} + \dfrac{3}{12}$

10. $\dfrac{3}{8} + \dfrac{7}{8}$ 11. $\dfrac{11}{9} - \dfrac{5}{9}$ 12. $\dfrac{17}{14} - \dfrac{9}{14}$

13. $\dfrac{1}{4} + \dfrac{2}{3}$ 14. $\dfrac{3}{5} + \dfrac{1}{2}$ 15. $\dfrac{5}{6} - \dfrac{3}{4}$

16. $\dfrac{3}{4} - \dfrac{1}{3}$ 17. $\dfrac{5}{12} + \dfrac{3}{8}$ 18. $\dfrac{11}{18} + \dfrac{5}{12}$

19. $\dfrac{7}{9} - \dfrac{5}{12}$ 20. $\dfrac{7}{20} - \dfrac{9}{30}$ 21. $\dfrac{2}{3} \cdot \left(\dfrac{3}{4} \div \dfrac{9}{12} \right)$

22. $\dfrac{4}{5} \div \left(\dfrac{8}{10} \div \dfrac{3}{4} \right)$ 23. $\dfrac{8}{9} \cdot \left(\dfrac{3}{4} - \dfrac{2}{3} \right)$ 24. $\dfrac{7}{5} \div \left(\dfrac{5}{6} - \dfrac{1}{4} \right)$

Add.

25. 3.1, 2.5, 0.2   26. 6.4, 0.3, 5.6

27. 23.2, 2.45, 6.012   28. 405.03, 21.105, 5.2

Subtract.

29. 25.32 from 43.05   30. 6.09 from 13.12

31. 23.56 from 103.2   32. 5.69 from 41.2

Multiply.

33. 2.5 by 13   **34.** 24 by 1.6

35. 4.26 by 0.002   **36.** 3.04 by 0.006

Convert to decimal fractions rounded to two decimal places.

37. $\dfrac{5}{6}$ **38.** $\dfrac{7}{9}$ **39.** $\dfrac{34}{46}$ **40.** $\dfrac{16}{24}$

Divide and round answers to one decimal place.

41. 84 by 2.2   **42.** 68 by 4.5

43. 36.2 by 4.6   **44.** 4.02 by 6.4

3-2

THE SET OF RATIONAL NUMBERS

- Rational Numbers
- Rational Numbers and the Number Line
- Opposite of and Absolute Value of a Rational Number
- Fundamental Principle of Fractions

This section introduces the set of rational numbers. Basic operations on the numbers are considered in Sections 3-3 and 3-4.

RATIONAL NUMBERS

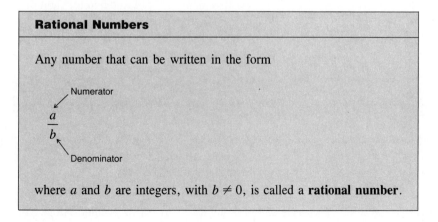

Rational Numbers

Any number that can be written in the form

Numerator

$$\dfrac{a}{b}$$

Denominator

where a and b are integers, with $b \neq 0$, is called a **rational number**.

Thus,

$$\frac{1}{3} \qquad \frac{3}{5} \qquad \frac{9}{1} \qquad \frac{-2}{7} \qquad \frac{10}{-5} \qquad \frac{-3}{-2} \qquad \frac{0}{3}$$

all name rational numbers. Every fraction represents a rational number, but the rational numbers also include ''fractions'' with negative numerator or denominator. Every integer is a rational number, but some rational numbers are not integers. For example, the integer 9 is also a rational number, since it can be written as the quotient of two integers:

$$9 = \frac{9}{1} \quad \text{or} \quad \frac{18}{2} \quad \text{or} \quad \frac{-27}{-3} \quad \text{and so on}$$

but the rational number $\frac{3}{5}$ is not an integer.

It would seem reasonable, from our experience with multiplying and dividing signed quantities in the preceding chapter, to define the quotient of any two integers with like signs as a **positive rational number** and the quotient of any two integers with unlike signs as a **negative rational number**. Thus,

$$\frac{+2}{+3} = \frac{2}{3} \qquad \frac{-2}{-3} = \frac{2}{3} \qquad \frac{-2}{+3} = -\frac{2}{3} \qquad \frac{+2}{-3} = -\frac{2}{3}$$

Therefore, we will use $-\frac{2}{3}$, $\frac{-2}{3}$, and $-2/3$ interchangeably, since they all represent the same rational number. (*Note:* We usually avoid writing $\frac{2}{-3}$ as a final form.)

RATIONAL NUMBERS AND THE NUMBER LINE

Locating rational numbers on a number line proceeds as one would expect: the positive numbers are located to the right of 0 and the negative numbers to the left. Where do we locate a number such as $\frac{7}{4}$? We divide each unit on the number line into four segments and identify $\frac{7}{4}$ with the endpoint of the seventh segment to the right of 0. Where is $-\frac{3}{2}$ located? Halfway between -1 and -2.

By proceeding as described, every rational number can be associated with a point on a number line.

Example 12   Locate $\frac{1}{2}$, $-\frac{3}{4}$, $\frac{5}{2}$, $-\frac{9}{4}$ on a number line.

Solution

Problem 12 Locate $\frac{3}{4}$, $-\frac{1}{2}$, $\frac{7}{4}$, $-\frac{5}{2}$ on a number line.

OPPOSITE OF AND ABSOLUTE VALUE OF A RATIONAL NUMBER

The **opposite of (negative of) a rational number** and the **absolute value of a rational number** are defined as in the integers. Thus,

$$-\left(\frac{2}{3}\right) = -\frac{2}{3} \qquad -\left(-\frac{2}{3}\right) = \frac{2}{3} \qquad \left|\frac{2}{3}\right| = \frac{2}{3} \qquad \left|-\frac{2}{3}\right| = \frac{2}{3}$$

FUNDAMENTAL PRINCIPLE OF FRACTIONS

We now consider a very important property of rational numbers and of fractions in general. Recall from arithmetic (see Section 3-1) the processes of reducing a fraction to lowest terms and that of raising a fraction to higher terms:

(A) $\dfrac{8}{12} = \dfrac{8 \div 4}{12 \div 4} = \dfrac{2}{3}$ or $\dfrac{8}{12} = \dfrac{4 \cdot 2}{4 \cdot 3} = \dfrac{2}{3}$ Lowest terms

(B) $\dfrac{3}{4} = \dfrac{5 \cdot 3}{5 \cdot 4} = \dfrac{15}{20}$ Higher terms

The **fundamental principle of fractions** is the basis for these processes.

Fundamental Principle of Fractions

For any nonzero integers b and k and any integer a,

(A) $\dfrac{ka}{kb} = \dfrac{\cancel{k}a}{\cancel{k}b} = \dfrac{a}{b}$ We may divide out a common factor k from both the numerator and denominator. This is called **reducing to lower terms.**† $\dfrac{6}{4} = \dfrac{2 \cdot 3}{2 \cdot 2} = \dfrac{3}{2}$

(B) $\dfrac{a}{b} = \dfrac{ka}{kb}$ We may multiply the numerator and denominator by the same nonzero factor k. This is called **raising to higher terms.** $\dfrac{1}{5} = \dfrac{1 \cdot 3}{5 \cdot 3} = \dfrac{3}{15}$

---

† The process of dividing out a common factor from both the numerator and denominator of a fraction is sometimes called **canceling.** This terminology is not used in this text.

Property (A) provides the basis for reducing fractions to lowest terms. To reduce a fraction to **lowest terms**, we divide the numerator and denominator by the largest nonzero common divisor. (That is, we remove *all* common factors from the numerator and denominator.)

Example 13   Replace question marks with appropriate numbers:

$$\textbf{(A)} \ \frac{27}{18} = \frac{?}{2} \qquad \textbf{(B)} \ \frac{6x}{9x} = \frac{?}{?} \qquad \textbf{(C)} \ \frac{3}{7} = \frac{?}{42} \qquad \textbf{(D)} \ \frac{5x}{3} = \frac{10x^2}{?}$$

Solution $\textbf{(A)} \ \dfrac{27}{18} = \dfrac{3 \cdot 9}{2 \cdot 9} = \dfrac{3}{2}$ Lowest terms

$\textbf{(B)} \ \dfrac{6x}{9x} = \dfrac{2 \cdot 3x}{3 \cdot 3x} = \dfrac{2}{3}$ Lowest terms

$\textbf{(C)} \ \dfrac{3}{7} = \dfrac{6 \cdot 3}{6 \cdot 7} = \dfrac{18}{42}$ Higher terms

$\textbf{(D)} \ \dfrac{5x}{3} = \dfrac{2x \cdot 5x}{2x \cdot 3} = \dfrac{10x^2}{6x}$ Higher terms

Problem 13   Replace question marks with appropriate symbols:

$$\textbf{(A)} \ \frac{24}{32} = \frac{?}{4} \qquad \textbf{(B)} \ \frac{8m}{12m} = \frac{2}{?} \qquad \textbf{(C)} \ \frac{2}{3} = \frac{?}{12y} \qquad \textbf{(D)} \ \frac{7}{4} = \frac{14y^2}{?}$$

When reducing fractions to lower terms, it is important to keep in mind that it is only common *factors* in products that can be divided out or removed. Common *terms* in sums or differences cannot be removed. For example:

Common Factors $\dfrac{2a}{3a} = \dfrac{2}{3}$ *a* is a common factor and can be divided out from both the numerator and the denominator.

Common Terms $\dfrac{2 + a}{3 + a} \neq \dfrac{2}{3}$ *a* is a common *term*, not a common *factor*, and cannot be divided out.

Example 14   Reduce to lowest terms:

$$\textbf{(A)} \ \frac{3xy}{15x^2} \qquad \textbf{(B)} \ \frac{33xy^2}{15x^2y} \qquad \textbf{(C)} \ \frac{6(x + 1)}{15(x + 2)}$$

Solution **(A)** $\dfrac{3xy}{15x^2} = \dfrac{3 \cdot x \cdot y}{3 \cdot 5 \cdot x \cdot x} = \dfrac{y}{5x}$

(B) $\dfrac{33xy^2}{15x^2y} = \dfrac{3 \cdot 11 \cdot x \cdot y \cdot y}{3 \cdot 5 \cdot x \cdot x \cdot y} = \dfrac{11y}{5x}$

(C) $\dfrac{6(x + 1)}{15(x + 2)} = \dfrac{3 \cdot 2(x + 1)}{3 \cdot 5(x + 2)} = \dfrac{2(x + 1)}{5(x + 2)}$ Note that *x* is *not* a common factor.

Problem 14 Reduce to lowest terms:

(A) $\dfrac{12x^2}{4xy}$ **(B)** $\dfrac{28x^2y^2}{16xy}$ **(C)** $\dfrac{8(y - 3)}{20(y + 3)}$

ANSWERS TO MATCHED PROBLEMS **12.**

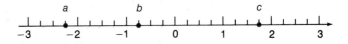

13. **(A)** 3   **(B)** 3   **(C)** $8y$ **(D)** $8y^2$

14. **(A)** $\dfrac{3x}{y}$ **(B)** $\dfrac{7xy}{4}$ **(C)** $\dfrac{2(y - 3)}{5(y + 3)}$

EXERCISE 3-2 *Do not change improper fractions to mixed fractions in your answers; that is, write $\tfrac{7}{2}$, not $3\tfrac{1}{2}$. All variables represent integers.*

A **1.** What rational numbers are associated with points a, b, and c?

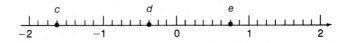

2. What rational numbers are associated with points c, d, and e?

3. What rational numbers are associated with points a, b, c, and d?

4. What rational numbers are associated with points c, d, e, and f?

Locate the given rational numbers on a number line.

5. $-\dfrac{3}{2}, -\dfrac{1}{4}, \dfrac{5}{4}, \dfrac{3}{2}$

6. $-\dfrac{4}{3}, -\dfrac{2}{3}, \dfrac{1}{3}, \dfrac{5}{3}$

7. $-\dfrac{5}{3}, -\dfrac{5}{6}, \dfrac{2}{3}, \dfrac{7}{6}$

8. $-\dfrac{7}{8}, -\dfrac{1}{2}, \dfrac{1}{4}, \dfrac{5}{8}$

Replace question marks with appropriate symbols.

9. $\dfrac{8}{12} = \dfrac{?}{3}$

10. $\dfrac{12}{16} = \dfrac{?}{4}$

11. $\dfrac{1}{5} = \dfrac{3}{?}$

12. $\dfrac{3}{4} = \dfrac{?}{20}$

13. $\dfrac{21x}{28x} = \dfrac{?}{4}$

14. $\dfrac{36y}{54y} = \dfrac{2}{?}$

B 15. $\dfrac{3}{7} = \dfrac{?}{21x^2}$

16. $\dfrac{4}{5} = \dfrac{28m^3}{?}$

17. $\dfrac{6x^3}{4xy} = \dfrac{?}{2y}$

18. $\dfrac{9xy}{12y^2} = \dfrac{3x}{?}$

19. $\dfrac{2ab}{3b^2} = \dfrac{2a}{?}$

20. $\dfrac{2a^2b}{5ab} = \dfrac{2a}{?}$

21. $\dfrac{10a^2b^2}{5ab} = \dfrac{?}{1}$

22. $\dfrac{12ab^2}{4a^2b} = \dfrac{3b}{?}$

Reduce to lowest terms.

23. $\dfrac{9x}{6x}$

24. $\dfrac{27y}{15y}$

25. $\dfrac{-3}{12}$

26. $\dfrac{18}{-8}$

C 27. $\dfrac{2y^2}{8y^3}$

28. $\dfrac{6x^3}{15x}$

29. $\dfrac{12a^2b}{3ab^2}$

30. $\dfrac{21x^2y^3}{35x^3y}$

31. $\dfrac{-2xy^2}{8x^2}$

32. $\dfrac{25mn^3}{-15m^2n^2}$

33. $\dfrac{60x^3y^4}{25x^4y^3}$

34. $\dfrac{60x^3y^4}{24x^2y^5}$

35. $\dfrac{4(x^2 + y)}{6(x^2 + y)}$

36. $\dfrac{3(a + b^2)}{9(a + b^2)}$

37. $\dfrac{4(x^2 + y)}{12(x + y^2)}$

38. $\dfrac{3(a + b^2)}{12(a^2 + b)}$

$3\text{-}3$

MULTIPLICATION
AND DIVISION

- Multiplication
- Sign Properties
- Division

In this section we will consider multiplication and division of algebraic forms representing rational numbers, and in the next section we will consider addition and subtraction.

MULTIPLICATION

In arithmetic you learned to multiply fractions by multiplying their numerators (tops) and multiplying their denominators (bottoms). This is exactly what we do with rational numbers in general.

Definition of Multiplication for Rational Numbers

If a, b, c, and d are integers with b and d different from 0, then

$$\frac{a}{b} \cdot \frac{c}{d} = \frac{a \cdot c}{b \cdot d} \qquad \frac{3}{4} \cdot \frac{5}{7} = \frac{3 \cdot 5}{4 \cdot 7} = \frac{15}{28}$$

Example 15 (A) $\dfrac{2}{5} \cdot \dfrac{3}{7} = \dfrac{2 \cdot 3}{5 \cdot 7} = \dfrac{6}{35}$

(B) $(-8) \cdot \dfrac{9}{5} = \dfrac{-8}{1} \cdot \dfrac{9}{5} = \dfrac{(-8)(9)}{(1)(5)} = \dfrac{-72}{5}$ or $-\dfrac{72}{5}$ or $-14\frac{2}{5}$ or -14.4

(C) $\dfrac{2x}{3y^2} \cdot \dfrac{x^2}{5y} = \dfrac{(2x)(x^2)}{(3y^2)(5y)} = \dfrac{2x^3}{15y^3}$

Problem 15 Multiply:

(A) $\dfrac{3}{4} \cdot \dfrac{3}{5}$ (B) $(-5) \cdot \dfrac{3}{4}$ (C) $\dfrac{3x^2}{2y} \cdot \dfrac{x}{4y^2}$

It follows from the definition of multiplication that we can continue to rearrange and regroup factors that represent rational numbers in the same way we rearrange and regroup factors that represent integers or natural numbers. That is, **the rational numbers are commutative and associative relative to multiplication**.

SIGN PROPERTIES

The following sign properties of rational numbers (and of fractions in general) are used with great frequency in mathematics. Their misuse accounts for many algebraic errors. The first property is a consequence of the Fundamental Principle of Fractions. The justification of the other two properties will be given in Section 3-4.

Sign Properties

For each integer a and each nonzero integer b:

(A) $\dfrac{-a}{-b} = \dfrac{a}{b}$ $\dfrac{-2}{-3} = \dfrac{2}{3}$

(B) $\dfrac{-a}{b} = \dfrac{a}{-b} = -\dfrac{a}{b}$ $\dfrac{-2}{3} = \dfrac{2}{-3} = -\dfrac{2}{3}$

(C) $(-1)\dfrac{a}{b} = -\dfrac{a}{b}$ $(-1)\dfrac{2}{3} = -\dfrac{2}{3}$ or $\dfrac{-2}{3}$ or $\dfrac{2}{-3}$

Note: If choosing among $\frac{-2}{3}$, $\frac{2}{-3}$, or $-\frac{2}{3}$ for a final answer, we would generally choose either $\frac{-2}{3}$ or $-\frac{2}{3}$, a form with a positive denominator.

We are now ready to consider multiplication examples of a more general type. Part (B) in the following example illustrates one use of the sign properties.

Example 16   Multiply and write your answer in lowest terms:

(A) $\dfrac{5x^2}{9y^2} \cdot \dfrac{6y}{10x}$ **(B)** $\dfrac{-3x}{2y} \cdot \dfrac{6y^2}{9x^2}$

Solution   **(A)** $\dfrac{5x^2}{9y^2} \cdot \dfrac{6y}{10x} = \dfrac{5xx \cdot 2 \cdot 3y}{3 \cdot 3yy \cdot 2 \cdot 5x}$ Factor numerator and denominator.

$= \dfrac{\cancel{5}x\cancel{x} \cdot \cancel{2} \cdot \cancel{3} \cdot \cancel{y}}{3 \cdot \cancel{3}y\cancel{y} \cdot \cancel{2} \cdot \cancel{5}\cancel{x}}$ Remove common factors.

$= \dfrac{x}{3y}$ Answer is in lowest terms.

After a little experience you will probably proceed by repeated division of the numerator and denominator by common factors until all common factors are eliminated. That is, you will proceed something like this:

$$\frac{5x^2}{9y^2} \cdot \frac{6y}{10x} = \frac{(5x^2)(6y)}{(9y^2)(10x)} = \frac{x}{3y}$$

(B) $$\frac{-3x}{2y} \cdot \frac{6y^2}{9x^2} = \frac{(-3x)(6y^2)}{(2y)(9x^2)} = \frac{-y}{x} \quad \text{or} \quad -\frac{y}{x}$$

We could also proceed as in the first part of part (A) by factoring the numerator and denominator and removing common factors.

Problem 16 Multiply and write your answer in lowest terms:

(A) $\dfrac{10x}{6y^2} \cdot \dfrac{12y}{5x^2}$ (B) $\dfrac{-7x^2}{3y^2} \cdot \dfrac{12y}{14x}$

DIVISION

In arithmetic courses you were probably told: "To divide one fraction by another, invert the divisor and multiply." It is not difficult to see why this mechanical rule is valid. To start, we define division for rational numbers as in the integers.

Definition of Division

If a/b and c/d are any two rational numbers with $c/d \neq 0$, then

$$\frac{a}{b} \div \frac{c}{d} = Q \qquad \text{if and only if} \qquad \frac{c}{d} \cdot Q = \frac{a}{b}$$

That is, the quotient Q is the number that c/d must be multiplied by to produce a/b.

$$\frac{2}{3} \div \frac{1}{5} = \frac{10}{3} \qquad \text{because} \qquad \frac{1}{5} \cdot \frac{10}{3} = \frac{2}{3}$$

As a result of this definition we can establish the following mechanical rule for carrying out division.

Mechanical Rule for Division

To divide one rational number by another rational number different from 0, invert the divisor and multiply. That is,

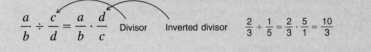

$$\frac{a}{b} \div \frac{c}{d} = \frac{a}{b} \cdot \frac{d}{c} \qquad \text{Divisor} \qquad \text{Inverted divisor} \qquad \frac{2}{3} \div \frac{1}{5} = \frac{2}{3} \cdot \frac{5}{1} = \frac{10}{3}$$

To establish this rule we have to show that the product of the divisor (c/d) and the quotient [$(a/b) \cdot (d/c)$] is equal to the dividend (a/b):

$$\frac{c}{d}\left(\frac{a}{b} \cdot \frac{d}{c}\right) = \frac{c}{d} \cdot \frac{ad}{bc}$$

$$= \frac{\overset{1}{\cancel{c}}a\overset{1}{\cancel{d}}}{\cancel{d}b\cancel{c}} = \frac{a}{b}$$

Example 17   Divide and reduce to lowest terms:

(A) $\dfrac{6}{14} \div \dfrac{21}{2}$ **(B)** $\dfrac{12}{5y} \div \dfrac{9y}{8x}$ **(C)** $\dfrac{18a^2b}{15c} \div \dfrac{12ab^2}{5c}$

(D) $\dfrac{-3x}{yz} \div 12x$

Solution   **(A)** $\dfrac{6}{14} \div \dfrac{21}{2} = \dfrac{\overset{2}{\cancel{6}}}{\underset{7}{\cancel{14}}} \cdot \dfrac{\overset{1}{\cancel{2}}}{\underset{7}{\cancel{21}}} = \dfrac{2}{49}$ Do not remove common factors in division before inverting the divisor.

(B) $\dfrac{12x}{5y} \div \dfrac{9y}{8x} = \dfrac{\overset{4x}{\cancel{12x}}}{5y} \cdot \dfrac{8x}{\underset{3y}{\cancel{9y}}} = \dfrac{32x^2}{15y^2}$

(C) $\dfrac{18a^2b}{15c} \div \dfrac{12ab^2}{5c} = \dfrac{\overset{\overset{a}{3a}}{\cancel{18a^2b}}}{\underset{3}{\cancel{15c}}} \cdot \dfrac{\overset{1}{\cancel{5c}}}{\underset{2b}{\cancel{12ab^2}}} = \dfrac{a}{2b}$

(D) $\dfrac{-3x}{yz} \div 12x = \dfrac{-3x}{yz} \div \dfrac{12x}{1} = \dfrac{\overset{-1}{\cancel{-3x}}}{yz} \cdot \dfrac{1}{\underset{4}{\cancel{12x}}} = \dfrac{-1}{4yz}$ or $-\dfrac{1}{4yz}$

Problem 17   Divide and reduce to lowest terms:

(A) $\dfrac{8}{9} \div \dfrac{4}{3}$ **(B)** $\dfrac{8x}{3y} \div \dfrac{6x}{9y}$ **(C)** $\dfrac{15mn^2}{12x} \div \dfrac{9m^2n}{8x}$

(D) $\dfrac{6x}{wz} \div (-3x)$

ANSWERS TO
MATCHED PROBLEMS

15. **(A)** $\dfrac{9}{20}$ **(B)** $\dfrac{-15}{4}$ or $-\dfrac{15}{4}$ **(C)** $\dfrac{3x^3}{8y^3}$

16. **(A)** $\dfrac{4}{xy}$ **(B)** $\dfrac{-2x}{y}$ or $-\dfrac{2x}{y}$

17. **(A)** $\dfrac{2}{3}$ **(B)** 4 **(C)** $\dfrac{10n}{9m}$ **(D)** $\dfrac{-2}{wz}$ or $-\dfrac{2}{wz}$

EXERCISE 3-3   *Do not change improper fractions to mixed fractions in your answers; that is, write $\tfrac{7}{2}$, not $3\tfrac{1}{2}$. All variables represent integers.*

A   *Multiply.*

1. $\dfrac{2}{5} \cdot \dfrac{3}{7}$ **2.** $\dfrac{3}{8} \cdot \dfrac{3}{5}$ **3.** $\dfrac{4}{5} \cdot \dfrac{7x}{3y}$

4. $\dfrac{5}{7} \cdot \dfrac{2x}{3y}$ **5.** $\dfrac{x}{2y} \cdot \dfrac{3x}{y^2}$ **6.** $\dfrac{2m}{n^2} \cdot \dfrac{3m^2}{5n^2}$

7. $\dfrac{3}{7} \cdot \dfrac{-2}{11}$ **8.** $\dfrac{-2}{5} \cdot \dfrac{4}{3}$ **9.** $\dfrac{-5}{3} \cdot \dfrac{2}{-7}$

10. $\dfrac{2}{-5} \cdot \dfrac{-3}{7}$

Divide.

11. $\dfrac{3}{5} \div \dfrac{5}{7}$ **12.** $\dfrac{3}{4} \div \dfrac{4}{5}$ **13.** $\dfrac{2x}{3} \div \dfrac{5}{7y}$

14. $\dfrac{3}{2u} \div \dfrac{5y}{11}$ **15.** $\dfrac{3}{7} \div \dfrac{-2}{3}$ **16.** $\dfrac{-4}{5} \div \dfrac{3}{7}$

B   *Multiply or divide as indicated and reduce to lowest terms.*

17. $\dfrac{3}{4} \cdot \dfrac{8}{9}$ 18. $\dfrac{2}{9} \cdot \dfrac{3}{10}$ 19. $\dfrac{1}{25} \div \dfrac{15}{4}$

20. $\dfrac{7}{3} \div \dfrac{2}{3}$ 21. $3 \cdot \dfrac{5}{3}$ 22. $\dfrac{5}{7} \cdot 7$

23. $\dfrac{2}{3} \div \dfrac{4}{9}$ 24. $\dfrac{5}{11} \div \dfrac{55}{44}$ 25. $\dfrac{4}{-5} \cdot \dfrac{15}{16}$

26. $\dfrac{8}{3} \cdot \dfrac{-12}{24}$ 27. $\dfrac{2x}{3yz} \cdot \dfrac{6y}{4x}$ 28. $\dfrac{2a}{3bc} \cdot \dfrac{9c}{a}$

29. $\dfrac{6x}{5y} \div \dfrac{3x}{10y}$ 30. $\dfrac{9m}{8n} \div \dfrac{3m}{4n}$ 31. $2xy \div \dfrac{x}{y}$

32. $\dfrac{x}{3y} \div 3y$ 33. $\dfrac{2x^2}{3y^2} \cdot \dfrac{9y}{4x}$ 34. $\dfrac{3x^2}{4} \cdot \dfrac{16y}{12x^3}$

35. $\dfrac{2x}{3y} \div \dfrac{4x}{6y^2}$ 36. $\dfrac{a}{4c} \div \dfrac{a^2}{12c^2}$ 37. $\dfrac{6a^2}{7c} \cdot \dfrac{21cd}{12ac}$

38. $\dfrac{8x^2}{3xy} \cdot \dfrac{12y^3}{6y}$ 39. $\dfrac{3uv^2}{5w} \div \dfrac{6u^2v}{15w}$ 40. $\dfrac{21x^2y^2}{12cd} \div \dfrac{14xy}{9d}$

41. $\dfrac{-6x^3}{5y^2} \div \dfrac{18x}{10y}$ 42. $\dfrac{9u^4}{4v^3} \div \dfrac{-12u^2}{15v}$

C   *Perform the operations as indicated and reduce to lowest terms.*

43. $\left(\dfrac{9}{10} \div \dfrac{4}{6}\right) \cdot \dfrac{3}{5}$ 44. $\dfrac{9}{10} \div \left(\dfrac{4}{6} \cdot \dfrac{3}{5}\right)$

45. $\dfrac{-21}{16} \cdot \dfrac{12}{-14} \cdot \dfrac{8}{9}$ 46. $\dfrac{18}{15} \cdot \dfrac{-10}{21} \cdot \dfrac{3}{-1}$

47. $\dfrac{2x^2}{3y^2} \cdot \dfrac{6yz}{2x} \cdot \dfrac{y}{-xz}$ 48. $\dfrac{-a}{-b} \cdot \dfrac{12b^2}{15ac} \cdot \dfrac{-10}{4b}$

49. $\left(\dfrac{a}{b} \div \dfrac{c}{d}\right) \div \dfrac{e}{f}$ 50. $\dfrac{a}{b} \div \left(\dfrac{c}{d} \div \dfrac{e}{f}\right)$

3-4   ■ Addition and Subtraction
■ Finding the LCD
ADDITION AND   ■ Order in the Rational Numbers
SUBTRACTION

In this section we consider the operations of addition and subtraction on rational numbers and conclude with some observations about the "greater than" relationship. A more detailed consideration of inequality on the rational numbers is, however, deferred until Chapter 5.

ADDITION AND SUBTRACTION

As in the preceding sections, we will again generalize from arithmetic. In adding $\frac{1}{2}$ and $\frac{2}{3}$ you probably proceed somewhat as follows:

$$\frac{1}{2} = \frac{3}{6}$$

$$\frac{2}{3} = \frac{4}{6}$$

$$\overline{\phantom{\frac{2}{3}} \quad \frac{7}{6}}$$

Note: In algebra we often leave fractions in what is called an improper form. That is, we write $\frac{7}{6}$ rather than $1\frac{1}{6}$, since the latter might be confused with the product $(1)(\frac{1}{6})$. However, if $\frac{7}{6}$ were the final answer in an applied problem, we would generally write it in the form $1\frac{1}{6}$.

That is, you changed each fraction to an equivalent form having a common denominator, then added the numerators and placed the sum over the common denominator. We will proceed in the same way with rational numbers, but we will find it more convenient to work horizontally. We start by defining addition and subtraction of rational numbers with common denominators.

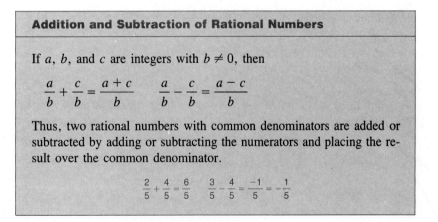

Addition and Subtraction of Rational Numbers

If a, b, and c are integers with $b \neq 0$, then

$$\frac{a}{b} + \frac{c}{b} = \frac{a+c}{b} \qquad \frac{a}{b} - \frac{c}{b} = \frac{a-c}{b}$$

Thus, two rational numbers with common denominators are added or subtracted by adding or subtracting the numerators and placing the result over the common denominator.

$$\frac{2}{5} + \frac{4}{5} = \frac{6}{5} \qquad \frac{3}{5} - \frac{4}{5} = \frac{-1}{5} = -\frac{1}{5}$$

An immediate consequence of this definition (and material in the preceding sections) is this: the rational numbers are commutative and associative relative to addition, and multiplication distributes over addition.

Example 18 Combine into single fractions:

$$\text{(A) } \frac{1}{8} + \frac{3}{8} \qquad \text{(B) } \frac{5x}{5x} - \frac{2}{5x} \qquad \text{(C) } \frac{2x}{6x^2} + \frac{5}{6x^2}$$

Solution **(A)** $\dfrac{1}{8} + \dfrac{3}{8} = \dfrac{1+3}{8} = \dfrac{4}{8} = \dfrac{1}{2}$ **(B)** $\dfrac{5x}{5x} - \dfrac{2}{5x} = \dfrac{5x-2}{5x}$

(C) $\dfrac{2x}{6x^2} + \dfrac{5}{6x^2} = \dfrac{2x+5}{6x^2}$

CAUTION

Note that in Example 18(B),

$$\frac{5x - 2}{5x} \neq -2$$

Only common factors can be divided out. $5x$ is a term in the numerator, not a factor. For example, if $x = 3$:

$$\frac{15 - 2}{15} \neq -2 \qquad \frac{15 - 2}{15} = \frac{13}{15}$$

15 cannot be   Right
divided out

Problem 18 Combine into single fractions:

$$\text{(A) } \frac{7}{3} - \frac{5}{3} \qquad \text{(B) } \frac{3}{2u} + \frac{2u}{2u} \qquad \text{(C) } \frac{3m^2}{12m^3} - \frac{2m}{12m^3}$$

FINDING THE LCD

How do we add or subtract rational numbers, or algebraic expressions representing rational numbers, when the denominators are not the same? We use the Fundamental Principle of Fractions:

$$\frac{a}{b} = \frac{ka}{kb} \qquad k,\, b \neq 0 \quad \text{Fundamental Principle of Fractions}$$

which states that we can multiply the numerator and denominator of a fraction by the same nonzero quantity, to obtain equivalent forms having common denominators. The common denominator that generally results in the least amount of computation is the least common multiple (LCM) of all the denominators. The LCM (see Section 1-1) of the denominators is the "smallest" quantity exactly divisible by each denominator and is called the **least common denominator** (LCD).

Finding the LCD

1. Determine the LCD (the ''smallest'' quantity exactly divisible by each denominator) by inspection, if possible.
2. If the LCD is not obvious, then it can always be found as follows:
   (A) Factor each denominator completely, representing multiple factors as powers.
   (B) The LCD must contain each *different* factor from these factorizations to the highest power it occurs in any one.

Note that step 2 is the same process that was used in Section 1-1 to find the LCM of natural numbers.

Example 19   Add or subtract and reduce to lowest terms:

$$\textbf{(A)}\ \frac{1}{3} + \frac{5}{12} \qquad \textbf{(B)}\ \frac{5}{24y} - \frac{7}{10y} \qquad \textbf{(C)}\ \frac{3}{8x} + \frac{7}{12x^2}$$

Solution   **(A)** *Step 1*   Find the LCD. The smallest number exactly divisible by 3 and 12 is 12. Therefore,

$$\text{LCD} = 12$$

Step 2   Use the Fundamental Principle of Fractions to convert each fraction into a form having the LCD as a denominator. Then combine into a single fraction and reduce to lowest terms:

$$\frac{1}{3} + \frac{5}{12} = \frac{4 \cdot 1}{4 \cdot 3} + \frac{5}{12} \qquad \text{Convert to forms having the same LCD.}$$

$$= \frac{4}{12} + \frac{5}{12} \qquad \text{Combine into a single fraction.}$$

$$= \frac{4 + 5}{12}$$

$$= \frac{9}{12} \qquad \text{Reduce to lowest terms.}$$

$$= \frac{3}{4}$$

(B) In this case the LCD is not obvious, so we factor each denominator completely:

$$24y = 8 \cdot 3y = 2 \cdot 2 \cdot 2 \cdot 3 \cdot y = 2^3 \cdot 3 \cdot y$$

$$10y = 2 \cdot 5 \cdot y$$

Since the LCD must contain each *different* factor from these factorizations to the highest power it occurs in any one, we first write down all the different factors:

$$2, 3, 5, y$$

Then we observe the highest power to which each occurs in any one factorization to obtain

$$\text{LCD} = 2^3 \cdot 3 \cdot 5 \cdot y = 120y$$

Now multiply numerators and denominators in the original problem by appropriate quantities to obtain $120y$ as a common denominator:

$$\frac{5}{24y} - \frac{7}{10y} = \frac{5 \cdot 5}{5 \cdot 24y} - \frac{12 \cdot 7}{12 \cdot 10y}$$

$$= \frac{25}{120y} - \frac{84}{120y}$$

$$= \frac{25 - 84}{120y}$$

$$= \frac{-59}{120y}$$

(C) Find the LCD:

$$8x = 2^3 \cdot x$$

$$12x^2 = 2^2 \cdot 3 \cdot x^2$$

$$\text{LCD} = 2^3 \cdot 3 \cdot x^2 = 24x^2$$

$$\frac{3}{8x} + \frac{7}{12x^2} = \frac{(3x)(3)}{(3x)(8x)} + \frac{2 \cdot 7}{2(12x^2)}$$

$$= \frac{9x}{24x^2} + \frac{14}{24x^2}$$

$$= \frac{9x + 14}{24x^2}$$

Problem 19 Add or subtract and reduce to lowest terms:

$$\text{(A) } \frac{4}{5} - \frac{2}{15} \qquad \text{(B) } \frac{5}{18xy} + \frac{3}{4xy} \qquad \text{(C) } \frac{2}{9x^2y} - \frac{7}{12xy^2}$$

Example 20 Combine into one fraction:

$$\text{(A) } \frac{-3}{4} - \frac{-1}{3} + \frac{5}{6} \qquad \text{(B) } \frac{3}{2x^2} - \frac{-5}{x} + 1$$

Solution **(A)** $\dfrac{-3}{4} - \dfrac{-1}{3} + \dfrac{5}{6} = \dfrac{3(-3)}{3(4)} - \dfrac{4(-1)}{4(3)} + \dfrac{2(5)}{2(6)}$ *Note:* LCD = 12

$$= \frac{-9}{12} - \frac{-4}{12} + \frac{10}{12}$$

$$= \frac{-9 - (-4) + 10}{12}$$

$$= \frac{-9 + 4 + 10}{12}$$

$$= \frac{5}{12}$$

(B) $\dfrac{3}{2x^2} - \dfrac{-5}{x} + 1 = \dfrac{3}{2x^2} - \dfrac{2x(-5)}{2x(x)} + \dfrac{2x^2}{2x^2}$ *Note:* LCD = $2x^2$

$$= \frac{3}{2x^2} - \frac{-10x}{2x^2} + \frac{2x^2}{2x^2}$$

$$= \frac{3 - (-10x) + 2x^2}{2x^2}$$

$$= \frac{3 + 10x + 2x^2}{2x^2}$$

Problem 20 Combine into one fraction:

$$\text{(A) } \frac{-1}{2} - \frac{-3}{4} + \frac{2}{3} \qquad \text{(B) } 2 - \frac{-3}{x} + \frac{4}{3x^2}$$

    Adding a number to its opposite should yield 0. This observation, together with the definition of addition of rational numbers, justifies some of the sign properties given in Sec. 3-3. For example,

$$\frac{-a}{b} = -\frac{a}{b} \quad \text{since} \quad \frac{a}{b} + \frac{-a}{b} = \frac{a + (-a)}{b} = \frac{0}{b} = 0$$

Thus, adding $\dfrac{-a}{b}$ to $\dfrac{a}{b}$ yields 0 so $\dfrac{-a}{b}$ is the opposite of $\dfrac{a}{b}$. The other parts of sign properties (B) and (C) on page 128 are explained similarly.

ORDER IN RATIONAL NUMBERS

There is a natural order on the set of rational numbers, just as on the set of integers. One number is greater than a second if the first lies to the right of the second on the number line. However, in contrast to the integers, it is not always obvious which of two rational numbers is greater. Compare, for example, $\frac{4}{7}$ and $\frac{6}{11}$. One way to compare them is to convert both to decimal fractions

$$\frac{4}{7} = 0.5714 \ldots \qquad \frac{6}{11} = 0.5454 \ldots$$

where it becomes clear that $\frac{4}{7}$ is the greater. Another approach follows that given in Section 2-4. Since

$$\frac{4}{7} - \frac{6}{11} = \frac{44}{77} - \frac{42}{77} = \frac{2}{77} \quad \text{and} \quad \frac{2}{77} \quad \text{is positive, then} \quad \frac{4}{7} > \frac{6}{11}.$$

Example 21   Select the larger rational number:

(A) $\dfrac{3}{13}, \dfrac{4}{17}$ (B) $\dfrac{5}{7}, \dfrac{14}{19}$

Solution   (A) $\dfrac{3}{13} = 0.2307 \ldots$ and $\dfrac{4}{17} = 0.2352 \ldots$

Thus $\dfrac{4}{17} > \dfrac{3}{13}$

(B) $\dfrac{14}{19} - \dfrac{5}{7} = \dfrac{14 \cdot 7}{19 \cdot 7} - \dfrac{5 \cdot 19}{7 \cdot 19} = \dfrac{98}{133} - \dfrac{95}{133} = \dfrac{3}{133} > 0$

Since $\dfrac{14}{19} - \dfrac{5}{7}$ is positive, $\dfrac{14}{19} > \dfrac{5}{7}$.

Problem 21 Select the larger rational number:

(A) $\dfrac{5}{21}, \dfrac{7}{31}$ (B) $\dfrac{8}{15}, \dfrac{14}{27}$

ANSWERS TO
MATCHED PROBLEMS

18. (A) $\dfrac{2}{3}$ (B) $\dfrac{3 + 2u}{2u}$ (C) $\dfrac{3m^2 - 2m}{12m^3}$

19. (A) $\dfrac{2}{3}$ (B) $\dfrac{37}{36xy}$ (C) $\dfrac{8y - 21x}{36x^2y^2}$

20. (A) $\dfrac{11}{12}$ (B) $\dfrac{6x^2 + 9x + 4}{3x^2}$

21. (A) $\dfrac{5}{21}$ (B) $\dfrac{8}{15}$

EXERCISE 3-4 A *Combine into single fractions and reduce to lowest terms (work horizontally).*

1. $\dfrac{2}{3} + \dfrac{4}{3}$

2. $\dfrac{3}{4} + \dfrac{5}{4}$

3. $\dfrac{-3}{5} + \dfrac{7}{5}$

4. $\dfrac{2}{3} + \dfrac{-5}{3}$

5. $\dfrac{3}{8} + \dfrac{1}{2}$

6. $\dfrac{2}{5} + \dfrac{3}{10}$

7. $\dfrac{2}{3} + \dfrac{3}{5}$

8. $\dfrac{1}{2} + \dfrac{4}{7}$

9. $\dfrac{7}{11} - \dfrac{3}{11}$

10. $\dfrac{5}{3} - \dfrac{2}{3}$

11. $\dfrac{7}{11} - \dfrac{-3}{11}$

12. $\dfrac{5}{3} - \dfrac{-2}{3}$

13. $\dfrac{1}{2} - \dfrac{3}{8}$

14. $\dfrac{2}{5} - \dfrac{3}{10}$

15. $\dfrac{3}{5} - \dfrac{2}{3}$

16. $\dfrac{1}{2} - \dfrac{4}{7}$

17. $\dfrac{3}{5xy} + \dfrac{-6}{5xy}$

18. $\dfrac{-6}{5x^2} + \dfrac{4}{5x^2}$

19. $\dfrac{3y}{x} + \dfrac{2y}{x}$

20. $\dfrac{x}{5y} + \dfrac{2x}{5y}$

21. $\dfrac{3}{7y} - \dfrac{-3}{7y}$

22. $\dfrac{-2}{3x} - \dfrac{2}{3x}$

23. $\dfrac{1}{2x} + \dfrac{2}{3x}$

24. $\dfrac{3}{5m} + \dfrac{5}{2m}$

25. $\dfrac{3x}{2} + \dfrac{2x}{3}$

26. $\dfrac{4m}{3} + \dfrac{m}{7}$

27. $\dfrac{3}{5x} - \dfrac{2}{3}$

28. $\dfrac{2}{3} - \dfrac{3}{4y}$

29. $\dfrac{2}{3} + \left(\dfrac{1}{4} \cdot \dfrac{3}{7}\right)$

30. $\left(\dfrac{2}{3} + \dfrac{1}{4}\right)\dfrac{3}{7}$

31. $\left(\dfrac{8}{3} - \dfrac{1}{2}\right)\left(\dfrac{4}{7} \div \dfrac{3}{5}\right)$

32. $\dfrac{8}{3} - \dfrac{1}{2}\left(\dfrac{4}{7} \div \dfrac{3}{5}\right)$

33. $\left(\dfrac{1}{3} - \dfrac{1}{4}\right) - \left(\dfrac{1}{5} - \dfrac{1}{6}\right)$

34. $\left(\dfrac{1}{3} - \dfrac{1}{5}\right) \div \left(\dfrac{1}{4} - \dfrac{1}{6}\right)$

B **35.** $\dfrac{x}{y} - \dfrac{y}{x}$

36. $\dfrac{a}{b} + \dfrac{b}{a}$

37. $\dfrac{x}{y} - 2$

38. $1 - \dfrac{1}{x}$

39. $5 - \dfrac{-3}{x}$

40. $\dfrac{-2}{m} - 4$

41. $\dfrac{1}{xy} - \dfrac{3}{y}$

42. $\dfrac{2a}{b} + \dfrac{-1}{ab}$

43. $\dfrac{3}{2x^2} + \dfrac{4}{3x}$

44. $\dfrac{5}{3y} + \dfrac{3}{4y^2}$

45. $\dfrac{5}{8m^3} - \dfrac{1}{12m}$

46. $\dfrac{2}{9n^2} - \dfrac{5}{12n^4}$

47. $\dfrac{1}{3} - \dfrac{-1}{2} + \dfrac{5}{6}$

48. $\dfrac{-3}{4} + \dfrac{2}{5} - \dfrac{-3}{2}$

49. $\dfrac{x^2}{4} - \dfrac{x}{3} + \dfrac{-1}{2}$

50. $\dfrac{2}{5} - \dfrac{x}{2} - \dfrac{-x^2}{3}$

51. $\dfrac{3}{4x} - \dfrac{2}{3y} + \dfrac{1}{8xy}$

52. $\dfrac{1}{xy} - \dfrac{1}{yz} + \dfrac{-1}{xz}$

53. $\dfrac{3}{y^3} - \dfrac{-2}{3y^2} + \dfrac{1}{2y} - 3$

54. $\dfrac{1}{5x^3} + \dfrac{-3}{2x^2} - \dfrac{-2}{3x} - 1$

C **55.** $\dfrac{y}{9} - \dfrac{-1}{28} - \dfrac{y}{42}$

56. $\dfrac{5x}{6} - \dfrac{3}{8} + \dfrac{x}{15} - \dfrac{3}{20}$

57. $\dfrac{x^2}{12} + \dfrac{x}{18} - \dfrac{1}{30}$

58. $\dfrac{3x}{50} - \dfrac{x}{15} - \dfrac{-2}{6}$

59. $\dfrac{x}{3}\left(\dfrac{1}{4} - \dfrac{x}{2}\right)$

60. $\left(\dfrac{x}{5} - \dfrac{x}{2}\right) \div \dfrac{x}{10}$

61. $x\left(\dfrac{1}{2} + \dfrac{x}{3}\right) - \dfrac{x^2}{6}$

62. $\dfrac{x^2}{2} \div \dfrac{x}{3} - \dfrac{x}{4}$

Select the larger rational number.

63. $\dfrac{2}{7}, \dfrac{7}{25}$

64. $\dfrac{6}{13}, \dfrac{5}{11}$

65. $\dfrac{8}{15}, \dfrac{10}{19}$ **66.** $\dfrac{5}{11}, \dfrac{16}{35}$

3-5
EQUATIONS INVOLVING FRACTIONS AND DECIMALS

- Equations Involving Fractions
- Equations versus Expressions
- Equations Involving Decimals

Most of the equations we solved earlier had integer coefficients. In most practical applications, rational number coefficients occur more frequently than integers. We now have the tools to convert any equation with rational coefficients in either fraction or decimal form into one with integer coefficients. This converts the equation to a form that can be solved using previous methods.

EQUATIONS INVOLVING FRACTIONS

We solve equations involving fractions by first eliminating the fractions. To do this we simply multiply each side of the equation by an appropriate integer.

Example 22   Solve $\dfrac{x}{4} = \dfrac{3}{8}$.

Solution   To isolate x on the left side with a coefficient of $+1$, we multiply both sides by 4 (that is, $\frac{4}{1}$) using the multiplication property of equality (Section 2-7):

$$\frac{4}{1} \cdot \frac{x}{4} = \frac{4}{1} \cdot \frac{3}{8}$$ Usually done mentally after some practice.

$$x = \frac{\overset{1}{\cancel{4}}}{1} \cdot \frac{3}{\underset{2}{\cancel{8}}} = \frac{3}{2}$$

Problem 22   Solve $\dfrac{x}{9} = \dfrac{2}{3}$.

Example 23   Solve $\dfrac{x}{3} - \dfrac{1}{2} = \dfrac{5}{6}$.

Solution   What operation can we perform on the equation to eliminate the denominators? If we could find a number exactly divisible by each denominator, then we would be able to use the multiplication property of equality to clear the denominators. The LCM (see Section 1-1) of the denominators is exactly what we are looking for. The LCM (the smallest number exactly divisible by 3, 2, and 6) is 6. Thus, we multiply both sides of the equation by 6 (or $\frac{6}{1}$):

$$\frac{6}{1} \cdot \left(\frac{x}{3} - \frac{1}{2} \right) = \frac{6}{1} \cdot \frac{5}{6}$$

Clear ( ) before dividing out common factors.

$$\frac{\overset{2}{\cancel{6}}}{1} \cdot \frac{x}{\underset{1}{\cancel{3}}} - \frac{\overset{3}{\cancel{6}}}{1} \cdot \frac{1}{\underset{1}{\cancel{2}}} = \frac{\overset{1}{\cancel{6}}}{1} \cdot \frac{5}{\underset{1}{\cancel{6}}}$$

All denominators should divide out, resulting in an equation with integer coefficients.

$$2x - 3 = 5 \qquad \text{Add 3 to each side.}$$

$$2x = 8 \qquad \text{Divide each side by 2.}$$

$$x = 4$$

With a little experience you will be able to do the dashed box steps mentally. Notice that each term on each side of the equation is multiplied by 6, and since 6 is the LCM of the denominators, each denominator will divide into 6 exactly.

Before you try the matched problem, observe that

$$\frac{5}{12}x$$

can also be written in the form

$$\frac{5x}{12}$$

since

$$\frac{5}{12}x = \frac{5}{12} \cdot \frac{x}{1} = \frac{5x}{12}$$

You should be able to shift easily from one form to the other.

Problem 23   Solve $\frac{1}{4}x - \frac{2}{3} = \frac{5}{12}x$. $\left(\textit{Hint:} \text{ First, write each term as a single fraction; that} \right.$ is, $\frac{1}{4}x = \frac{x}{4}$ and $\frac{5}{12}x = \frac{5x}{12}.\Big)$

Example 24   Solve $5 - \dfrac{2x - 1}{4} = \dfrac{x + 2}{3}$.

Solution   It is a good idea to enclose any numerator with more than one term in parentheses first before multiplying both sides by the LCM of the denominators. The LCM of 4 and 3 is 12.

$$5 - \frac{(2x - 1)}{4} = \frac{(x + 2)}{3}$$

$$12 \cdot 5 - \overset{3}{\cancel{12}} \cdot \frac{(2x - 1)}{\underset{1}{\cancel{4}}} = \overset{4}{\cancel{12}} \cdot \frac{(x + 2)}{\underset{1}{\cancel{3}}}$$ Eliminate denominators.

$$60 - 3(2x - 1) = 4(x + 2)$$ Clear ( ).

$$60 - 6x + 3 = 4x + 8$$ Combine like terms.

$$-6x + 63 = 4x + 8$$ Subtract 63 from each side.

$$-6x = 4x - 55$$ Subtract 4x from each side.

$$-10x = -55$$ Divide both sides by -10.

$$x = \frac{-55}{-10}$$ Reduce your answer.

$$x = \frac{11}{2} \quad \text{or} \quad 5.5$$

Problem 24 Solve $\dfrac{x + 3}{4} - \dfrac{x - 4}{2} = \dfrac{3}{8}$.

EQUATIONS VERSUS EXPRESSIONS

A very common error occurs about now—expressions involving fractions tend to be confused with equations involving fractions. Consider the two problems:

(A) Solve: $\dfrac{x}{2} + \dfrac{x}{3} = 10$.   **(B)** Add: $\dfrac{x}{2} + \dfrac{x}{3} + 10$.

The problems look very much alike, but they are actually quite different. To solve the equation in part (A) we multiply both sides by 6 to clear the fractions. This works so well for equations, students want to do the same thing for problems like (B). The only catch is that part (B) is not an equation and the multiplication property of equality does not apply. If we multiply the expression in part (B) by 6, we obtain an expression 6 times as large as the original. To add in part (B) we find the LCD and proceed as in Sec. 3-4.

Compare the following:

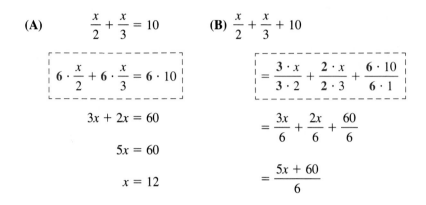

(A) $\dfrac{x}{2} + \dfrac{x}{3} = 10$ (B) $\dfrac{x}{2} + \dfrac{x}{3} + 10$

$$6 \cdot \dfrac{x}{2} + 6 \cdot \dfrac{x}{3} = 6 \cdot 10$$ $$= \dfrac{3 \cdot x}{3 \cdot 2} + \dfrac{2 \cdot x}{2 \cdot 3} + \dfrac{6 \cdot 10}{6 \cdot 1}$$

$$3x + 2x = 60$$ $$= \dfrac{3x}{6} + \dfrac{2x}{6} + \dfrac{60}{6}$$

$$5x = 60$$

$$x = 12$$ $$= \dfrac{5x + 60}{6}$$

EQUATIONS INVOLVING DECIMALS

If an equation contains decimal coefficients, we can often transform it into one with integer coefficients by multiplying each side by a power of 10. Multiplying by 10 moves a decimal point one place to the right; by 100, two places to the right; by 1,000, three places to the right; and so on. Example 25 illustrates the process.

Example 25   Solve $0.1x + 0.5(x - 5) = 3.5$.

Solution $0.1x + 0.5(x - 5) = 3.5$ Multiply each side by 10.

$$10(0.1x) + 10[0.5(x - 5)] = 10(3.5)$$

$$1x + 5(x - 5) = 35$$ The equation is now free of decimals.

$$x + 5x - 25 = 35$$

$$6x = 60$$

$$x = 10$$

Of course, we could retain the decimals and solve the equation as follows:

$$0.1x + 0.5(x - 5) = 3.5$$

$$0.1x + 0.5x - 2.5 = 3.5$$

$$0.6x = 6$$

$$x = \dfrac{6}{0.6} = 10$$

You may find the first method easier.

Problem 25 Solve $0.25x - 0.05(x - 3) = 1.75$.

ANSWERS TO **22.** 6   **23.** -4 **24.** $\frac{19}{2}$ or 9.5   **25.** 8
MATCHED PROBLEMS

EXERCISE 3-5 *Solve each equation.*

A **1.** $\dfrac{x}{7} = -5$ **2.** $\dfrac{x}{3} = -2$ **3.** $\dfrac{x}{4} = \dfrac{3}{2}$

4. $\dfrac{x}{9} = \dfrac{1}{6}$ **5.** $\dfrac{x}{6} = \dfrac{5}{8}$ **6.** $\dfrac{x}{8} = \dfrac{5}{12}$

7. $\dfrac{x}{7} - 1 = \dfrac{1}{7}$ **8.** $\dfrac{x}{5} - 2 = \dfrac{3}{5}$ **9.** $\dfrac{y}{4} + \dfrac{y}{2} = 9$

10. $\dfrac{x}{3} + \dfrac{x}{6} = 4$ **11.** $\dfrac{x}{2} + \dfrac{x}{3} = 5$ **12.** $\dfrac{y}{4} + \dfrac{y}{3} = 7$

13. $\dfrac{x}{3} - \dfrac{1}{4} = \dfrac{3x}{8}$ **14.** $\dfrac{y}{5} - \dfrac{1}{3} = \dfrac{2y}{15}$ **15.** $\dfrac{n}{5} - \dfrac{n}{6} = \dfrac{6}{5}$

16. $\dfrac{m}{4} - \dfrac{m}{3} = \dfrac{1}{2}$ **17.** $\dfrac{2}{3} - \dfrac{x}{8} = \dfrac{5}{6}$ **18.** $\dfrac{5}{12} - \dfrac{m}{3} = \dfrac{4}{9}$

19. $0.8x = 16$ **20.** $0.5x = 35$

21. $0.3x + 0.5x = 24$ **22.** $0.7x + 0.9x = 32$

B **23.** $\dfrac{x + 3}{2} - \dfrac{x}{3} = 4$ **24.** $\dfrac{x - 2}{3} + 1 = \dfrac{x}{7}$

25. $\dfrac{2x + 1}{4} = \dfrac{3x + 2}{3}$ **26.** $\dfrac{4x + 3}{9} = \dfrac{3x + 5}{7}$

27. $3 - \dfrac{x - 1}{2} = \dfrac{x - 3}{3}$ **28.** $4 - \dfrac{x - 3}{4} = \dfrac{x - 1}{8}$

29. $3 - \dfrac{2x - 3}{3} = \dfrac{5 - x}{2}$ **30.** $1 - \dfrac{3x - 1}{6} = \dfrac{2 - x}{3}$

31. $0.4(x + 5) - 0.3x = 17$ **32.** $0.1(x - 7) + 0.05x = 0.8$

33. $0.05x + 0.1(x - 5) = 1.15$ **34.** $0.25x - 0.2(x + 1) = 0.35$

C **35.** $\dfrac{3x - 1}{8} - \dfrac{2x + 1}{3} = \dfrac{1 - x}{12} - 1$

36. $\dfrac{2x - 3}{9} - \dfrac{x + 5}{6} = \dfrac{3 - x}{2} + 1$

37. $0.4312x = 3.1205$ **38.** $2.1038x = 24.6109$

39. $4.3292x = 6.0791x + 38.7415$

40. $23.9308x = 21.0753 - 4.3387x$

3-6
NUMBER AND GEOMETRIC PROBLEMS

- A Strategy for Solving Word Problems
- Number Problems
- Geometric Problems

We are now ready to consider a variety of word problems and significant applications. This section deals with relatively simple number and geometric problems to give you more practice in translating words into symbolic forms. You may be surprised at the number and variety of applications that are now within your reach after having had less than three chapters of algebra. Additional problems are considered in Sections 3-7, 3-8, and 3-9. Applications of a slightly more difficult nature are included in Chapter 4.

A STRATEGY FOR SOLVING WORD PROBLEMS

To start our discussion, we will restate a strategy for solving word problems:

A Strategy for Solving Word Problems

1. Read the problem carefully—several times if necessary—that is, until you understand the problem, know what is to be found, and know what is given.
2. If appropriate, draw figures or diagrams, and label given and unknown parts. Look for formulas connecting the given with the unknown.
3. Let one of the unknown quantities be represented by a variable, say x, and try to represent all other unknown quantities in terms of x. This is an important step and must be done carefully.
4. Form an equation relating the unknown quantities with known quantities.
5. Solve the equation and write answers for all parts of the problem requested.
6. Check and interpret all solutions in terms of the original problem and not just in the equation found in step 4. (A mistake might have been made in setting up the equation in step 4.)

NUMBER PROBLEMS

Recall that if x is a number, then two-thirds x can be written

$$\frac{2}{3}x \quad \text{or} \quad \frac{2x}{3}$$

The latter form will be more convenient for our purposes.

Example 26   Find a number such that 10 less than two-thirds the number is one-fourth the number.

Solution   Let $x =$ The number. Symbolize each part of the problem:

$$\frac{2x}{3} - 10 \quad = \quad \frac{x}{4}$$

$$\underbrace{\begin{pmatrix} \text{10 less than} \\ \text{two-thirds} \\ \text{the number} \end{pmatrix}}_{} \quad \text{is} \quad \underbrace{\begin{pmatrix} \text{one-fourth} \\ \text{the number} \end{pmatrix}}_{}$$

Write an equation involving the symbolic forms and solve:

$$\frac{2x}{3} - 10 = \frac{x}{4}$$

$$12 \cdot \frac{2x}{3} - 12 \cdot 10 = 12 \cdot \frac{x}{4} \qquad \text{Multiply by 12, the LCM of 3 and 4.}$$

$$8x - 120 = 3x \qquad \text{Divide out denominators and simplify.}$$

$$5x = 120$$

$$x = 24$$

Check $\frac{2}{3}(24) - 10 = 16 - 10 = 6$ Left side

$\frac{1}{4}(24) = 6$ Right side

Problem 26   Find a number such that 6 more than one-half the number is two-thirds the number.

GEOMETRIC PROBLEMS

Recall that the **perimeter** of a triangle or rectangle is the distance around the figure. Symbolically:

$$P = a + b + c \qquad\qquad P = 2a + 2b$$

Example 27   If one side of a triangle is one-third the perimeter, the second side is 7 centi-meters, and the third side is one-fifth the perimeter, what is the perimeter of the triangle?

Solution   Let P = Perimeter. Draw a triangle and label the sides, as shown. Thus,

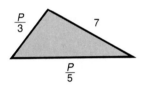

$$P = \frac{P}{3} + 7 + \frac{P}{5}$$

$$15 \cdot P = 15 \cdot \frac{P}{3} + 15 \cdot 7 + 15 \cdot \frac{P}{5} \qquad \text{15 is LCM of 3 and 5.}$$

$$15P = 5P + 105 + 3P$$

$$7P = 105$$

$$P = 15 \text{ centimeters}$$

Check $\dfrac{15}{3} + 7 + \dfrac{15}{5} = 5 + 7 + 3 = 15 \qquad$ The perimeter

Problem 27   If one side of a triangle is one-fourth the perimeter, the second side is 7 meters, and the third side is two-fifths the perimeter, what is the perimeter?

Example 28   Find the dimensions of a rectangle with perimeter 176 centimeters if its width is three-eighths its length.

Solution   Let x = Length. Draw a rectangle and label the sides, as shown. Thus,

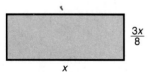

$$2x + 2 \cdot \frac{3x}{8} = 176 \qquad \text{Use the perimeter formula } 2a + 2b = P.$$

$$2x + \frac{3x}{4} = 176$$

$$4 \cdot 2x + 4 \cdot \frac{3x}{4} = 4 \cdot 176$$

$$8x + 3x = 704$$

$$11x = 704$$

$$x = 64 \text{ centimeters}$$

$$\frac{3x}{8} = 24 \text{ centimeters}$$

Check $2 \cdot 64 + 2 \cdot 24 = 128 + 48 = 176$ centimeters   The perimeter. Be sure to add all four sides, not just two.

Problem 28   Find the dimensions of a rectangle with perimeter 84 centimeters if its width is two-fifths its length.

ANSWERS TO MATCHED PROBLEMS   **26.** 36   **27.** 20 meters   **28.** 30 centimeters by 12 centimeters

EXERCISE 3-6   A   *If x represents a number, write an algebraic expression for each of the following numbers:*

1. One-half x
2. One-sixth x
3. Two-thirds x
4. Three-fourths x
5. 2 more than one-third x
6. 5 more than one-fourth x
7. 8 less than two-thirds x
8. 6 less than three-fourths x
9. One-half the number that is 3 less than twice x
10. One-third the number that is 5 less than four times x

Find numbers meeting each of the indicated conditions.
(A) *Write an equation using x.*   **(B)** *Solve the equation.*

11. 2 more than one-fourth the number is $\frac{1}{2}$.
12. 3 more than one-sixth the number is $\frac{2}{3}$.
13. 2 less than one-half the number is one-third the number.
14. 3 less than one-third the number is one-fourth the number.

B   **15.** 5 less than half the number is 3 more than one-third the number.

16. 2 less than one-sixth the number is 1 more than one-fourth the number.

17. 5 more than two-thirds the number is 10 less than one-fourth the number.

18. 4 less than three-fifths the number is 8 more than one-third the number.

Solve.

19. If one side of a triangle is one-fourth the perimeter, the second side is 3 meters, and the third side is one-third the perimeter, what is the perimeter?

20. If one side of a triangle is two-fifths the perimeter, the second side is 70 centimeters, and the third side is one-fourth the perimeter, what is the perimeter?

21. An electrical transmission tower is located in a lake. If one-fifth of the tower is in the sand, 10 meters is in the water, and two-thirds of it is in the air, what is the total height of the tower from the rock foundation to the top (see the figure)?

22. On a safari in Africa a group traveled one-half the distance by Land Rover, 55 kilometers by horse, and the last one-third of the distance by boat. How long was the trip?

23. Find the dimensions of a rectangle with perimeter 72 centimeters if its width is one-third its length.

24. Find the dimensions of a rectangle with perimeter 84 meters if its width is one-sixth its length.

25. Find the dimensions of a rectangle with perimeter 216 meters if its width is two-sevenths its length.

26. Find the dimensions of a rectangle with perimeter 100 centimeters if its width is two-thirds its length.

C **27.** Find the dimensions of a rectangle with perimeter 112 centimeters if its width is 7 centimeters less than two-fifths its length.

28. Find the dimensions of a rectangle with perimeter 264 centimeters if its width is 11 centimeters less than three-eighths its length.

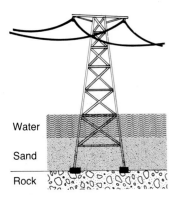

Water

Sand

Rock

3-7 PERCENT

- Percent
- Converting between Percent and Decimal
- Percent Problems

This section presents a brief review of percent and the sorts of applied problems where percentages arise. Students thoroughly familiar with the percent concept can cover the first two subsections quickly.

PERCENT

If 1 is divided into 100 equal parts, then each part is called **1 percent**. The symbol % is read "percent." Thus,

FRACTION		DECIMAL		PERCENT
$\dfrac{23}{100}$	=	0.23	=	23%
$\dfrac{4}{100}$	=	0.04	=	4%
$\dfrac{162}{100}$	=	1.62	=	162%
$\dfrac{0.3}{100}$	=	0.003	=	0.3%

CONVERTING BETWEEN PERCENT AND DECIMAL

It will often be necessary to convert back and forth between percent and decimal forms.

> To convert a percent to a decimal, remove the percent symbol and move the decimal point two places to the left.

Example 29 **(A)** 43% $\boxed{= 43.\%}$ = 0.43   **(B)** 7% $\boxed{= 07.\%}$ = 0.07

(C) 234% $\boxed{= 234.\%}$ = 2.34   **(D)** 0.3% $\boxed{= 00.3\%}$ = 0.003

Problem 29 Convert each percent to a decimal:

(A) 59%   **(B)** 2%   **(C)** 105%   **(D)** 0.7%

> To convert a decimal or whole number to percent, shift the decimal point two places to the right and use the percent symbol.

Example 30 **(A)** 0.23 $\boxed{= 0.23}$ = 23%   **(B)** 0.06 $\boxed{= 0.06}$ = 6%

(C) 4.37 $\boxed{= 4.37}$ = 437%   **(D)** 0.064 $\boxed{= 0.064}$ = 6.4%

Problem 30   Convert each decimal to a percent:

(A) 0.71   **(B)** 0.05   **(C)** 1.09   **(D)** 0.003

PERCENT PROBLEMS

Applied problems frequently require taking a percent of a given quantity.

> To find a percent of a given quantity, convert the percent to a decimal and multiply.

Example 31   **(A)** Find 23% of 45.   **(B)** Find 6.2% of 28.

Solution   **(A)** 23% of 45 = 0.23 × 45 = 10.35
(B) 6.2% of 28 = 0.062 × 28 = 1.736

Problem 31   Find each:

(A) 4% of 64   **(B)** 108% of 22   **(C)** 23% of 5   **(D)** 0.5% of 30

Example 32   The sales tax in a given state is $5\frac{1}{2}$% of the total charges. Compute the tax on a bill of $114.

Solution $5\frac{1}{2}$% of $114 = 5.5% of 114 = 0.055 × 114 = 6.27. The tax is $6.27.

Problem 32   The tax on hotel rooms in a certain city is 11%. Find the tax if the room charge is $65.

Example 33   A retail store marks up an item 20% above cost. Find the original cost of an item that the store sells for $45.60.

Solution   Let x be the original cost. The markup is 20% of x, that is $0.2x$. The selling price is cost plus markup:

$$\text{Cost} + \text{Markup} = \text{Selling price}$$
$$x + 0.2x = 45.60$$
$$1.2x = 45.60$$
$$x = \frac{45.60}{1.2} = 38$$

so the cost to the store was $38.

This problem can also be set up by recognizing that 20% above cost is 120% of the cost. Therefore the selling price is 120% of the cost, that is,

$$1.2x = 45.60$$

Problem 33   A worker receives a raise of 6.25%. If the worker's new pay rate is $10.20 per hour, what was her previous rate?

ANSWERS TO   **29. (A)** 0.59   **(B)** 0.02   **(C)** 1.05   **(D)** 0.007
MATCHED PROBLEMS   **30. (A)** 71%   **(B)** 5%   **(C)** 109%   **(D)** 0.3%
                   31. (A) 2.56   **(B)** 23.76   **(C)** 1.15   **(D)** 0.15
                   32. $7.15   **33.** $9.60

EXERCISE 3-7 A *Change percents to decimals.*

1. 67%	**2.** 14%	**3.** 9%	**4.** 1%
5. 216%	**6.** 308%	**7.** 0.6%	**8.** 0.1%
9. 7.4%	**10.** 2.8%	**11.** 23.1%	**12.** 64.5%

Change decimals to percents.

13. 0.12	**14.** 0.21	**15.** 0.08	**16.** 0.02
17. 3.25	**18.** 6.04	**19.** 0.007	**20.** 0.004
21. 0.072	**22.** 0.069	**23.** 0.405	**24.** 0.236

Find each.

25. 12% of 403	**26.** 18% of 40	**27.** 6% of 4,000
28. 8% of 2,000	**29.** 125% of 200	**30.** 150% of 44
31. 6.5% of 24	**32.** 4.8% of 36	**33.** 0.4% of 20
34. 0.7% of 80		

B   **35.**   If you paid $168 for a camera after receiving a 20% discount, what was the original price of the camera?

36.   The retail price of a record is $9.80. The markup on the cost is 40%. What did the store pay for the record?

Interest rates are usually expressed as annual rates. To convert an annual rate to a monthly rate, divide by 12. For example, 9% annual rate is equivalent to 0.75% per month.

37.   A checking account pays interest monthly at an annual rate of 5.4% on the average monthly balance. What is the interest for a month where the average balance is $440.00?

38. A money market fund pays interest monthly at an annual rate of 6.6%. What is the monthly return on an investment of $1,500?

39. If the unemployment rate is 5.6% and the total eligible workforce is 140 million people, how many persons are unemployed?

40. The attrition rate at a certain university is 14% from freshman to sophomore year, meaning that 14% of a typical freshman class does not return to the school the following year. If the school enrolls 650 freshman, how many does it expect to return as sophomores?

41. Wage increases are often tied to the Consumer Price Index (CPI), also called the cost of living index. If the CPI increase for a given year is 4.6%, how much must an hourly wage of $8.40 be increased to match the cost-of-living increase?

42. Book royalties are often determined as a percentage of gross sales. If a best-selling author gets a royalty of 18%, how much income does she receive from a book that has gross sales of $400,000?

C   **43.** A person borrowed a sum of money from a lending group at 12% simple interest. At the end of 2.5 years the loan was cleared by paying $520. How much was originally borrowed? [*Hint:* $A = P + Prt$, where A is the amount repaid, P is the amount borrowed, r is the interest rate expressed as a decimal, and t is time in years.]

44. A money market fund pays interest monthly at an annual rate of 6.6%. If $2,000 is placed in the fund and the interest reinvested, how much is in the fund after 2 months?

45. If the CPI (see Problem 41) increases from 318 to 332.3, how much must an annual salary of $22,000 be increased to keep pace with the cost of living?

46. A retail store has a markup of 20%. An item is subsequently offered for 15% off the list price. What is the sale price if the item cost the store $30?

47. A retail store with a markup of 30% offers an item on sale for 20% off at a price of $54.08. What was the store's original cost?

48. A checking account pays monthly interest at an annual rate of 5.4% on the average monthly balance. If the account had no activity during the month and the balance at the end of the month was $662.97, what was the balance at the start of the month?

3-8
RATIO AND PROPORTION

- Ratio
- Proportion
- Direct Variation
- Metric Conversion

One of the first applications of algebra in elementary science and technology courses you are likely to encounter deals with ratio and proportion. Many problems in these courses can be solved using the methods developed in this section. Moreover, we will find a convenient way to convert metric units into English units and English units into metric units.

RATIO

The use of ratios is very common. You have no doubt been using ratios for many years and will recall that the ratio of two quantities is the first divided by the second. That is:

Ratio of a to b

The ratio of a to b, assuming $b \neq 0$, is $\dfrac{a}{b}$.

(It is also written $a:b$ or a/b and is read "a to b.")

Thus a ratio of two integers is a rational number.

Example 34 If there are 10 men and 20 women in a class, what is the ratio of men to women?

Solution The ratio is $\frac{10}{20}$ or $\frac{1}{2}$ (which is also written $1:2$ and is read "1 to 2").

Problem 34 If there are 500 men and 400 women in a school, what is the ratio of:

(A) Men to women?   **(B)** Women to men?

PROPORTION

In addition to comparing known quantities, another reason we want to know something about ratios is that they often lead to a simple way of finding unknown quantities.

Example 35 Suppose you are told that the ratio of women to men in a college is $3:5$ and there are 1,450 men. How many women are in the college?

Solution   Let x = The number of women; then the ratio of women to men is $x/1{,}450$. Thus,

$$\frac{x}{1{,}450} = \frac{3}{5} \qquad \text{To isolate } x \text{, multiply both sides by 1,450.}$$

$$x = 1{,}450 \cdot \frac{3}{5}$$

$$= 870 \text{ women}$$

Problem 35   If in a college the ratio of men to women is $2:3$ and there are 1,200 women, how many men are in the school?

A statement of equality between two ratios is called a proportion. That is:

Proportion
$\dfrac{a}{b} = \dfrac{c}{d} \qquad b, d \neq 0$

Example 36   If a car can travel 192 miles on 8 gallons of gas, how far will it go on 15 gallons?

Solution   Let x = Distance traveled on 15 gallons. Thus,

$$\frac{x}{15} = \frac{192}{8} \qquad \text{Both ratios represent miles per gallon.}$$

$$x = 15 \cdot \frac{192}{8} \qquad \begin{array}{l}\text{We can isolate } x \text{ by multiplying both sides by 15—we do not need}\\ \text{to use the LCM of 15 and 8.}\end{array}$$

$$= 360 \text{ miles}$$

Problem 36   If a truck can travel 180 kilometers on 24 liters of gas, how far will it travel on 30 liters? Set up a proportion and solve.

Example 37   If there are 24 milliliters of hydrochloric acid in 64 milliliters of solution, how many milliliters of hydrochloric acid will be in 48 milliliters of the same solution? Set up a proportion and solve.

Solution   Let x = Number of milliliters of acid in 48 milliliters of solution; then

$$\frac{x}{48} = \frac{24}{64}$$

$$x = 48 \cdot \frac{24}{64} = 18 \text{ milliliters}$$

Problem 37   If there are 4 cups of milk in a recipe for 6 people, how many cups of milk should be used in the same recipe for 10 people?

DIRECT VARIATION

In applied problems, ratios of certain quantities may be constant. In this case the quantities are said to vary directly or to be directly proportional.

Direct Variation

A quantity a is said to **vary directly** with another quantity b if the ratio $\frac{a}{b}$ is a constant. We also say a is **directly proportional** to b.

For example, at a constant speed, distance d is proportional to time t, since

$$\frac{d}{t} = \text{speed (constant)}$$

If a car travels at a constant speed of 20 miles per hour, then the distance is given by $d = 20t$, so $\frac{d}{t} = 20$.

The variation in the two quantities distance and time is "direct" in the sense that as one increases so does the other.

Example 38   Successful telephone solicitations for a charity are directly proportional to the number of calls made. If an organization receives 3 donations for every 50 calls made, how many donations will it receive if it makes 1,500 solicitation calls?

Solution   The ratio $\dfrac{\text{donation}}{\text{calls}}$ is a constant and this constant is $\dfrac{3}{50} = 0.06$. Let x be the number of donations resulting from 1,500 calls. Then

$$\frac{x}{1,500} = 0.06$$

$$x = 0.06 \times 1,500 = 90$$

Another way of looking at this problem is to observe that the number of calls increased to 1,500, that is, to 30 times the original number 50. The number of donations should therefore do the same, increasing from 3 to 30 times 3, or 90.

Problem 38   The number of traffic accidents on a particular stretch of highway varies directly with the number of vehicles traveling the highway. If 2 accidents are expected per 5,000 vehicles, how many should be expected if 12,500 vehicles use the highway on a busy day?

METRIC CONVERSION

A summary of metric units is located inside the back cover of the text. Here we show how proportion can be used to convert from one system to the other.

Example 39   If there are 2.2 pounds in 1 kilogram, how many kilograms are in 100 pounds?

Solution   Let x = Number of kilograms in 100 pounds. Set up a proportion with x in a numerator; that is, a proportion of the form

$$\frac{\text{Kilograms}}{\text{Pounds}} = \frac{\text{Kilograms}}{\text{Pounds}} \quad \text{Each ratio represents kilograms per pound.}$$

Thus,

$$\frac{x}{100} = \frac{1}{2.2}$$

$$x = \frac{100}{2.2}$$

$$= 45.45 \text{ kilograms}$$

Problem 39   If there is 0.45 kilogram in 1 pound, how many pounds are in 90 kilograms? Set up a proportion (with the variable in the numerator) and solve.

Example 40   If there are 1.09 yards in 1 meter, how many meters are in 80 yards?

Solution   Let x = Number of meters in 80 yards. Set up a proportion of the form

$$\frac{\text{Meters}}{\text{Yards}} = \frac{\text{Meters}}{\text{Yards}}$$

Thus,

$$\frac{x}{80} = \frac{1}{1.09}$$

$$x = \frac{80}{1.09}$$

$$= 73.39 \text{ meters}$$

Problem 40   If there is 0.94 liter in 1 quart, how many quarts are in 50 liters? Set up a proportion (with the variable in a numerator) and solve.

ANSWERS TO
MATCHED PROBLEMS

34. **(A)** $\frac{5}{4}$ or 5:4   **(B)** $\frac{4}{5}$ or 4:5
35. 800 men   **36.** 225 kilometers   **37.** $6\frac{2}{3}$ cups
38. 5 accidents
39. $\dfrac{x}{90} = \dfrac{1}{0.45}$, x = 200 pounds   **40.** $\dfrac{x}{50} = \dfrac{1}{0.94}$, x = 53.19 quarts

EXERCISE 3-8   A   *Write as a ratio.*

1.   16 men to 64 women

2.   64 women to 16 men

3.   25 centimeters to 5 centimeters

4.   30 meters to 10 meters

5.   30 square kilometers to 90 square kilometers

6.   25 square meters to 100 square meters

Solve each proportion.

7. $\dfrac{x}{12} = \dfrac{2}{3}$ **8.** $\dfrac{y}{16} = \dfrac{5}{4}$ **9.** $\dfrac{d}{12} = \dfrac{27}{18}$

10. $\dfrac{y}{13} = \dfrac{21}{39}$ **11.** $\dfrac{18}{27} = \dfrac{h}{6}$ **12.** $\dfrac{35}{56} = \dfrac{x}{32}$

Set up proportions and solve.

13. If in a college the ratio of men to women is $\frac{5}{7}$ and there are 840 women, how many men are there?

14. If the ratio of women to men is $\frac{7}{9}$ and there are 630 men, how many women are there?

15. If the ratio of the length of a rectangle to its width is $\frac{3}{2}$ and the width is 24 centimeters, how long is the rectangle?

16. If the ratio of the width of a rectangle to its length is $\frac{3}{5}$ and its length is 30 meters, how wide is it?

17. If the ratio of grade points to the total number of units for a student is $\frac{7}{2}$ and the student has completed 60 units, how many grade points does the student have?

18. If the ratio of grade points to the total number of units for a student is $\frac{14}{5}$ and the student has completed 90 units, how many grade points does the student have?

19. If a car can travel 100 kilometers on 12 liters of gas, how far will it go on 15 liters?

20. If an airplane can fly 2,400 miles in 9 hours, how far will it fly in 6 hours?

B   21. *Mixture* If there are 8 grams of sulfuric acid in 70 grams of solution, how many grams of sulfuric acid are in 21 grams of the same solution?

22. *Mixture* If 1.5 cups of sugar are needed in a recipe for 4 people, how many cups of sugar are needed for 6 people?

23. *Photography* If you enlarge a 3- by 6-inch picture so that the longer side is 8 inches, how wide will the enlargement be?

24. *Scale drawings* An architect wishes to make a scale drawing of a building that is 12 meters long by 8 meters wide. If she uses 9 centimeters for the length, what should she use for the width?

25. *Price/earning ratio* If the price/earning ratio for a common stock is $\frac{5}{2}$ and the stock earns $36 per share, what is the price of the stock?

26. *Commissions* If you were charged a commission of $144 on the purchase of 300 shares of stock, what would be the proportionate commission on 500 shares of the same stock?

27. *Engineering* If an engineer knows that a 1.5-meter piece of steel rod weighs 12 kilograms, how much would a 5-meter piece of the same rod weigh?

28. **Engineering** In the figure the area *a* of the small pipe is 2 square centimeters and the area *A* of the larger pipe is 136 square centimeters. How much force *f* in kilograms is required to lift a car weighing 1,700 kilograms (3,740 pounds)?

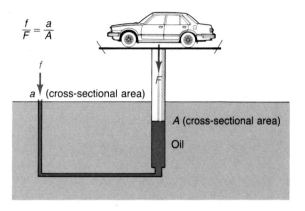

29. **Metric conversion** If there is 1 kilogram in 2.2 pounds, how many kilograms are in 12 pounds?

30. **Metric conversion** If there is 1 liter in 1.06 quarts, how many liters are in 1 gallon (4 quarts)?

31. **Metric conversion** If there are 1.61 kilometers in 1 mile, how many miles are in 40 kilometers?

32. **Metric conversion** If there are 1.09 yards in 1 meter, how many meters are in 100 yards?

33. **Metric conversion** If there are 28.57 grams in 1 ounce, how many ounces are in 1 kilogram (1,000 grams)?

34. **Metric conversion** If there are 39.37 inches in 1 meter, how many meters are in 10 feet?

35. **Metric conversion** If there is 0.92 meter in 1 yard, how many yards are in 50 meters?

36. **Metric conversion** If there is 0.94 liter in 1 quart, how many quarts are in 20 liters?

C 37. **Wildlife management** Zoologists Green and Evans (1940) estimated the total population of snowshoe hares in the Lake Alexander area of Minnesota as follows. They captured and banded 948 hares and then released them. After an appropriate period for mixing, they again captured a sample of 421 and found 167 of these marked. Assuming that the ratio of marked hares to the total number captured in the second sample is the same as the ratio of those banded in the first sample to the total population, set up a proportion and estimate the total hare population in the region.

38. *Wildlife management* Estimate the total number of trout in a lake if a sample of 500 are netted, marked, and released and after a period for mixture, a second sample of 375 produces 25 marked ones. (See Problem 37.)

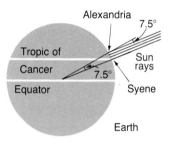

39. *Astronomy* Do you have any idea how one might measure the circumference of the earth? In 240 B.C. Eratosthenes measured the size of the earth from its curvature. At Syene, Egypt (lying on the Tropic of Cancer), the sun was directly overhead at noon on June 21. At the same time in Alexandria, a town 500 miles directly north, the sun's rays fell at an angle of 7.5° to the vertical. Using this information and a little knowledge of geometry (see the figure), Eratosthenes was able to approximate the circumference of the earth by using the following proportion: 360° is to 7.5° as the circumference of the earth is to 500 miles. Compute Eratosthenes' estimate.

3-9
SUPPLEMENTAL APPLICATIONS

Now that you have had experience in solving several types of word problems, we present a supplemental exercise set with a wide variety of real-world applications from several fields. Some are easy and others are more difficult to solve. The more difficult problems are marked with either a double or single asterisk.

It is again worthwhile noting that with less than three chapters of algebra behind you, you are in a position to solve a fair number of practical problems. In the following chapters we will increase our problem-solving power even more.

If you are having difficulty in solving word problems (most people do at first), do not become discouraged. Keep working on the easier problems, then gradually work up to the more difficult ones.

EXERCISE 3-9

This supplemental exercise set contains a variety of applications arranged according to subject area. The most difficult problems are marked with two stars (★★) and the moderately difficult problems with one star (★). The easier problems are not marked.

BUSINESS

1. If an IBM electronic card sorter can sort 1,250 cards in 5 minutes, how long will it take the card sorter to sort 11,250 cards?

DOMESTIC

2. A father, in order to encourage his daughter to do better in algebra, agrees to pay her 25 cents for each problem she gets right on a test and to fine her 10 cents for each problem she misses. On a test with 20 problems she received $3.60. How many problems did she get right?

3. A car rental company charges $20 per day and 15 cents per mile. If a car was rented for 2 days, how far was it driven if the total rental bill was $100?

★★4. The cruising speed of an airplane is 150 miles per hour (relative to ground). You wish to hire the plane for a 3-hour sightseeing trip. You instruct the pilot to fly north as far as possible and still return to the airport at the end of the allotted time.

  (A) How far north should the pilot fly if there is a wind of 30 miles an hour blowing from the north?

  (B) How far north should the pilot fly if there is no wind blowing?

CHEMISTRY

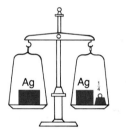

5. Two-thirds of a standard bar of silver (Ag) balances exactly with one-half of a standard bar of silver and a $\frac{1}{4}$-kilogram weight (see the figure). How much does one whole standard bar of silver weigh?

6. In the study of gases there is a simple law called Boyle's law that expresses a relationship between volume and pressure. It states that the product of the pressure and volume, as these quantities change and all other variables are held fixed, remains constant. Stated as a formula, $P_1V_1 = P_2V_2$. If 500 cubic centimeters of air at 70-centimeter pressure were converted to 100-centimeter pressure, what volume would it have?

LIFE SCIENCE

7. A fairly good approximation for the normal weight of a person over 60 inches (5 feet) tall is given by the formula $w = 5.5h - 220$, where h is height in inches and w is weight in pounds. How tall should a 121-pound person be?

★8. A wildlife management team estimated the number of bears in a national forest by the popular capture-mark-recapture technique. Using live traps, they captured and marked 30 bears and then released them. After a period for mixing, they captured another 30 and found 5 marked among them. Assuming that the ratio of the total bear population to the bears marked in the first sample is the same as the ratio of bears in the second sample to those found marked in the second sample, estimate the bear population in the forest.

EARTH SCIENCE

9. About one-ninth of the height of an iceberg is above water. If 20 meters are observed above water, what is the total height of the iceberg?

10. Pressure in seawater increases by 1 atmosphere (15 pounds per square inch) for each 33 feet of depth; it is 15 pounds per square inch at the surface. Thus, $p = 15 + 15(d/33)$, where p is the pressure in pounds per square inch at a depth of d feet below the surface. How deep is a diver if she observes that the pressure is 165 pounds per square inch?

11. As dry air moves upward, it expands and in so doing cools at the rate of about 5.5°F for each 1,000 feet in rise. This ascent is known as the "adiabatic process." If the ground temperature is 80°F, write an equation that relates temperature T with altitude h (in feet). How high is an airplane if the pilot observes that the temperature is 25°F?

MUSIC   **12.** Starting with a string tuned to a given note, one can move up and down the scale simply by decreasing or increasing its length (while maintaining the same tension) according to simple whole-number ratios (see the figure). Chords can also be formed by taking two strings whose lengths form ratios involving certain whole numbers. Find the lengths of seven strings (each less than 30 inches) that will produce the following seven chords when paired with a 30-inch string:

(A)	Octave	1:2	**(B)**	Fifth	2:3
(C)	Fourth	3:4	**(D)**	Major third	4:5
(E)	Minor third	5:6	**(F)**	Major sixth	3:5
(G)	Minor sixth	5:8			

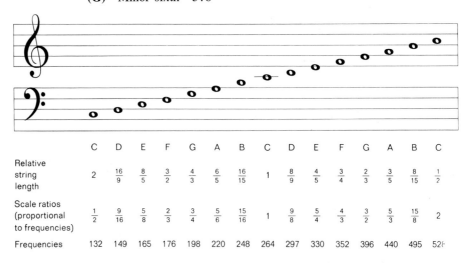

	C	D	E	F	G	A	B	C	D	E	F	G	A	B	C
Relative string length	2	$\frac{16}{9}$	$\frac{8}{5}$	$\frac{3}{2}$	$\frac{4}{3}$	$\frac{6}{5}$	$\frac{16}{15}$	1	$\frac{8}{9}$	$\frac{4}{5}$	$\frac{3}{4}$	$\frac{2}{3}$	$\frac{3}{5}$	$\frac{8}{15}$	$\frac{1}{2}$
Scale ratios (proportional to frequencies)	$\frac{1}{2}$	$\frac{9}{16}$	$\frac{5}{8}$	$\frac{2}{3}$	$\frac{3}{4}$	$\frac{5}{6}$	$\frac{15}{16}$	1	$\frac{9}{8}$	$\frac{5}{4}$	$\frac{4}{3}$	$\frac{3}{2}$	$\frac{5}{3}$	$\frac{15}{8}$	2
Frequencies	132	149	165	176	198	220	248	264	297	330	352	396	440	495	528

Diatonic scale

PHYSICS AND ENGINEERING   **13.** An important problem in physics and engineering is the lever problem shown in the figure. In order for the system to be balanced (not move), the product of the force and distance on one side must equal the product of the force and distance on the other. If a person has a 1-meter wrecking bar and places a fulcrum 10 centimeters from one end, how much can be lifted with a force of 25 kilograms on the long end?

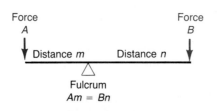

Force
A

Force
B

Distance m Distance n

Fulcrum
$Am = Bn$

Lever system

14. How heavy a rock can be moved with an 8-foot steel rod if the fulcrum is placed 1 foot from the rock end and a force of 100 pounds is exerted on the other end?

★15. How far would a fulcrum have to be placed from an end with a 65-kilogram weight to balance 85 kilograms on the other end if the bar is 3 meters long? (See Problem 13.)

PSYCHOLOGY   **16.** Psychologists define IQ (intelligence quotient) as

$$IQ = \frac{\text{Mental age}}{\text{Chronological age}} \times 100$$

$$= \frac{\text{MA}}{\text{CA}} \times 100$$

If a person has an IQ of 120 and a mental age of 18 years, what is the person's chronological (actual) age?

3-10
CHAPTER REVIEW

A **fraction** represents parts of a whole. The fraction $\frac{a}{b}$, where a and b are positive integers, represents a parts of a whole divided into b equal parts. Fractions may be represented as **decimals**.   *(3-1)*

A **rational number** is a number that can be written in the form $\frac{a}{b}$, where the **numerator** a and **denominator** b are integers with $b \neq 0$. The rational number $\frac{a}{b}$ is **positive** when a and b have like signs and **negative** when their signs are opposite. The **absolute value** and **opposite** of a rational number are defined as for integers. A rational number $\frac{a}{b}$ can be **raised to higher terms** or the rational number $\frac{ak}{bk}$ **reduced to lower terms** by using the **fundamental principle of fractions**: $\frac{a}{b} = \frac{ak}{ab}$. A fraction is reduced to **lowest terms** if the numerator and denominator have no common factor greater than 1. Rational numbers have the following **sign properties**:

$$\frac{-a}{-b} = \frac{a}{b} \qquad \frac{-a}{b} = \frac{a}{-b} = -\frac{a}{b} = (-1)\frac{a}{b} \quad (3\text{-}2)$$

Multiplication and **division** of rational numbers are defined by

$$\frac{a}{b} \cdot \frac{c}{d} = \frac{ac}{bd} \quad \text{and} \quad \frac{a}{b} \div \frac{c}{d} = \frac{a}{b} \cdot \frac{d}{c} = \frac{ad}{bc} \quad (3\text{-}3)$$

Addition and **subtraction** of rational numbers with common denominators are defined by

$$\frac{a}{b} + \frac{c}{b} = \frac{a+c}{b} \quad \text{and} \quad \frac{a}{b} - \frac{c}{b} = \frac{a-c}{b}$$

To add or subtract rational numbers when the denominators are not the same, convert them to equivalent forms with a common denominator by using the fundamental principle of fractions. Computation is generally minimized by using the **least common denominator** (LCD)—that is, the LCM of the denominators.   *(3-4)*

Equations involving fractions or decimals are solved by first clearing the equation of fractions and decimals by multiplication.   *(3-5)*

The strategy for solving word problems, first introduced in Chapter 2, is applied again in Sections 3-6 to 3-9. **Percent** means parts per 100.   *(3-7)*

A **ratio** of two quantities is the first divided by the second, written $\frac{a}{b}$ or $a:b$

and read "*a* to *b*." A **proportion** is an equality between two ratios. A quantity **varies directly** with another, or is **directly proportional** to another, if their ratio is constant.   *(3-8)*

REVIEW EXERCISE 3-10

Work through all the problems in this chapter review and check answers in the back of the book. (Answers to all problems are there, and following each answer is a number in italics indicating the section in which that type of problem is discussed.) Where weaknesses show up, review appropriate sections in the text.

All variables represent nonzero integers.

A   **1.**   Graph $\{-\frac{7}{4}, -\frac{3}{4}, \frac{3}{2}\}$ on a number line.

Perform the indicated operations and reduce to lowest terms.

2. $\dfrac{3}{2y} \cdot \dfrac{5x}{4}$ **3.** $\dfrac{3}{2y} \div \dfrac{5x}{4}$ **4.** $\dfrac{y}{2} + \dfrac{y}{3}$ **5.** $\dfrac{3}{2y} - \dfrac{5x}{4}$

Solve.

6. $6x = 5$ **7.** $3x - 5 = 5x - 8$ **8.** $\dfrac{y}{8} = \dfrac{3}{4}$

9. $0.7x = 4.2$

10. $\dfrac{x}{2} - \dfrac{1}{3} = \dfrac{x}{6}$

11. Three-tenths of what number is $\frac{2}{5}$?
(A) Write an equation.   (B) Solve.

12. If the width of a rectangle with perimeter 80 centimeters is three-fifths the length, what are the dimensions of the rectangle?

13. The response rate in a mail survey is 46%. If 3,000 surveys were mailed, how many were returned?

B   *Perform the indicated operations and reduce to lowest terms.*

14. $\dfrac{3y}{5xz} \cdot \dfrac{10z}{15xy}$

15. $\dfrac{3y}{5xy} \div \dfrac{10z}{15xy}$

16. $\dfrac{3}{4xy^2} - \dfrac{1}{3x^2y}$

17. $\dfrac{3}{x^2} - \dfrac{2}{x} + 1$

18. $\dfrac{1}{4y} + \dfrac{3}{2z} - \dfrac{1}{3x} - 2$

19. $\dfrac{-4}{9} - \dfrac{35}{18} - \dfrac{-10}{3}$

20. $\dfrac{x}{3}\left(6y - \dfrac{9}{x}\right)$

Solve.

21. $\dfrac{x}{4} - \dfrac{x-3}{3} = 2$

22. $0.4x - 0.3(x - 3) = 5$

23. If the ratio of all the trout in a lake to the ones that had been captured, marked, and released is 20:3 and there are 450 marked trout, how many trout are in the lake? Set up an equation and solve.

24. If there are 2.54 centimeters in 1 inch, how many inches are in 40 centimeters? Set up a proportion and solve.

25. Find a number such that 1 less than three quarters of the number is 12 less than the number itself.

26. The federal income tax rate for single taxpayers on net taxable incomes of $16,800 to $27,000 is $2,448 plus 28% of the amount over $16,800. What is the tax on a taxable income of $22,800?

27. Solve: $0.4x - \dfrac{x}{0.12} = -4.76$.

C   *Perform the indicated operations and reduce to lowest terms.*

28. $\dfrac{10x}{9y} \div \left(\dfrac{15xy}{2z} \div \dfrac{3y^2}{-z} \right)$

29. $\dfrac{3}{10x^2} - \dfrac{2}{15xy} + \dfrac{5}{18y^2}$

30. Solve: $\dfrac{x+3}{10} - \dfrac{x-2}{15} = \dfrac{3-x}{6} - 1.$

31. Estimate the total number of squirrels in a forest if a sample of 140 is captured, marked, and released; and after a period for mixing, a second batch of 70 is captured and it is found that 20 of these are marked.

32. A retail store buys an item for $60 and adds a mark up of 30%. A customer pays $82.68 including sales tax. What is the sales tax rate?

4

GRAPHING AND LINEAR EQUATIONS

By extending the integers to the rational numbers in Chapter 3, we significantly increased our ability to perform certain operations, to solve equations, and to attack practical problems. It appears that the rational numbers are capable of satisfying all our number needs. Can we stop here or do we need to go further? We will see in this chapter that there are lengths, and therefore points, on the number line that do not correspond to rational numbers. An expanded number system, the *real numbers,* is needed.

The real number system provides an exact correspondence between numbers and points on the number line. This correspondence is utilized in Section 4-1 to identify points in the plane with pairs of numbers, which provides a link between algebra and geometry that is explored in the rest of the chapter.

4-1

REAL NUMBERS AND THE CARTESIAN COORDINATE SYSTEM

- The Set of Real Numbers
- Cartesian Coordinates
- Graphing Ordered Pairs (a, b)

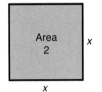

Suppose we wish to find the length of the side of a square with area 2. Referring to the figure in the margin, we see that

$$x^2 = 2$$

We ask: Are there any rational numbers whose square is 2? It turns out that one can prove that there is no rational number whose square is 2. If a square of area 2 is to have a number that represents the length of a side, then we must invent a new kind of number. This new kind of number is called an **irrational number**.† In this case a number whose square is 2 is called a square root of 2 and is symbolized by $\sqrt{2}$.

The rational and irrational numbers together provide a number associated with each point on the number line. In this section we will also see how pairs of such numbers are associated with every point in a plane.

THE SET OF REAL NUMBERS

Every rational number has a repeating decimal representation. For example:

$$5 = 5.000 \ldots = 5.\overline{0} \qquad 3.14 = 3.1400 \ldots = 3.14\overline{0}$$

$$\tfrac{4}{3} = 1.33 \ldots = 1.\overline{3} \qquad \tfrac{5}{7} = 0.\overline{714285} \qquad \tfrac{71}{330} = 0.21515 \ldots = 0.2\overline{15}$$

where the overbar indicates the block of numbers that continues to repeat indefinitely.‡

Every irrational number, when represented in decimal form, has an infinite nonrepeating decimal representation. For example:

$$\sqrt{2} = 1.4142135 \ldots \qquad \pi = 3.1415926 \ldots \qquad -\sqrt{6} = -2.4494897 \ldots$$

and no block of numbers will continue to repeat.

The set of rational and irrational numbers form the **real number system**, the number system in which most of you will operate most of the time. Table 1 (next page) compares the various sets of numbers we have discussed, and Figure 1 shows some of these numbers on a **real number line**.

† Irrational numbers were "discovered" by the Pythagoreans, mathematical followers of the Greek mathematician Pythagoras (fifth century B.C.). If we apply the Pythagorean theorem to a right triangle with each side having length 1, as shown, the square of the hypotenuse $h^2 = 1^2 + 1^2 = 2$. Thus, h is $\sqrt{2}$. The Pythagoreans could prove that this number was not the ratio of two integers.
‡ Decimals of the form $5 = 5.000 \ldots = 5.\overline{0}$ where the zeros repeat indefinitely are often called **terminating decimals**.

TABLE 1 THE SET OF REAL NUMBERS

SYMBOL	NUMBER SET	DESCRIPTION	EXAMPLES
N	Natural numbers	Counting numbers (positive integers)	1, 3, 3,525
J	Integers	Set of counting numbers, their opposites, and 0	-31, -1, 0, 4, 702
Q	Rationals	Any number that can be represented in the form $\dfrac{a}{b}$, $b \neq 0$, where a and b are integers	-4, $-\frac{3}{5}$, 0, $\frac{4}{3}$, 3.57
R	Reals	Set of all rational and irrational numbers	$-\sqrt{2}$, $\frac{-4}{7}$, 0, 62.48, $\sqrt{5}$, π, 3,407

Note: Each set in the left-hand column is a subset of every set below it.

FIGURE 1 A real number line

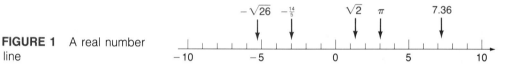

When associating rational numbers with points on a number line, it may appear (since between any two points with a rational number as a label one can always find another point with a rational number as a label) that the rational numbers name all the points. This, of course, is false, since the length of the side of the square on page 170 corresponds to a point on the number line that cannot be labeled with a rational number. It may surprise you to learn that in a certain sense there are more points on a number line that have not been named by rational numbers than have been named.

To make a long story short, all the points on a number line that have not been named by rational numbers are named by irrational numbers; that is, using the two sets of numbers, every point on the line will be named and no numbers will be left over.

If we write

$$\sqrt{2} \approx 1.414 \qquad \text{and} \qquad \pi \approx 3.1415$$

where $\approx$ means **approximately equal to**, then we are using rational number approximations for the irrational numbers $\sqrt{2}$ and π. We will return to irrational numbers again in Chapter 8.

All the common properties of the number systems we have developed thus far extend to the real numbers. These are summarized on the inside front cover of the text. Our next goal is to extend the identification of numbers with points on a line to pairs of numbers with points in a plane. We accomplish this by introducing a *cartesian coordinate system*.

CARTESIAN COORDINATES

Figure 1 illustrates the real number line. We now move to a plane and develop a system, called a **cartesian coordinate system**, that will enable us to graph equations and inequalities with two variables instead of just one.

To form a cartesian coordinate system in a plane we select two real number lines, one vertical and one horizontal, and let them cross at their respective zero points (Figure 2). Up and to the right are the usual choices for the positive directions. These two number lines are called the **vertical axis** and the **horizontal axis** or (together) **coordinate axes**. The coordinate axes divide the plane into four parts called **quadrants**. The quadrants are numbered counterclockwise from I to IV. The point where the two axes cross is called the **origin**.

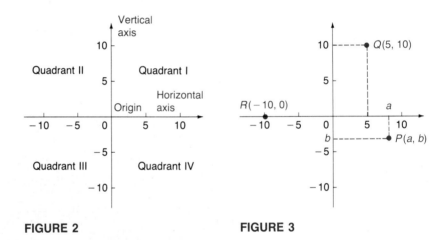

FIGURE 2   **FIGURE 3**

Pick a point P in the plane at random (see Figure 3). Pass horizontal and vertical lines through the point. The vertical line will intersect the horizontal axis at a point with coordinate a, and the horizontal line will intersect the vertical axis at a point with coordinate b. The coordinates of each point of intersection, a and b, respectively, form the **coordinates**

(a, b)

of the point P in the plane. In particular, point Q has coordinates $(5, 10)$ and point R has coordinates $(-10, 0)$.

The coordinates (a, b) of a point give directed distances to the axes. A **directed distance** includes a sign; a negative distance means to the left or below the origin. The first number a in the ordered pair (a, b) is the directed distance of the point from the vertical axis (measured on the horizontal scale);

the second number b is the directed distance of the point from the horizontal axis (measured on the vertical scale).†

We know that coordinates a and b exist for each point in the plane, since every point on each axis has a real number associated with it. Hence, by the procedure described, every point in the plane can be labeled with an ordered pair of real numbers. Conversely, by reversing the process, every ordered pair of real numbers can be associated with a point in the plane. Examples 1 and 2 illustrate the procedure.

The system that we have just described is called a **cartesian coordinate system** or a **rectangular coordinate system**.

Example 1 Find the coordinates of each of the points A, B, C, D, E, and F.

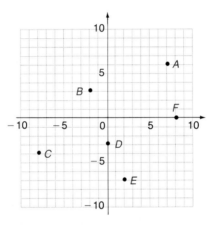

Solution $A(7, 6)$ $B(-2, 3)$ $C(-8, -4)$ $D(0, -3)$ $E(2, -7)$ $F(8, 0)$

Problem 1 Find the coordinates, using the figure in Example 1, for each of the following points:

(A) 2 units to the right and 1 unit up from A
(B) 2 units to the left and 2 units down from C
(C) 1 unit up and 1 unit to the left of E
(D) 2 units to the right of B

GRAPHING ORDERED PAIRS (a, b)

To graph an ordered pair of numbers, we start at the origin; then move left or right depending on whether the first number (coordinate) is negative or posi-

---

† The first coordinate a in (a, b) is called the **abscissa** of the point; the second b is called the **ordinate**.

tive; then move down or up depending on whether the second number (coordinate) is negative or positive. Consider the four cases shown in Figure 4.

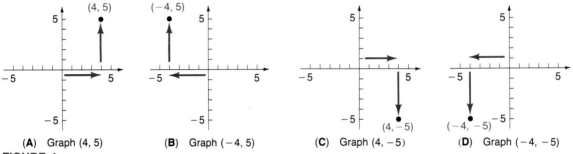

(**A**) Graph (4, 5)   (**B**) Graph (−4, 5)   (**C**) Graph (4, −5)   (**D**) Graph (−4, −5)

FIGURE 4

Example 2   Graph (associate each ordered pair of numbers with a point in the cartesian coordinate system): (2, 7), (7, 2), (−8, 4), (4, −8), (−8, −4), (−4, −8).

Solution

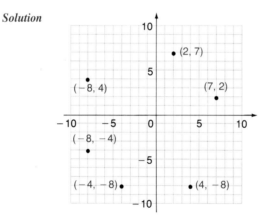

It is very important to note that the ordered pair (2, 7) and the set {2, 7} are not the same thing: {2, 7} = {7, 2} but (2, 7) ≠ (7, 2).

Problem 2   Graph in the same coordinate system: (3, 4), (−3, 2), (−2, −2), (4, −2), (0, 1), (−4, 0).

ANSWERS TO
MATCHED PROBLEMS

1.   (**A**)   (9, 7)   (**B**)   (−10, −6)   (**C**)   (1, −6)   (**D**)   (0, 3)

2.

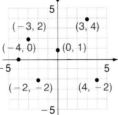

EXERCISE 4-1   A   *Indicate whether true (T) or false (F).*

1. 5 is a natural number.

2. $\frac{2}{3}$ is a rational number.

3. -3 is an integer.

4. $\frac{3}{4}$ is a natural number.

5. 0 is an integer.

6. $-\frac{2}{3}$ is an integer.

7. $\sqrt{2}$ is an irrational number.

8. π is an irrational number.

9. $\sqrt{5}$ is a real number.

10. 7 is a real number.

11. -5 is a real number.

12. $\frac{3}{7}$ is a real number.

Write down the coordinates for each labeled point.

13.   **14.**

15.   **16.**

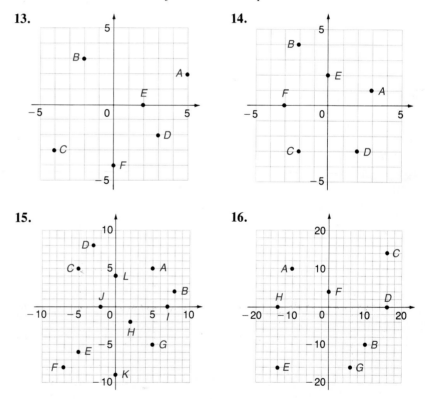

Graph each set of ordered pairs of numbers on the same coordinate system.

17. $(3, 1), (-2, 3), (-5, -1), (2, -1), (4, 0), (0, -5)$

18. $(4, 4), (-4, 1), (-3, -3), (5, -1), (0, 2), (-2, 0)$

19. $(-9, 8), (8, -9), (0, 5), (4, -8), (-3, 0), (7, 7), (-6, -6)$

20. $(2, 7), (7, 2), (-6, 3), (-4, -7), (2, 3), (0, -8), (9, 0)$

B   *Write down the coordinates of each labeled point to the nearest quarter of a unit.*

21.   **22.**

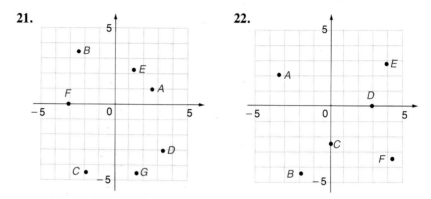

23.   Graph the following ordered pairs of numbers on the same coordinate system: $A(1\frac{1}{2}, 3\frac{1}{2})$, $B(-3\frac{1}{4}, 0)$, $C(3, -2\frac{1}{2})$, $D(-4\frac{1}{2}, 1\frac{3}{4})$, $E(-2\frac{1}{2}, -4\frac{1}{4})$.

24.   Graph the following ordered pairs of numbers on the same coordinate system: $A(3\frac{1}{2}, 2\frac{1}{2})$, $B(-4\frac{1}{2}, 3)$, $C(0, -3\frac{3}{4})$, $D(-2\frac{3}{4}, -3\frac{3}{4})$, $E(4\frac{1}{4}, -3\frac{3}{4})$.

25.   Without graphing, tell which quadrants contain the graph of each of the following ordered pairs (see Figure 2):
(A) $(-20, -4)$ (B) $(-3, 22\frac{3}{4})$
(C) $(4, 35{,}000)$ (D) $(\sqrt{2}, -3)$

26.   Without graphing, tell which quadrants contain the graph of each of the following ordered pairs (see Figure 2):
(A) $(-23, 403)$ (B) $(32\frac{1}{2}, -430)$
(C) $(201, 25)$ (D) $(-0.008, -3.2)$

C   *Express each rational number as a repeating decimal. (Divide each denominator into the numerator, and continue until a repeating pattern is observed.)*

27. $\frac{1}{4}$ **28.** $\frac{7}{4}$ **29.** $\frac{23}{9}$ **30.** $\frac{10}{6}$

Express each rational number as a repeating decimal with the aid of a hand calculator.

31. $\frac{32}{99}$ **32.** $\frac{10}{33}$ **33.** $\frac{4}{7}$ **34.** $\frac{7}{13}$

35.   In which quadrants is the product of the two coordinates of a point positive?

36.   In which quadrants is the product of the two coordinates of a point negative?

4-2
EQUATIONS AND STRAIGHT LINES

- Graphing Straight Lines
- Vertical and Horizontal Lines
- Graphing with Different Scales and Restricted Values

The development of the cartesian coordinate system represented a very important advance in mathematics. It was through the use of this system that René Descartes (1596–1650), a French philosopher-mathematician, was able to transform geometric problems requiring long, tedious reasoning into algebraic problems that could be solved almost mechanically. This joining of algebra and geometry has now become known as **analytic geometry**.

When an equation involves only one variable, a solution is a number that can replace the variable and that makes the equation true (see Section 2-7.) The set of all solutions is called the **solution set**. When an equation involves two variables, a **solution** must consist of a pair of numbers, one for each variable. The set of solution pairs is again called the **solution set** and the graph of all these pairs is called the **graph of the equation**.

Two fundamental problems of analytic geometry are the following:

1. Given an equation, find its graph. That is, find the graph of its solution set.
2. Given a geometric figure, such as a straight line, circle, or ellipse, find an equation that has this figure as the graph of its solution set.

In this course we will be interested mainly in the first problem, with particular emphasis on equations whose graphs are straight lines. We explore these equations in this and the next section.

GRAPHING STRAIGHT LINES

We begin with a simple equation

$$y = 2x + 3$$

and ask what is its solution set and what does the graph of its solution set look like?

The solutions will be pairs of numbers. For example, $x = 0$ and $y = 3$ is a solution, since

$$3 = 2 \cdot 0 + 3$$

We agree to write such a solution as $(0, 3)$ with the value of x first and y second. We can find other solutions by assigning any value to x and solving for y. If $x = 1$, then

$$y = 2 \cdot 1 + 3 = 5$$

and if $x = 2$,

$$y = 2 \cdot 2 + 3 = 7$$

Therefore $(1, 5)$ and $(2, 7)$ are also solutions to the equation. Since we can assign any value to x, it should be clear that the solution set will be infinite. We can list some of the solutions in a table:

TABLE 2

ASSIGN VALUE TO x	COMPUTE $2x + 3 = y$	SOLUTION (x, y)
-3	$2(-3) + 3 = -3$	$(-3, -3)$
-2	$2(-2) + 3 = -1$	$(-2, -1)$
-1	$2(-1) + 3 = 1$	$(-1, 1)$
0	$2 \cdot 0 + 3 = 3$	$(0, 3)$
1	$2 \cdot 1 + 3 = 5$	$(1, 5)$
2	$2 \cdot 2 + 3 = 7$	$(2, 7)$
3	$2 \cdot 3 + 3 = 9$	$(3, 9)$

We can graph these points in a cartesian coordinate system. Since we have identified the first coordinate with a value for x, we label the horizontal axis as the **x axis**. The vertical axis then becomes the **y axis**:

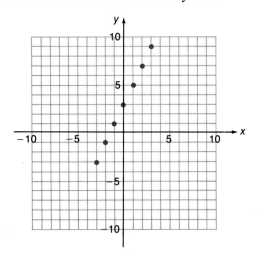

It appears that these seven solutions lie in a straight line, and this suggests that perhaps all the solutions lie on this line. This, in fact, is true, not only for this example but also for equations like this in general. We will use, but not prove, the following result.

Equations and Straight Lines

The graph of any equation of the form

$$Ax + By = C$$

where A, B, and C are constants (A and B not both 0) and x and y are variables, is a straight line. Every straight line in a cartesian coordinate system is the graph of an equation of this form.

Our equation $y = 2x + 3$ is easily rewritten as $-2x + y = 3$ to fit the form of the result. Similarly, any equation of the form

$$y = mx + b$$

where m and b are constants, is also a straight line, since it can be written in the form $-mx + y = b$, which is a special case of $Ax + By = C$.

Since graphing a straight line requires only two points, we have a simple procedure for graphing equations of the form

$$Ax + By = C \qquad \text{or} \qquad y = mx + b$$

Mechanics of Graphing Equations of the Form
$Ax + By = C$ or $y = mx + b$

1. Find any two solutions to the equation. (A third solution is useful as a check point.)
2. Draw coordinate axes and label them.
3. Indicate a scale on each axis by numbering appropriate points on each axis.
4. Plot (graph) the solutions found in step 1.
5. Draw a line through points plotted in step 4, using a ruler.

Our graphs, of course, are only part of the complete graph, since the line extends infinitely far in either direction. We usually are most interested in the portion of the graph near the origin.

Example 3   Graph:

(A) $y = 2x + 3$ **(B)** $x + 2y = 6$

Solution   **(A)** Since this is the same example with which we started this section, choose two points from the table already constructed, say, $(-3, -3)$ and $(2, 7)$. Plot these two points and graph the line through them with a straightedge or ruler.

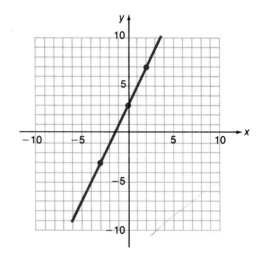

We can use a third point, say, $(0, 3)$, as a check. If this point had not been on the line, we would check for an error in finding our solutions.

(B) Find two solutions by assigning a value to one variable and solving for the other. If we let $x = 0$, then

$$0 + 2y = 6$$
$$2y = 6$$
$$y = 3$$

so $(0, 3)$ is a solution. If we let $y = 0$, then

$$x + 2 \cdot 0 = 6$$
$$x = 6$$

so $(6, 0)$ is a solution. Plot the two points and the line they determine:

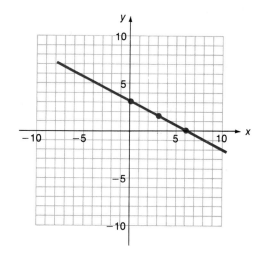

Find a check point by assigning another value to one variable, say, $x = 3$, and solving for the other:

$$3 + 2y = 6$$
$$2y = 3$$
$$y = \tfrac{3}{2}$$

Thus $(3, \tfrac{3}{2})$ should lie on the line and it does.

The choices of $x = 0$ and $y = 0$ used in part (B) above are often convenient ones, since they make for easy calculations in solving for the other variable. Geometrically, the points are where the line crosses the two coordinate axes, and they are therefore called the **x and y intercepts**. To find the x intercept, let $y = 0$ and solve for x. To find the y intercept, let $x = 0$ and solve for y.

Problem 3 Graph:

(A) $y = 2x - 1$ **(B)** $2x + y = 4$

VERTICAL AND HORIZONTAL LINES

Vertical and horizontal lines are graphed easily and have simple equations. The x coordinate at any point on a vertical line is constant. Thus, to graph a vertical line, we need to know only the x coordinate common to all points on the line. The equation will be $x = $ a constant. Similarly, a horizontal line will have equation $y = $ a constant.

Example 4   Graph the equations $x = 3$ and $y = -2$.

Solution   To graph $x = 3$, recognize that this is the same as $x + 0 \cdot y = 3$, so the graph is a line. No matter what value is assigned to y, $x = 3$, so the points $(3, 0)$ and $(3, 1)$ are on the line and the line is vertical:

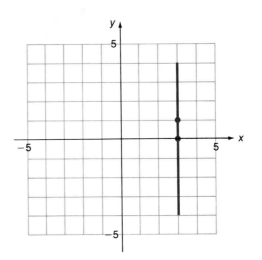

Similarly, $y = -2$ is the same as $0 \cdot x + y = -2$, so this equation represents a horizontal line with x assuming any value and $y = -2$:

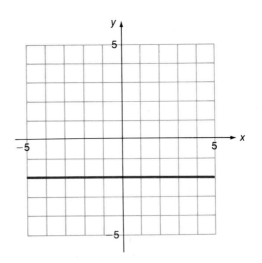

In general:

Vertical and Horizontal Lines

$x = a$ represents a vertical line through $(a, 0)$

$y = b$ represents a horizontal line through $(0, b)$

Problem 4 Graph the equations $x = -3$ and $y = 2$

An equation of the form $Ax + By = C$ or $y = mx + b$ is called a **linear equation** because its graph is a straight line. As a special case, this applies to the equations in one variable such as were solved in Section 2-7 where the term "linear" equation was first used.

GRAPHING WITH DIFFERENT SCALES AND RESTRICTED VALUES

We may be interested in graphing an equation with one or both of the variables restricted to a particular set of values. Such restrictions often arise in applied problems because of real-world considerations. It may also occur that the values of interest for one variable are significantly larger than those for the other. In such instances, it is helpful to use a different scale on the two axes.

Example 5 Graph $y = 55x$ for x between 0 and 5.

Solution Find three solutions (two points and a check point). Since x is restricted to be between 0 and 5, we plot the extreme values of x, 0 and 5, and an intermediate value $x = 3$ as a check. We note the large values of y corresponding to the smaller values for x, so we adjust the scale on the y axis accordingly. We also note that the whole graph will be drawn in the first quadrant.

x	y
0	0
5	275
3	165

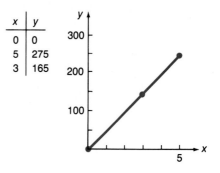

If we think of x as representing time in hours traveled, and 55 as representing a speed in miles per hour, then y represents the distance traveled in miles.

Problem 5   Graph $y = 30x + 10$ for x between 0 and 6.

ANSWERS TO
MATCHED PROBLEMS

3.   **(A)**   **(B)**

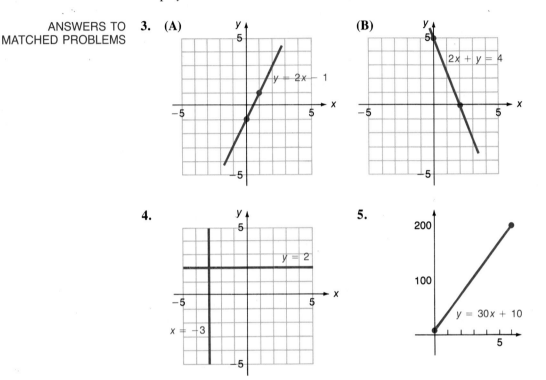

4.   **5.**

EXERCISE 4-2   *Graph each equation in Problems 1–32 in a cartesian coordinate system.*

A   **1.** $y = x + 3$ **2.** $y = x - 4$ **3.** $y = -x + 1$

     4. $y = -x + 2$ **5.** $y = -x$ **6.** $y = x$

     7. $y = 3x$ **8.** $y = -2x$ **9.** $y = -3x + 2$

    10. $y = 2x - 3$ **11.** $x + 2y = 4$ **12.** $2x - y = 4$

    13. $3x - 2y = 6$ **14.** $2x + 3y = 6$ **15.** $x = 4$

    16. $x = -2$ **17.** $y = -3$ **18.** $y = 1$

B   **19.** $y = \frac{1}{3}x$ **20.** $y = -\frac{1}{3}x$ **21.** $y = -\frac{1}{2}x + 1$

    22. $y = \frac{1}{2}x + 1$ **23.** $x + 2y = 3$ **24.** $x - 2y = 3$

    25. $3x - 2y = 4$ **26.** $3x + 2y = 4$ **27.** $y = \frac{1}{2}x + \frac{1}{5}$

28. $y = -\frac{1}{2}x + \frac{2}{3}$ **29.** $y = -\frac{1}{2}x + \frac{1}{5}$ **30.** $y = \frac{1}{2}x - \frac{2}{3}$

31. $x = 0$ **32.** $y = 0$

Write each equation in the form $y = mx + b$ and graph. For example, to write $y - 3x + 1 = x - 2$ in the form $y = mx + b$, we proceed as follows:

$$y - 3x + 1 = x - 2$$

$$\boxed{y - 3x + 1 + 3x - 1 = x - 2 + 3x - 1}$$

$$y = 4x - 3 \quad \text{Form } y = mx + b; m = 4, b = -3$$

33. $3x + 4y = 12$ **34.** $4x - 3y = 12$

35. $5x - 2y = 10$ **36.** $-5x + 2y = 10$

Write in the form $Ax + By = C$, $A > 0$, and graph. For example, to write $3x - 1 + 2y = x + 5y + 5$ in the form $Ax + By = C$, $A > 0$, we proceed as follows:

$$3x - 1 + 2y = x + 5y + 5$$

$$\boxed{3x - 1 + 2y - x - 5y + 1 = x + 5y + 5 - x - 5y + 1}$$

$$2x - 3y = 6 \quad \text{Form } Ax + By = C, A > 0;$$
$$A = 2, B = -3, C = 6$$

37. $y = \frac{1}{2}x - 1$ **38.** $y = \frac{2}{3}x + 4$

39. $x = \frac{3}{4}y + 2$ **40.** $x = \frac{5}{3}y - 1$

C *Use a different scale on the vertical axis to keep the size of the graph within reason.*

41. $y = 65x$ for x between 0 and 5

42. $y = 20x$ for x between 0 and 15

43. $y = 30x + 100$ for x between 0 and 6

44. $y = 40x + 50$ for x between 0 and 8

45. Graph $y = 2x + 3$ and $x + y = 0$ on the same coordinate system. Estimate the coordinates of the point where the lines intersect. Substitute these coordinates into both equations and see if the equations are satisfied.

46. Repeat Exercise 45 with $2x + y = 4$ and $y = 3x - 1$.

47. Graph $y = \frac{1}{2}x + b$ for $b = -4$, $b = 0$, and $b = 4$ all on the same coordinate system.

48. Graph $y = mx + 1$ for $m = -2$, $m = -\frac{1}{2}$, $m = 0$, $m = \frac{1}{2}$, and $m = 2$ all on the same coordinate system.

49. Graph $y = |x|$. [*Hint:* Graph $y = x$ for $x \geq 0$ and $y = -x$ for $x < 0$.]

50. Graph $y = |2x|$ and $y = |\frac{1}{2}x|$ on the same coordinate system.

APPLICATIONS   *Choose horizontal and vertical scales to produce maximum clarity in graphs.*

51. *Biology*   In biology there is an approximate rule, called the bioclimatic rule, for temperate climates which states that in spring and early summer periodic phenomena such as blossoming for a given species, appearance of certain insects, and ripening of fruit usually come about 4 days later for each 500 feet of altitude. Stated as a formula,

$$d = 4\left(\frac{h}{500}\right)$$

where d = Change in days and h = Change in altitude in feet. Graph the equation for $0 \leq h \leq 4{,}000$.

52. *Psychology*   In 1948 Professor Brown, a psychologist, trained a group of rats (in an experiment on motivation) to run down a narrow passage in a cage to receive food in a box. He then put a harness on each rat and connected it to an overhead wire that was attached to a scale. In this way he could place the rat at different distances (in centimeters) from the food and measure the pull (in grams) of the rat toward the food. He found that a relation between motivation (pull) and position was given approximately by the equation $p = -\frac{1}{5}d + 70$, $30 \leq d \leq 175$. Graph this equation for the indicated values of d.

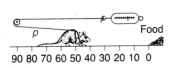

53. *Earth science*   As dry air moves upward, it expands and in doing so cools at the rate of about 5.5°F for each 1,000 feet in rise (see Problem 11, Section 3-9). If the ground temperature is 80°F, the equation

$$T = 80 - 5.5h$$

relates temperature T with altitude h measured in 1,000-foot units. Graph this equation for h between 0 and 20.

54. *Earth science*   Pressure in seawater increases by 1 atmosphere (15 pounds per square inch) for each 33 feet of depth; it is 15 pounds per square inch at the surface. Thus, $p = 15 + 15(d/33)$, where p is pressure in pounds per square inch at a depth of d feet below the surface (see Problem 10, Section 3-9). Graph this equation for d between 0 and 330.

4-3
SLOPE OF A LINE

- Slope of a Line
- Slope–Intercept Form
- Parallel and Perpendicular Lines

From Section 4-2 we know that every linear equation has a graph that is a straight line, and given a particular linear equation we can graph it. In this section we will consider the reverse situation: given a straight line, or at least certain information about it, find an equation to describe it.

Two points are sufficient to determine a line. It is also enough to know one point and the "direction" or "steepness" of the line. The notion of direction or steepness is measured as the *slope* of the line and is considered in this section.

SLOPE OF A LINE

Given two points on a line, say, the points $(-3, -3)$ and $(2, 7)$ on the line $y = 2x + 3$, we define the **slope** of the line as the ratio of the change in y to the change in x as we move from one point to the other. For the given points, moving from $(-3, -3)$ to $(2, 7)$, the slope would be

$$\frac{\text{Change in } y}{\text{Change in } x} = \frac{7 - (-3)}{2 - (-3)} = \frac{10}{5} = 2$$

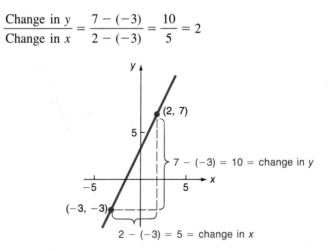

If we reverse the order of the two points, we calculate

$$\frac{-3 - 7}{-3 - 2} = \frac{-10}{-5} = 2$$

If we use the point $(0, 3)$ on the line instead of $(-3, -3)$, we calculate

$$\frac{7 - 3}{2 - 0} = \frac{4}{2} = 2$$

Thus it appears that no matter what two points on the line we choose, and no matter in what order we choose them, we obtain the same ratio, namely, 2. The slope of this line is therefore 2. The same thing happens in general, so we can define slope:

Slope Formula

If a line passes through $P_1(x_1, y_1)$ and $P_2(x_2, y_2)$, then its slope is given by the formula

$$m = \frac{y_2 - y_1}{x_2 - x_1} \qquad x_1 \neq x_2$$

$$= \frac{\text{Vertical change (rise)}}{\text{Horizontal change (run)}}$$

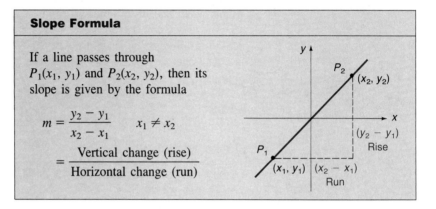

CAUTION

Note, however, that we must be consistent: whichever y component we use first in the numerator, we must use the x coordinate of the same point first in the denominator. That is, the slope is *not* equal to

$$\frac{y_2 - y_1}{x_1 - x_2}$$

Example 6   Find the slope of the line passing through $(2, 1)$ and $(4, -3)$.

Solution   Let $(x_1, y_1) = (2, 1)$ and $(x_2, y_2) = (4, -3)$. Then

$$\text{Slope} = m = \frac{y_2 - y_1}{x_2 - x_1} = \frac{-3 - 1}{4 - 2} = \frac{-4}{2} = -2$$

Problem 6   Find the slope of the line passing through $(-3, 2)$ and $(1, 0)$.

For a vertical line, the slope is not defined. Such a line has equation $x = a$, so $x_1 = x_2 = a$. Therefore, $x_2 - x_1 = 0$, and we cannot divide by zero in

$$\frac{y_2 - y_1}{x_2 - x_1}$$

On the other hand, for a horizontal line $y = b$, $y_1 = y_2 = b$, $y_2 - y_1 = 0$, and the slope is 0.

In general, the slope of a line may be positive, negative, 0, or not defined. Each of these cases is interpreted geometrically as shown in Table 3.

TABLE 3 GOING FROM LEFT TO RIGHT

LINE	SLOPE	EXAMPLE
Rising	Positive	
Falling	Negative	
Horizontal	0	
Vertical	Not defined	

SLOPE–INTERCEPT FORM

In our first example above, the slope of the line $y = 2x + 3$ turned out to be 2. The fact that the slope and the coefficient of x are the same is not a coincidence: the constant m in the form $y = mx + b$ is always equal to the slope of the line.

The constant b in the form $y = mx + b$ also has geometric significance. If we let $x = 0$, then

$$y = m \cdot 0 + b = 0 + b = b$$

Thus, b is the y coordinate when $x = 0$, that is, b is the y intercept. Therefore, in the example $y = 2x + 3$, the y intercept is 3, as we already knew from Example 3.

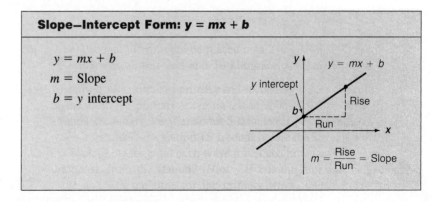

Slope–Intercept Form: $y = mx + b$

$y = mx + b$
m = Slope
$b = y$ intercept

Example 7   **(A)** Find the slope and y intercept for the line

$$y = 3x - 1$$

(B) Find an equation for the line with slope $-\frac{2}{3}$ and y intercept 1.

Solution   **(A)** $y = 3x - 1$

$$y = \mathbf{3}x + (\mathbf{-1})$$

slope y intercept

(B) Since $m = -\frac{2}{3}$ and $b = 1$, then $y = mx + b$ becomes

$$y = -\tfrac{2}{3}x + 1$$

Problem 7   **(A)** Find the slope and y intercept for the line

$$y = \tfrac{2}{3}x + 2$$

(B) Find an equation for the line with slope $\frac{1}{2}$ and y intercept -1.

In Example 7(B), we found the equation of the line given the slope and y intercept. In this case the line was specified by one point (the y intercept) and its direction (slope). Frequently, however, the given point will not be the y intercept. Also, the line may be specified by two points instead of a point and direction. These situations are only slightly more difficult to handle. The following example shows how to proceed:

Example 8   **(A)** Find the equation of the line that passes through the point (1, 3) and has slope $-\frac{1}{3}$.
(B) Find the equation of the line that passes through (1, 3) and (4, 1).

Solution   **(A)** Since the slope is $-\frac{1}{3}$, the equation must have the form

$$y = -\tfrac{1}{3}x + b$$

To find b, use the fact that (1, 3) lies on the line. Thus

$$3 = -\tfrac{1}{3} \cdot 1 + b$$

$$3 = -\tfrac{1}{3} + b$$

$$\tfrac{10}{3} = b$$

Therefore, the equation is $y = -\frac{1}{3}x + \frac{10}{3}$.

(B) First find the slope m:

$$m = \frac{y_2 - y_1}{x_2 - x_1} = \frac{1 - 3}{4 - 1} = \frac{-2}{3}$$

Now we can proceed as in part (A), using the coordinates of either point to find b:

USING (1, 3)	USING (4, 1)
$y = -\frac{2}{3}x + b$	$y = -\frac{2}{3}x + b$
$3 = -\frac{2}{3} \cdot 1 + b$	$1 = -\frac{2}{3} \cdot 4 + b$
$\frac{11}{3} = b$	$1 = -\frac{8}{3} + b$
	$\frac{11}{3} = b$

The equation is therefore $y = -\frac{2}{3}x + \frac{11}{3}$.

Problem 8 **(A)** Find the equation of the line that passes through the point (1, 2) and has slope $\frac{3}{4}$.

(B) Find the equation of the line that passes through $(-2, 1)$ and $(3, 4)$.

An equation in slope–intercept form allows us to graph its line very efficiently, as the following example shows.

Example 9 Graph $y = \frac{3}{4}x - 2$

Solution The y intercept is -2 so the point $(0, -2)$ is on the graph. Since the slope is

$$\frac{\text{Change in } y}{\text{Change in } x} = \frac{3}{4}$$

we know that if we increase x by 4, y must increase by 3. Starting from $(0, -2)$ this yields the point $(4, 1)$, and the line can be graphed:

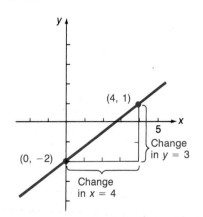

Problem 9   Graph $y = -\frac{1}{2}x + 1$.

Any linear equation with coefficient of y not zero can be rewritten in the form $y = mx + b$ by dividing by the coefficient of y and shifting all terms except y to the other side. For example, if the equation is $3x + 4y = 5$, then

$$\tfrac{3}{4}x + y = \tfrac{5}{4}$$
$$y = -\tfrac{3}{4}x + \tfrac{5}{4}$$

If the coefficient of y is zero, the line must be vertical and is also easily graphed.

PARALLEL AND PERPENDICULAR LINES

Since the slope of a line gives an indication of direction, it should not be surprising that the slopes can provide information about parallel or perpendicular lines. Vertical lines are parallel. Nonvertical parallel lines must have the same slope and vice versa. Two lines with different slopes must, therefore, intersect. If one of the lines is vertical, only horizontal lines are perpendicular to it. If neither line is vertical, it can be shown that the two lines are perpendicular exactly when the product of their slopes is -1.

ANSWERS TO
MATCHED PROBLEMS

6. $-\frac{1}{2}$

7. **(A)** Slope $= \frac{2}{3}$, y intercept $= 2$
    (B) $y = \frac{1}{2}x - 1$

8. **(A)** $y = \frac{3}{4}x + \frac{5}{4}$ **(B)** $y = \frac{3}{5}x + \frac{11}{5}$

9.

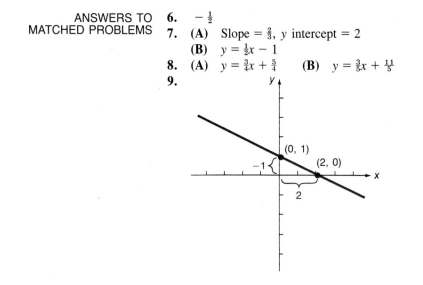

EXERCISE 4-3   A   *Find the slope of the line determined by the given points.*

1. (2, 3) and (4, 5)   **2.** (3, 2) and (6, 5)

3. (1, 5) and (3, 9)   **4.** (0, 2) and (3, 4)

Find the slope and y intercept of the line with the given equation.

5. $y = 3x + 5$ **6.** $y = 2x - 7$

7. $y = -2x + 4$ **8.** $y = -2x - 1$

Find the slope–intercept form of the equation for the line with slope and y intercept as given.

9. slope $= 3$, y intercept $= -1$

10. slope $= 2$, y intercept $= 5$

11. slope $= -4$, y intercept $= 1$

12. slope $= -1$, y intercept $= -4$

Find the slope–intercept form of the equation for the line that passes through the given point and has the indicated slope.

13. point $(1, 2)$; $m = 2$ **14.** point $(4, 3)$; $m = 3$

15. point $(1, 2)$; $m = -2$ **16.** point $(4, 3)$; $m = -3$

Find the slope–intercept form of the equation of the line that passes through the given two points.

17. $(2, 3)$ and $(4, 5)$ **18.** $(3, 2)$ and $(6, 5)$

19. $(1, 5)$ and $(3, 9)$ **20.** $(0, 2)$ and $(3, 4)$

B *Find the slope of the line determined by the given points.*

21. $(1, 2)$ and $(5, -1)$ **22.** $(4, 1)$ and $(-1, 7)$

23. $(-1, 1)$ and $(4, -4)$ **24.** $(3, -1)$ and $(-2, 3)$

Find the slope and y intercept of the line with the given equation.

25. $2x - 3y = 4$ **26.** $-2x + 5y = -7$

27. $-3x + 5y = 4$ **28.** $4x - 3y = 2$

Find the slope–intercept form of the equation for the line that passes through the given point and has the indicated slope.

29. $(1, 3)$; $m = \frac{1}{5}$ **30.** $(2, 3)$; $m = -\frac{3}{4}$

31. $(\frac{1}{3}, 1)$; $m = -\frac{1}{2}$ **32.** $(1, \frac{2}{3})$; $m = \frac{1}{2}$

Find the slope–intercept form of the equation for the line that passes through the given two points.

33. (1, 2) and (5, −1)   **34.** (4, 1) and (−1, 7)

35. (−1, 1) and (4, −4)   **36.** (3, −1) and (−2, 3)

Graph.

37. $y = 3x + 5$ **38.** $y = 2x - 7$

39. $y = -2x + 4$ **40.** $y = -2x - 1$

41. $2x - 3y = 4$ **42.** $-2x + 5y = -7$

43. $-3x + 5y = 4$ **44.** $4x - 3y = 2$

C **45.** $y = \frac{1}{3}x + 1$ **46.** $y = \frac{1}{2}x - 1$

47. $y = -\frac{1}{2}x + 2$ **48.** $y = -\frac{1}{3}x + 1$

49. $y - 3x = 1$ **50.** $y + x = -1$

51. $x - 2y = 6$ **52.** $-x + 3y = 6$

53. $x + \frac{1}{2}y = 3$ **54.** $2x - \frac{1}{3}y = 1$

55. $3x - \frac{1}{2}y = 2$ **56.** $x + \frac{2}{3}y = 2$

APPLICATIONS **57.** ***Earth science*** Pressure in seawater increases by 1 atmosphere (15 pounds per square inch) for each 33 feet of depth; it is 15 pounds per square inch at the surface. Thus,

$$p = 15 + 15\left(\frac{d}{33}\right) = 15 + \tfrac{15}{33}d$$

where p is pressure in pounds per square inch at a depth of d feet below the surface (see Problem 10, Section 3-9). What is the slope of this line, and how is it related to the physical problem?

58. ***Earth science*** As dry air moves upward, it expands and in doing so cools at the rate of about 5.5°F for each 1,000 feet in rise (see Problem 11, Section 3-9). Let the ground temperature be 80°F.
(A) If the altitude h is expressed in feet, the equation

$$T = -\frac{5.5}{1,000}h + 80$$

relates temperature and altitude. What is the slope of this line, and how is it related to the physical problem?

(B) If the altitude is expressed in 1,000-foot units, the equation becomes

$$T = -5.5h + 80$$

What is the slope of this line, and how is it related to the physical problem?

59. *Business* A sporting goods store sells a pair of cross-country ski boots costing $40 for $61 and a pair of cross-country skis costing $110 for $159.

(A) If the markup policy of the store for items costing over $10 is assumed to be linear and is reflected in the pricing of these two items, write an equation that relates retail price R with cost C.

(B) Find the slope and y intercept for the line determined by this equation.

(C) The store's markup policy depends on the cost of an item, a fixed charge that is the same for all items, and a percentage of the cost. Describe the exact policy in words. How are the slope and y intercept related to this policy?

60. *Business* The management of a company manufacturing ballpoint pens estimates costs for running the company to be $200 per day at zero output and $700 per day at an output of 1,000 pens.

(A) Assuming that total cost per day C is linearly related to total output per day x, write an equation relating these two quantities.

(B) What is the slope of the line determined by this equation and how is it related to the problem?

61. *Physics* Water freezes at 32°F and 0°C and boils at 212°F and 100°C. Find the linear relationship between the two scales.

4-4

SYSTEMS OF EQUATIONS AND SOLVING BY GRAPHING

- Systems of Equations
- Solving by Graphing

In Section 2-8, we considered the following problem: find the dimensions of a rectangle with perimeter 52 centimeters if its length is 5 more than twice its width. We solved the problem by letting x be the width, so $2x + 5$ is the length, and then solving the equation $2(2x + 5) + 2x = 52$. The width turned out to be 7 and the length 19. We set the problem up in terms of one variable x, but we could also have set it up using two variables as follows:

Let $x =$ width, $y =$ length.

Then

$$2x + 2y = 52 \qquad \text{Perimeter is 52}$$
$$y = 2x + 5 \qquad \text{Length is 5 more than twice width}$$

In this way we obtain a system of equations—two equations in two variables. We consider such systems in the next three sections.

SYSTEMS OF EQUATIONS

A solution of a system of equations such as

$$2x + 2y = 52$$
$$y = 2x + 5$$

is an ordered pair of real numbers that satisfy both equations. Thus, (7, 19) is a solution to this system, since

$$2 \cdot 7 + 2 \cdot 19 = 52$$
$$19 = 2 \cdot 7 + 5$$

To solve the system means to find all such pairs. We will see below that (7, 19) is the only solution to this system. More generally, we will consider systems of two linear equations in two variables, that is, systems of the type

$$ax + by = m$$
$$cx + dy = n$$

where a, b, c, d, m, and n are real-number constants and x and y are variables.

SOLVING BY GRAPHING

Since each equation in our system represents a straight line, the system represents two straight lines. Geometrically, two different lines are parallel or they intersect at one point. The two lines in the system may not be different. That is, the two equations might represent the same line. We can determine the nature of the solution of a system of equations and get an approximation to the solution itself by graphing the lines.

Example 10   Solve by graphing:

$$2x + 2y = 52$$
$$y = 2x + 5$$

Solution Graph the two equations on the same coordinate system. It is clear that the lines intersect so there is exactly one solution.

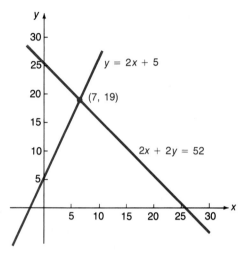

The intersection point appears to be (7, 19). We already know this is the solution, as we have checked by substituting $x = 7$ and $y = 19$ into both equations.

In general, we cannot hope to read the exact solution from the graph. If the solution in Example 10 had been (7.01, 18.93), we would not have found it exactly by graphing but we could have approximated it. A good graph can, however, suggest integer solutions.

Problem 10 Solve by graphing and check. (The solution has integer values.)

$$2x + 3y = 12$$
$$3x - 4y = 1$$

The following three systems show all three solution possibilities for a system of two equations in two unknowns:

(A) $2x - 3y = 2$
$\qquad x + 2y = 8$

(B) $4x + 6y = 12$
$\qquad 2x + 3y = -6$

(C) $2x - 3y = -6$
$\qquad -x + \frac{3}{2}y = 3$

See Figure 5, page 198.

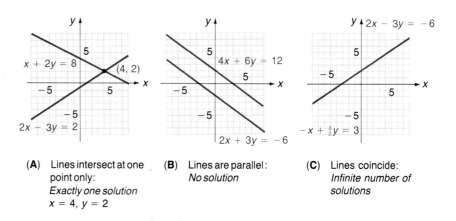

(A) Lines intersect at one point only:
Exactly one solution
x = 4, y = 2

(B) Lines are parallel:
No solution

(C) Lines coincide:
Infinite number of solutions

FIGURE 5

The nature of the solution can be determined by considering the slopes of the lines involved. Rewrite each equation in the form $y = mx + b$ and recall that m represents the slope:

(A) $\begin{cases} 2x - 3y = 2 \\ x + 2y = 8 \end{cases}$ $\begin{cases} y = \frac{2}{3}x - \frac{2}{3} \\ y = -\frac{1}{2}x + 4 \end{cases}$ Slope $= \frac{2}{3}$
Slope $= -\frac{1}{2}$

Since the slopes are different, the lines intersect at one point.

(B) $\begin{cases} 4x + 6y = 12 \\ 2x + 3y = -6 \end{cases}$ $\begin{cases} y = -\frac{2}{3}x + 3 \\ y = -\frac{2}{3}x - 2 \end{cases}$ Slope $= -\frac{2}{3}$
Slope $= -\frac{2}{3}$

Since the slopes are equal, the lines are parallel. Since the lines have different y intercepts, they will never meet.

(C) $\begin{cases} 2x - 3y = -6 \\ -x + \frac{3}{2}y = 3 \end{cases}$ $\begin{cases} y = \frac{2}{3}x + 2 \\ y = \frac{2}{3}x + 2 \end{cases}$

Both equations can be transformed into the same one, so both represent the same line.

Now we know exactly what to expect when solving a system of two linear equations in two unknowns:

Exactly one pair of numbers as a solution

No solutions

An infinite number of solutions

In most applications the first case prevails. If we find a pair of numbers that satisfies the system of equations and the graphs of the equations meet at only one point, then that pair of numbers is the only solution of the system, and we need not look further for others.

The graphing method of solving systems of equations yields considerable information about what to expect in the way of solutions to a system of two linear equations in two unknowns. Moreover, graphs frequently reveal relationships in problems that would otherwise be hidden. On the other hand, if one is interested in solutions with accuracy to several decimal places, the graphing method is not practical. The methods of elimination, to be considered in the next two sections, will take care of this deficiency.

ANSWERS TO   **10.** $x = 3$, $y = 2$
MATCHED PROBLEM

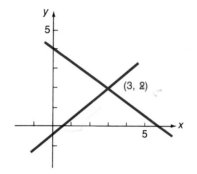

EXERCISE 4-4   *Solve Problems 1–16 by graphing and check.*

A   **1.** $x + y = 5$ **2.** $x + y = 6$ **3.** $x + y = 5$
         $x - y = 1$ $x - y = 2$ $2x - y = 4$

    4. $2x + y = 6$ **5.** $x - 3y = 3$ **6.** $x - 2y = -4$
         $x - y = -3$ $x - y = 7$ $2x - y = 10$

B   **7.** $3x - y = 2$ **8.** $x - 2y = 2$
         $x + 2y = 10$ $2x + y = 9$

    9. $-2x + 3y = 12$ **10.** $3x - 2y = 12$
         $2x - y = 4$ $7x + 2y = 8$

    11. $-3x + y = 9$ **12.** $x + 5y = -10$
          $3x + 4y = -24$ $-x + 2y = 3$

    13. $x + 2y = 4$ **14.** $3x + 5y = 15$
           $2x + 4y = -8$ $6x + 10y = -30$

    15. $\frac{1}{2}x - y = -3$ **16.** $3x - 5y = 15$
           $-x + 2y = 6$ $x - \frac{5}{3}y = 5$

C   **17.** Show that the lines in Problem 13 are parallel.

18. Show that the lines in Problem 14 are parallel.

19. Show that the lines in Problem 15 coincide.

20. Show that the lines in Problem 16 coincide.

4-5

SOLVING SYSTEMS OF LINEAR EQUATIONS USING ELIMINATION BY SUBSTITUTION

We now consider another method—called **elimination by substitution**, or more simply just **substitution**—for solving systems of linear equations. This method will produce solutions (if they exist) to any decimal accuracy desired. The method is most useful when one of the equations in the system can easily be solved for one variable in terms of the other. A couple of examples should make the process clear.

Example 11 Solve by substitution and check:

$$y = 2x - 3$$
$$2x - 3y = 1$$

Solution Since in the first equation y is already expressed in terms of x, we substitute the right side of this equation for y in the second equation and then solve for x. After finding x, we substitute it into the first equation to find y.

$$y = \underbrace{2x - 3}_{} \qquad \text{Substitute } 2x - 3 \text{ for } y \text{ in the second equation.}$$
$$2x - 3y = 1$$
$$2x - 3(2x - 3) = 1 \qquad \text{Now solve this equation for } x.$$
$$2x - 6x + 9 = 1$$
$$-4x + 9 = 1$$
$$-4x = -8$$
$$\boxed{x = 2}$$

Replace x with 2 in the first equation, $y = 2x - 3$, to find y:

$$y = 2x - 3$$
$$y = 2(2) - 3$$
$$\boxed{y = 1}$$

The solution is $x = 2$, $y = 1$.

Check
$$y = 2x - 3 \qquad\qquad 2x - 3y = 1$$
$$(1) \overset{?}{=} 2(2) - 3 \qquad 2(2) - 3(1) \overset{?}{=} 1$$
$$1 \overset{\checkmark}{=} 1 \qquad\qquad\qquad 1 \overset{\checkmark}{=} 1$$

Note: It is not sufficient to check just one equation. The solution must satisfy *both* equations.

Problem 11   Solve by substitution and check:

$$y = 3x + 1$$
$$3x - 2y = 1$$

Example 12   Solve by substitution and check:

$$5x + y = 4$$
$$2x - 3y = 5$$

Solution   Solve either equation for one variable in terms of the other; then proceed as in Example 11. In this example we can avoid fractions by choosing the first equation and solving for y in terms of x:

$5x + y = 4$	Solve first equation for y in terms of x.
$y = 4 - 5x$	Substitute into second equation.
$2x - 3y = 5$	Second equation.
$2x - 3(\mathbf{4 - 5x}) = 5$	Solve for x.
$2x - 12 + 15x = 5$	
$17x = 17$	
$\boxed{x = 1}$	

Now replace x with 1 in $y = 4 - 5x$ to find y:

$$y = 4 - 5x$$
$$y = 4 - 5(\mathbf{1})$$
$$\boxed{y = -1}$$

The solution is $x = 1$, $y = -1$.

Check

$$5x + y = 4 \qquad\qquad 2x - 3y = 5$$
$$5(1) + (-1) \overset{?}{=} 4 \qquad 2(1) - 3(-1) \overset{?}{=} 5$$
$$4 \overset{\checkmark}{=} 4 \qquad\qquad 5 \overset{\checkmark}{=} 5$$

Problem 12   Solve by substitution and check:

$$3x + 2y = -2$$
$$2x - y = -6$$

ANSWERS TO   **11.** $x = -1$, $y = -2$ **12.** $x = -2$, $y = 2$
MATCHED PROBLEMS

EXERCISE 4-5   *Solve by substitution and check.*

A   **1.** $y = x + 1$ **2.** $y = x - 1$
                  $x + y = 5$ $x + y = 7$

3. $y = 4x + 11$ 4. $y = 3x + 5$
         $x + 2y = 4$ $x - 3y = -7$

5. $y = 2x - 7$ 6. $y = 3x + 2$
    $y = x - 4$ $y = 2x + 1$

B   7. $2x + y = 6$ 8. $2x - y = 3$ 9. $3x - y = 2$
        $x - y = -3$ $x + 2y = 14$ $x + 2y = 10$

10. $x - y = 4$ 11. $2m - n = 10$ 12. $3m - n = 7$
      $x + 3y = 12$ $m - 2n = -4$ $2m + 3n = 1$

13. $3u - v = -3$ 14. $2u - 3v = 9$
      $5u + 3v = -19$ $u + 2v = -13$

C   15. $y = 0.4x$ 16. $y = 0.6x$
       $y = 50 + 0.2x$ $y = 30 + 0.3x$

17. $y = 0.07x$ 18. $y = 0.08x$
     $y = 80 + 0.05x$ $y = 100 + 0.04x$

4-6

SOLVING SYSTEMS OF LINEAR EQUATIONS USING ELIMINATION BY ADDITION

- Equivalent Systems
- Solution by Elimination by Addition
- Inconsistent and Dependent Systems

In this section we consider a third method for solving systems of equations, *elimination by addition*. This method concerns the replacement of systems of equations with simpler equivalent systems (by performing appropriate operations) until we get a system whose solution is obvious.

EQUIVALENT SYSTEMS

Equivalent systems are, as you might expect, systems with the same solution set. What operations on a system produce equivalent systems? The following operations produce the results we are looking for.

Operations Producing Equivalent Systems

An equivalent system will result if

(A) An equation is multiplied by a nonzero constant.
(B) One of the equations is added to the other.

These are direct results of the properties of equality first listed in Section 2-7.

SOLUTION BY ELIMINATION BY ADDITION

Through the appropriate use of the above operations, we can eliminate one of the variables in one of the equations and obtain a system that has an obvious solution. We will refer to the method as **elimination by addition**. It is a very important method in that it generalizes to large-scale systems involving many equations and many variables. Solving linear systems by this method is best illustrated through examples.

Example 13 Solve, using elimination by addition, and check:

$$3x + 2y = 13$$
$$2x - y = 4$$

Solution We use the operations presented above to eliminate one of the variables and thus obtain a system whose solution is obvious:

$$3x + 2y = 13$$ If we multiply the bottom equation by 2 and add this to the top
$$2x - y = 4$$ equation, we can eliminate y.

$$3x + 2y = 13$$
$$\underline{4x - 2y = 8}$$
$$7x \qquad = 21$$ Now solve for x.
$$\boxed{x = 3}$$

$$2 \cdot 3 - y = 4$$ Substitute $x = 3$ back into either of the two original equations,
$$-y = -2$$ the simpler of the two. and solve for y. We choose the second
$$\boxed{y = 2}$$ equation.

The solution is $x = 3$, $y = 2$.

Check
$$3x + 2y = 13 \qquad\qquad 2x - y = 4$$
$$3(3) + 2(2) \overset{?}{=} 13 \qquad 2(3) - 2 \overset{?}{=} 4$$
$$9 + 4 \overset{\checkmark}{=} 13 \qquad\qquad 6 - 2 \overset{\checkmark}{=} 4$$

Problem 13 Solve the system:

$$2x + 3y = 7$$
$$3x - y = 5$$

Example 14 Solve the system:

$$2x + 3y = 1$$
$$5x - 2y = 12$$

Solution

$$2x + 3y = 1$$
$$5x - 2y = 12$$

If we multiply the top equation by 2 and the bottom equation by 3 and add, we can eliminate y.

$$4x + 6y = 2$$
$$\underline{15x - 6y = 36}$$
$$19x \qquad = 38$$
$$\boxed{x = 2}$$

$$2 \cdot 2 + 3y = 1$$
$$3y = -3$$
$$\boxed{y = -1}$$

Substitute $x = 2$ back into either of the two original equations, then solve for y.

The solution is $x = 2$, $y = -1$.

Check

$$2x + 3y = 1 \qquad\qquad 5x - 2y = 12$$
$$2(2) + 3(-1) \overset{?}{=} 1 \qquad 5(2) - 2(-1) \overset{?}{=} 12$$
$$4 - 3 \overset{\checkmark}{=} 1 \qquad\qquad 10 + 2 \overset{\checkmark}{=} 12$$

Problem 14   Solve the system:

$$3x - 2y = 8$$
$$2x + 5y = -1$$

INCONSISTENT AND DEPENDENT SYSTEMS

Systems of equations do not always have a single solution. As we saw in Section 4-4, a system may not have a solution at all or it may have infinitely many. How do we recognize these cases when solving a system using elimination by addition? Let us consider a couple of examples to see how.

Example 15   Solve the system:

$$x + 3y = 2$$
$$2x + 6y = -3$$

Solution

$$x + 3y = 2$$
$$2x + 6y = -3$$

Multiply the top equation by -2 and add.

$$-2x - 6y = -4$$
$$\underline{2x + 6y = -3}$$
$$0 = 7$$

A contradiction!

Hence, there is no solution.

    Our assumption that there are values for x and y that satisfy both equations simultaneously must be false (otherwise, we have proved that $0 = 7$); thus, the system has no solutions. Systems of this type are said to be **inconsistent**—conditions have been placed on the unknowns x and y that are impossible to meet. Geometrically, the graphs of the two equations must be parallel lines.

Problem 15   Solve the system:

$$2x - y = 2$$
$$-4x + 2y = 1$$

Example 16   Solve the system:

$$-2x + y = -8$$
$$x - \tfrac{1}{2}y = 4$$

Solution $-2x + y = -8$ Multiply the bottom equation by 2 and add.
$$x - \tfrac{1}{2}y = 4$$

$$-2x + y = -8$$
$$\underline{2x - y = 8}$$
$$0 = 0$$

Both unknowns have been eliminated! Actually, if we had multiplied the bottom equation by -2, we would have obtained the top equation. When one equation is a constant multiple of the other, the system is said to be **dependent**, and their graphs will coincide. There are infinitely many solutions to the system—any solution of one equation is a solution of the other.

Problem 16   Solve the system:

$$4x - 2y = 3$$
$$-2x + y = -\tfrac{3}{2}$$

ANSWERS TO
MATCHED PROBLEMS

13. $x = 2, y = 1$ **14.** $x = 2, y = -1$ **15.** No solution
16. Infinitely many solutions—any solution of one equation is a solution of the other.

EXERCISE 4-6   *Solve Problems 1–26 by the elimination method and check.*

A   **1.** $x + y = 5$ **2.** $x - y = 6$ **3.** $x + 3y = 13$
       $x - y = 1$ $x + y = 10$ $-x + y = 3$

4. $-x + y = 1$ **5.** $2x + y = 0$ **6.** $x + 5y = 16$
       $x - 2y = -5$ $3x + y = 2$ $x - 2y = 2$

7. $2x + 3y = 1$ **8.** $3x - y = -3$ **9.** $3x - 4y = 1$
       $3x - y = 7$ $5x + 3y = -19$ $-x + 3y = 3$

10. $-x + 5y = -3$
$2x - 3y = -1$

11. $2x + 4y = 6$
$-3x + y = 5$

12. $3x + y = -8$
$-5x + 3y = 4$

B   **13.** $3x + 2y = -2$
$4x + 5y = 2$

14. $5x + 7y = 8$
$3x + 2y = 7$

15. $6x + 5y = 4$
$7x + 2y = -3$

16. $9x + 4y = 1$
$4x + 3y = -2$

17. $11x + 2y = 1$
$9x - 3y = 24$

18. $3x - 11y = -7$
$4x + 3y = 26$

19. $3p + 8q = 4$
$15p + 10q = -10$

20. $5m - 3n = 7$
$7m + 12n = -1$

21. $4m + 6n = 2$
$6m - 9n = 15$

22. $5a - 4b = 1$
$3a - 6b = 6$

23. $3x + 5y = 15$
$6x + 10y = -5$

24. $x + 2y = 4$
$2x + 4y = -9$

25. $3x - 5y = 15$
$x - \frac{5}{3}y = 5$

26. $\frac{1}{2}x - y = -3$
$-x + 2y = 6$

Write in standard form

$$ax + by = c$$
$$dx + ey = f$$

and solve.

27. $y = 3x - 3$
$6x = 8 + 3y$

28. $3x = 2y$
$y = -7 - 2x$

29. $3m + 2n = 2m + 2$
$2m + 3n = 2n - 2$

30. $2x - 3y = 1 - 3x$
$4y = 7x - 2$

31. If 3 limes and 12 lemons cost 81 cents, and 2 limes and 5 lemons cost 42 cents, what is the cost of 1 lime and of 1 lemon?

32. Find the capacity of each of two trucks if 3 trips of the larger and 4 trips of the smaller result in a total haul of 41 tons, and if 4 trips of the larger and 3 trips of the smaller result in a total haul of 43 tons.

C   *Solve by using elimination by addition. [Hint: Multiply both sides of each equation first by a constant that will eliminate decimals or fractions.]*

33. $0.3x - 0.6y = 0.18$
$0.5x + 0.2y = 0.54$

34. $0.8x - 0.3y = 0.79$
$0.2x - 0.5y = 0.07$

35. $\dfrac{x}{3} + \dfrac{y}{2} = 4$

$\dfrac{x}{3} - \dfrac{y}{2} = 0$

36. $\dfrac{x}{4} + \dfrac{y}{3} = 0$

$-\dfrac{x}{4} + \dfrac{y}{3} = -4$

37. $\dfrac{x}{2} + \dfrac{y}{3} = 1$

$\dfrac{2x}{3} + \dfrac{y}{2} = 2$

38. $\dfrac{a}{4} - \dfrac{2b}{3} = -2$

$\dfrac{a}{2} - b = -2$

4-7
RATE–TIME PROBLEMS

- Rate–Time Formulas
- Rate–Time Examples

Many problems that can be solved using the one-equation–one-variable methods discussed in Chapter 3 can also be solved using two-equation–two-variable methods. In fact, many practical problems are more naturally set up using two variables rather than one. It is important to remember that if you introduce two variables into a problem, you will need two linear equations involving those two variables.

In this and the following two sections, we will work a variety of problems using both one- and two-variable methods.

RATE–TIME FORMULAS

If a car travels 400 kilometers in 5 hours, then the ratio

$$\frac{400 \text{ kilometers}}{5 \text{ hours}} \qquad \text{or} \qquad 80 \text{ kilometers per hour}$$

is called the rate of motion, or speed. It is the number of kilometers traveled in each unit of time. Similarly, if a person types 420 words in 6 minutes, the ratio

$$\frac{420 \text{ words}}{6 \text{ minutes}} \qquad \text{or} \qquad 70 \text{ words per minute}$$

is the rate of typing. It is the number of words produced in each unit of time. In general, if q is the quantity produced in t units of time, then

$$\frac{\text{Quantity}}{\text{Time}} = \text{Rate}$$

or

$$\frac{q}{t} = r \qquad\qquad (1)$$

Thus, the **rate** *r* is the amount of *q* produced in each unit of time. If both sides of Equation (1) are multiplied by *t*, we obtain the more commonly encountered form

$$q = rt \qquad\qquad (2)$$

If *q* is distance *d*, then

$$d = rt \qquad\qquad (3)$$

a special form of Equation (2) with which you are likely familiar. Formulas (2) and (3) enter into the solutions of many rate–time problems.

Important Rate–Time Formulas
Quantity = (Rate)(Time)
$q = rt$ (2)
Distance = (Rate)(Time)
$d = rt$ (3)

RATE–TIME EXAMPLES

We now consider a variety of examples involving the rate–time concept.

Example 17   If a woman jogs 9 miles in 2 hours, what is her rate of motion (in miles per hour)?

Solution   This problem can be set up as a one-variable problem. We write Equation (3) in the form

$$rt = d$$

and let *t* = 2 and *d* = 9, then solve for *r*:

$$r \cdot 2 = 9$$

$$r = \tfrac{9}{2} = 4.5 \text{ miles per hour}$$

Problem 17   If a gas station pump pumps 10 gallons in 4 minutes, what is its rate of pumping (in gallons per minute)?

Example 18   If an IBM card sorting machine can sort 350 cards per minute, how long will it take the machine to sort 3,850 cards?

Solution   We write Equation (2) in the form

$$rt = q$$

and let $r = 350$ and $q = 3,850$, then solve for t:

$$350t = 3,850$$

$$t = \tfrac{3,850}{350} = 11 \text{ minutes}$$

Problem 18   If an airplane flies at 800 kilometers per hour, how long will it take to fly 2,600 kilometers?

Example 19   An airplane flew out to an island from the mainland and back in 5 hours. How far is the island from the mainland if the pilot averaged 600 miles per hour going to the island and 400 returning?

Solution   The problem can be solved using only one variable, the unknown distance to the island. Let x be this distance. Since $d = rt$, $t = \dfrac{d}{r}$, so the time to fly to the island is $\dfrac{x}{600}$ and the time to fly back is $\dfrac{x}{400}$. The total time is 5 hours; thus

$$\frac{x}{600} + \frac{x}{400} = 5$$

Multiply by 1,200 to clear fractions and solve:

$$2x + 3x = 6,000$$
$$5x = 6,000$$
$$x = 1,200 \text{ miles}$$

Problem 19   An airplane flew from San Francisco to a distressed ship at sea and back in 7 hours. How far was the ship from San Francisco if the pilot averaged 400 miles per hour going and 300 returning?

Example 20   A car leaves a town traveling at 60 kilometers per hour. How long will it take a second car traveling at 80 kilometers per hour to catch up to the first car if it leaves 2 hours later?

Solution   Here we can use either one- or two-variable methods.

Using One Variable: Let t = Number of hours for the second car to catch up. Then draw a diagram and label known and unknown parts:

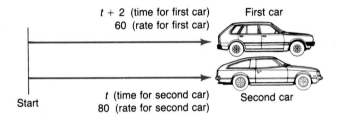

$t + 2$ (time for first car)   First car
60 (rate for first car)

Start

t (time for second car)   Second car
80 (rate for second car)

When the second car catches up to the first car, both cars will have traveled the same distance; hence,

$$\left(\begin{array}{c}\text{Distance first}\\ \text{car travels}\end{array}\right) = \left(\begin{array}{c}\text{Distance second}\\ \text{car travels}\end{array}\right)$$

$$\left(\begin{array}{c}\text{Rate of}\\ \text{first car}\end{array}\right)\left(\begin{array}{c}\text{Time for}\\ \text{first car}\end{array}\right) = \left(\begin{array}{c}\text{Rate of}\\ \text{second car}\end{array}\right)\left(\begin{array}{c}\text{Time for}\\ \text{second car}\end{array}\right)$$

$$60 \quad \cdot \quad (t + 2) \quad = \quad 80 \quad \cdot \quad t$$
$$60t + 120 = 80t$$
$$-20t = -120$$
$$t = \frac{-120}{-20} = 6 \text{ hours}$$

Using Two Variables: Let x be the time the first car travels, y be the time the second car travels. The distance traveled is then $60x$ for the first car and $80y$ for the second. We thus obtain this system of equations:

$60x = 80y$ The distances traveled must be the same.

$x = y + 2$ The first car leaves 2 hours earlier so travels 2 hours more.

We can solve this system by substitution, substituting $y + 2$ for x:

$60(y + 2) = 80y$
$60y + 120 = 80y$

This is the same equation solved in the first solution, so $y = 6$ hours. Since $x = y + 2$, $x = 8$ hours. Thus, it takes 6 hours for the second car to catch up to the first.

Problem 20   An older printing press can print 50 handbills per minute and a newer press can print 75 per minute. If the newer press is brought on the job 5 minutes after the first press starts and both continue until the job is done, how long will it take to print 1,500 handbills?

ANSWERS TO
MATCHED PROBLEMS

17. $r \cdot 4 = 10$, $r = 2.5$ gallons per minute

18. $800t = 2,600$, $t = 3.25$ hours

19. $\dfrac{x}{400} + \dfrac{x}{300} = 7$, $x = 1,200$ miles

20. $50t + 75(t - 5) = 1,500$, $t = 15$ minutes

EXERCISE 4-7

Solve using either a one-variable or a two-variable method.

A   **1.**   A car is traveling at an average rate of 48 miles per hour. How long will it take to go 156 miles?

2.   If a typist can type 76 words per minute, how long will it take to type 1,520 words?

3.   If a water pump on a boat can pump at the rate of 12 gallons per minute, how long will it take to pump 30 gallons?

4.   If the labor costs for a painter are $480, how long did the painter spend on the job if she receives $16 per hour?

5.   If a person earns $220 for a 40-hour week, what is the rate per hour?

6.   If a typist can type 2,400 words in 50 minutes, what is the rate per minute?

7.   If a car travels 550 kilometers in 5.5 hours, what is its rate?

8.   If a printing press can print the evening run of 12,000 papers in 2.5 hours, what is its rate?

9.   Two cars leave New York at the same time and travel in opposite directions. If one travels at 55 miles per hour and the other at 50 miles per hour, how long will it take them to be 630 miles apart?

10.   Two airplanes leave Atlanta at the same time and fly in opposite directions. If one travels at 600 kilometers per hour and the other at 500 kilometers per hour, how long will it take them to be 3,850 kilometers apart?

B   **11.**   If one machine can fill and cap 20 bottles per minute, and another machine can do 30, how long will it take both together to complete a 30,000-bottle order?

12. Two people volunteer to fold and stuff envelopes for a political campaign. If one person can produce 6 per minute and the other 8, how long will it take both together to prepare 1,267 envelopes?

13. A car leaves town traveling at 45 miles per hour. How long will it take a second car traveling at 50 miles per hour to catch up to the first car if it leaves 1 hour later?

14. Repeat Problem 13 if the second car leaves 2 hours later and travels at 55 miles per hour.

15. Find the total amount of time to complete the job in Problem 11 if the second (faster) machine is brought on the job 1 hour after the first machine starts and both continue until the job is finished.

16. Find the total amount of time to complete the job in Problem 12 if the second (faster) person is brought on the job 28 minutes after the first person starts and both continue until the job is finished.

17. A research chemist charges $35 per hour for her services and $21 per hour for her assistant. On a given job a customer received a bill for $1,505. If the chemist worked 5 hours less on the job than her assistant, how much time did each spend?

18. A contractor has just finished constructing a swimming pool in your backyard, and you have turned on the large water valve to fill it. The large valve lets water into the pool at a rate of 60 gallons per minute. After 2 hours you get impatient and turn on the garden hose, which lets water in at 15 gallons per minute. If the swimming pool holds 30,000 gallons of water, what will be the total time required to fill it?

C 19. An earthquake emits a primary wave and a secondary wave. Near the surface of the earth, the primary wave travels at about 5 miles per second and the secondary wave at about 3 miles per second. From the time lag between the two waves arriving at a given seismic station, it is possible to estimate the distance to the quake. (The "epicenter" can be located by getting distance bearings at three or more stations.) Suppose a station measured a time difference of 12 seconds between the arrival of the two waves. How far would the earthquake be from the station?

20. A skydiver free falls (because of air resistance) at about 176 feet per second or 120 miles per hour; with parachute open the rate of fall is about 22 feet per second or 15 miles per hour. If the skydiver opened the chute halfway down and the total time for the descent was 6 minutes, how high was the plane when the skydiver jumped?

<table>
<tr><td rowspan="2">4-8

MIXTURE PROBLEMS</td><td>■ Money Problems</td></tr>
<tr><td>■ Solution Problems</td></tr>
</table>

A variety of applications can be classified as mixture problems. Even though the problems come from different areas, their mathematical treatment is essentially the same.

MONEY PROBLEMS

When working coin problems, students often confuse value with the number of coins. Before we work Example 21, let us consider a few questions about collections of coins and their value.

How much are 8 nickels worth in cents?

$$\begin{pmatrix}\text{Value of one}\\\text{nickel in cents}\end{pmatrix} \times \begin{pmatrix}\text{Number of}\\\text{nickels}\end{pmatrix} = \begin{pmatrix}\text{Total value of all}\\\text{nickels in cents}\end{pmatrix}$$

$$5 \qquad \times \qquad 8 \qquad = \qquad 40 \text{ cents}$$

How much are x nickels worth in cents?

$$5 \qquad \times \qquad x \qquad = \qquad 5x$$

How much are 10 quarters worth in cents?

$$\begin{pmatrix}\text{Value of one}\\\text{quarter in cents}\end{pmatrix} \times \begin{pmatrix}\text{Number of}\\\text{quarters}\end{pmatrix} = \begin{pmatrix}\text{Total value of all}\\\text{quarters in cents}\end{pmatrix}$$

$$25 \qquad \times \qquad 10 \qquad = \qquad 250 \text{ cents}$$

How much are $(40 - x)$ quarters worth in cents?

$$25 \qquad \times \qquad (40 - x) \qquad = \qquad 25(40 - x)$$

Now Example 21 should be easier for you to understand.

Example 21 Suppose you have 40 coins consisting only of nickels and quarters in your pocket that are worth \$4. How many of each type of coin do you have?

Solution **1.** We solve the problem first using two variables. Let

x = Number of nickels
y = Number of quarters

Then

$$x + y = 40 \qquad \text{Number of coins}$$

$$5x + 25y = 400 \qquad \text{Value of coins in cents}$$

To solve, multiply the top equation by -5 and add:

$$
\begin{array}{r}
-5x - 5y = -200 \\
\underline{5x + 25y = 400} \\
20y = 200
\end{array}
$$

$$y = 10 \qquad \text{Quarters}$$

$$x + 10 = 40 \qquad \text{Now solve for } x \text{ using the top equation}$$

$$x = 30 \qquad \text{Nickels}$$

Check $30 + 10 = 40$ coins; $30 \cdot 5 + 10 \cdot 25 = 150 + 250 = 400$ cents $= \$4.$

2.   We can also solve the problem using only one variable. Let

$$x = \text{Number of nickels}$$

Then

$$40 - x = \text{Number of quarters}$$

Value before mixing   Value after mixing

$$
\begin{pmatrix} \text{Value of} \\ \text{nickels} \\ \text{in cents} \end{pmatrix} + \begin{pmatrix} \text{Value of} \\ \text{quarters} \\ \text{in cents} \end{pmatrix} = \begin{pmatrix} \text{Total value} \\ \text{of mixture} \\ \text{in cents} \end{pmatrix}
$$

$$5x + 25(40 - x) = 400 \qquad \text{Not 4.00}$$

$$5x + 1{,}000 - 25x = 400$$

$$-20x = -600$$

$$x = 30 \qquad \text{Nickels}$$

$$40 - x = 10 \qquad \text{Quarters}$$

Problem 21   A noon concert brought in \$2,000 on the sale of 1,500 tickets. If tickets sold for \$1 and \$2, how many of each were sold?

Example 22   A coffee shop wishes to blend coffee that sells for \$3 per pound with coffee that sells for \$4.25 per pound. How much of each should be used to produce 50 pounds of the new blend selling at \$3.50 per pound?

Solution   We will solve the problem using two variables. Let

x = Amount of \$3-per-pound coffee used
y = Amount of \$4.25-per-pound coffee used

Then

$$x + y = 50 \qquad \text{Pounds in blend}$$
$$3x + 4.25y = 3.5(50) = 175 \quad \text{Value of blend}$$

To solve, multiply the top equation by -3 and add:

$$
\begin{array}{r}
-3x - 3y = -150 \\
\underline{3x + 4.25y = 175} \\
1.25y = 25
\end{array}
$$

$$y = \frac{25}{1.25} = 20 \text{ pounds of \$4.25-per-pound coffee}$$

$$x + 20 = 50 \quad \text{Now solve for } x \text{ using the top equation}$$

$$x = 30 \text{ pounds of \$3-per-pound coffee}$$

Check $20 + 30 = 50$ pounds; $3(30) + 4.25(20) = 90 + 85 = \$175 =$ value   of blend.

The problem could also be solved by one-variable methods, replacing y by $50 - x$ in the solution given.

Problem 22   Repeat Example 22 but suppose that the two coffees to be used in the blend cost \$4 and \$6.50 per pound, respectively, and the final blend is to sell for \$5 per pound.

SOLUTION PROBLEMS

We now consider mixture problems involving percent. Recall from Section 3-7 that 12% in decimal form is 0.12, and 3.5% is 0.035, and so on. Also recall that 30% of 50 means 0.30×50 and 2.5% of 50 means 0.025×50.

Example 23   How many centiliters of pure alcohol must be added to 35 centiliters of a 20% solution to obtain a 30% solution?

Solution   There is only one variable in this problem. We let x = Number of centiliters of pure alcohol to be added. Let us illustrate the situation before and after mixing. The amount of alcohol present before mixing must equal the amount of alcohol present after mixing. (Note that pure alcohol is 100% alcohol.)

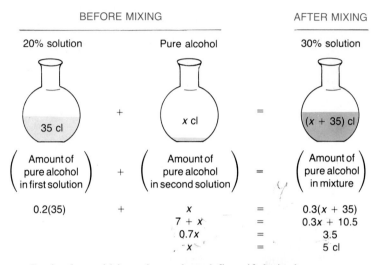

BEFORE MIXING   AFTER MIXING

20% solution   Pure alcohol   30% solution

35 cl   +   x cl   =   (x + 35) cl

$$\left(\begin{array}{c}\text{Amount of}\\\text{pure alcohol}\\\text{in first solution}\end{array}\right) + \left(\begin{array}{c}\text{Amount of}\\\text{pure alcohol}\\\text{in second solution}\end{array}\right) = \left(\begin{array}{c}\text{Amount of}\\\text{pure alcohol}\\\text{in mixture}\end{array}\right)$$

$0.2(35)$	+	x	=	$0.3(x + 35)$
		$7 + x$	=	$0.3x + 10.5$
		$0.7x$	=	3.5
		x	=	5 cl

Note: Decimals could have been cleared first, if desired.

The information provided by the illustration also can be given in tabular form:

	VOLUME IN CENTILITERS	PERCENT ALCOHOL	AMOUNT OF ALCOHOL
COMPONENT 1: 20% SOLUTION	35	20%	0.2(35)
COMPONENT 2: PURE ALCOHOL	x	100%	x
MIXTURE: 30% SOLUTION	$35 + x$	30%	$0.3(35 + x)$

The equation is then obtained from the right-hand column of the table. The amount of alcohol is to be 30% of the volume, that is,

$$0.2(35) + x = 0.3(35 + x)$$

Problem 23   How many centiliters of distilled water must be added to 80 centiliters of a 60% acid solution to obtain a 50% acid solution? Set up an equation and solve. [*Note:*   Distilled water has 0% acid.]

Example 24   A chemical storeroom has a 40% acid solution and an 80% solution. How many deciliters must be used from each to obtain 12 deciliters of a 50% solution?

Solution   Let

x = Amount of 40% solution used
y = Amount of 80% solution used

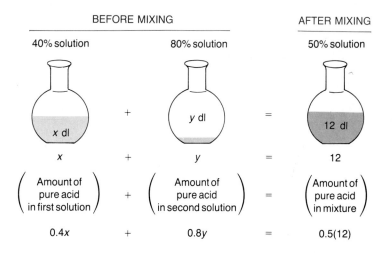

BEFORE MIXING				AFTER MIXING
40% solution		80% solution		50% solution

$$x \quad + \quad y \quad = \quad 12$$

$$\begin{pmatrix} \text{Amount of} \\ \text{pure acid} \\ \text{in first solution} \end{pmatrix} + \begin{pmatrix} \text{Amount of} \\ \text{pure acid} \\ \text{in second solution} \end{pmatrix} = \begin{pmatrix} \text{Amount of} \\ \text{pure acid} \\ \text{in mixture} \end{pmatrix}$$

$$0.4x \quad + \quad 0.8y \quad = \quad 0.5(12)$$

Thus, we obtain two equations and two variables:

$$\begin{aligned} x + \quad y &= 12 \\ 0.4x + 0.8y &= 6 \end{aligned} \qquad \text{Multiply by 10 to clear decimals.}$$

$$\begin{aligned} x + \quad y &= 12 \\ 4x + \quad 8y &= 60 \end{aligned} \qquad \text{Divide by } -4 \text{ to simplify.}$$

$$\begin{aligned} x + \quad y &= 12 \\ -x - \quad 2y &= -15 \qquad \text{Add to eliminate } x. \\ \hline -y &= -3 \\ y &= 3 \text{ deciliters of 80\% solution} \\ x + \quad y &= 12 \qquad \text{Now solve for } x \text{ using the top equation.} \\ x + \quad 3 &= 12 \\ x &= 9 \text{ deciliters of 40\% solution} \end{aligned}$$

The information provided by the illustration also can be given in tabular form:

	VOLUME IN DECILITERS	PERCENT ACID	AMOUNT OF ACID
COMPONENT 1: 40% SOLUTION	x	40%	$0.4x$
COMPONENT 2: 80% SOLUTION	y	80%	$0.8y$
MIXTURE: 50% SOLUTION	12	50%	$0.5(12)$

The volumes and amounts of acid in the components must add to that in the mixture, that is,

$$x + y = 12$$
$$0.4x + 0.8y = 0.5(12)$$

The problem also can be solved using one variable, replacing y with $12 - x$ in the solution given.

Problem 24   In Example 24 how many deciliters of each stockroom solution must be used to obtain 20 deciliters of a 70% solution?

ANSWERS TO
MATCHED PROBLEMS

21. $1x + 2(1,500 - x) = 2,000$; $x = 1,000$ ($1 tickets);
      $1,500 - x = 500$ ($2 tickets)
22. $4x + 6.5(50 - x) = 5(50)$; $x = 30$ pounds ($4 coffee);
      $50 - x = 20$ pounds ($6.50 coffee)
23. $0.6(80) + 0.0x = 0.5(x + 80)$; $x = 16$ centiliters
24. $0.4x + 0.8(20 - x) = 0.7(20)$; $x = 5$ deciliters (40% solution);
      $20 - x = 15$ deciliters (80% solution)

EXERCISE 4-8   A

1.   A parking meter takes only nickels and dimes. If it contains 50 coins at a total value of $3.50, how many of each type of coin are in the meter?

2.   An all-day parking meter takes only dimes and quarters. If it contains 100 coins at a total value of $14.50, how many of each type of coin are in the meter?

3.   A jazz concert brought in $60,000 on the sale of 8,000 tickets. If the tickets sold for $6 and $10 each, how many of each type were sold?

4.   A student production brought in $7,000 on the sale of 3,000 tickets. If tickets sold for $2 and $3 each, how many of each type were sold?

B

5.   How many deciliters of pure alcohol must be added to 12 deciliters of a 30% solution to obtain a 40% solution?

6.   How many milliliters of pure acid must be added to 100 milliliters of a 40% acid solution to obtain a 50% acid solution?

7.   How many milliliters of distilled water must be added to 500 milliliters of a solution of 60% acid to obtain a 50% solution?

8.   How many centiliters of distilled water must be added to 140 centiliters of an 80% acid solution to obtain a 70% acid solution?

9.   A chemist has two solutions in a stockroom—one is 30% acid and the other is 70% acid. How many milliliters of each should be mixed to obtain 100 milliliters of a 40% solution?

10.   A chemical stockroom has a 20% acid solution and a 50% acid solution.

How many centiliters must be taken from each to obtain 90 centiliters of a 30% solution?

11. A coffee and tea shop wishes to blend a $3.50-per-pound coffee with a $4.75-per-pound coffee in order to produce a blend selling for $4 per pound. How much of each would have to be used to produce 100 pounds of the new blend?

12. A coffee and tea shop wishes to blend a $2.50-per-pound tea with a $3.25-per-pound tea to produce a blend selling for $3 per pound. How much of each should be used to produce 75 pounds of the new blend?

13. You have just inherited $10,000 and wish to invest part at 8% interest and the rest at 12% interest. How much should be invested at each rate in order to produce the same yield as if you had invested it all at 9%?

14. An investor has $20,000 to invest. If part is to be invested at 8% and the rest at 12%, how much should be invested at each rate to yield the same amount as if all had been invested at 11%?

C **15.** A 10-liter radiator contains a 60% solution of antifreeze in distilled water. How much should be drained and replaced with pure antifreeze to obtain an 80% solution?

16. A 3-gallon radiator contains a 50% solution of antifreeze in distilled water. How much should be drained and replaced with pure antifreeze to obtain a 70% solution?

17. It is known that a carton contains 100 packages and that some of the packages weigh $\frac{1}{2}$ pound each and the rest weigh $\frac{1}{3}$ pound each. To save time counting each type of package in the carton, you can weigh the whole contents of the box (45 pounds) and determine the number of each kind of package by use of algebra. How many are there of each kind?

4-9
SUPPLEMENTAL
APPLICATIONS

This section provides another supplemental exercise set with a variety of applications. Some of the problems may be solved by one-variable methods, but all can be approached using two variables.

EXERCISE 4-9

The problems in this exercise are grouped according to subject area. The most difficult problems are marked with two stars (★★) and the moderately difficult problems with one star (★). The easier problems are not marked. Solve all problems using two-equation–two-unknown methods.

GEOMETRY   **1.** An 18-foot board is cut into two pieces so that one piece is 4 feet longer than the other piece. How long is each piece?

2. If the sum of two angles in a right triangle is 90° and their difference is 14°, find the two angles.

★**3.** Find the dimensions of a rectangle with perimeter 72 centimeters if its length is 1.25 times its width.

★**4.** Find the dimensions of a rectangle with perimeter 168 centimeters if its length is 1.8 times its width.

BUSINESS   **5.** A jazz concert brought in $75,000 on the sale of 8,200 tickets. If the tickets sold for $7 and $11 each, how many of each type were sold?

6. A student production brought in $7,000 on the sale of 3,000 tickets. If tickets sold for $2 and $3 each, how many of each type were sold?

★**7.** A person has $8,000 to invest. If part is invested at 6% and the rest at 8%, how much should be invested at each rate to have a total return of $520 per year?

★**8.** You have just inherited $10,000 and wish to invest part at 8% and the rest at 12%. How much should be invested at each rate to produce the same return as if you had invested it all at 9%?

★**9.** A coffee shop wishes to blend a $3.70-per-pound coffee with a $5.20-per-pound coffee to produce a blend selling for $4.60 per pound. How much of each should be used to produce 100 pounds of the new blend?

★**10.** A coffee and tea shop wishes to blend a $2.50-per-pound tea with a $3.25-per-pound tea to produce a blend selling for $3 per pound. How much of each should be used to produce 75 pounds of the new blend?

CHEMISTRY   **11.** Alcohol and distilled water were mixed to produce 120 centiliters of solution. If 20 centiliters more water was used than alcohol, how many centiliters of each was mixed?

12. Hydrochloric acid and distilled water were mixed to produce 96 milliliters of solution. If 36 milliliters more water was used than acid, how much of each was mixed?

★**13.** A chemist has two solutions in a stockroom. One is a 30% acid solution and the other is a 70% acid solution. How many milliliters of each should be mixed to obtain 100 milliliters of a 60% solution?

★**14.** A chemical storeroom has a 20% acid solution and a 50% acid solution. How many centiliters must be taken from each to obtain 90 centiliters of a 40% solution?

LIFE SCIENCE **15.** If laboratory animals in a diet experiment have a combined weight of 800 grams and one weighs 200 grams more than the other, how much does each weigh?

16. If two monkeys have a combined weight of 10 kilograms and one weighs 2 kilograms more than the other, how much does each weigh?

★★17. Animals in an experiment are to be kept on a strict diet. Each animal is to receive, among other things, 20 grams of protein and 6 grams of fat. The laboratory technician is able to purchase two food mixes of the following compositions:

	PROTEIN	FAT
Mix 1	10%	6%
Mix 2	20%	2%

How many grams of each mix should be used to obtain the right diet for a single animal?

★★18. A farmer placed an order with a chemical company for a fertilizer that would contain, among other things, 120 pounds of nitrogen and 90 pounds of phosphoric acid. The company had two mixtures on hand with the following compositions:

	NITROGEN	PHOSPHORIC ACID
Mixture *A*	20%	10%
Mixture *B*	6%	6%

How many pounds of each mixture should the company mix to fill the order?

PHYSICS AND ENGINEERING

19. Where should the fulcrum be placed on a 12-foot bar if it is to balance with a 14-pound weight on one end and a 42-pound weight on the other?

Hint:

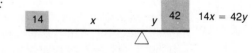

EARTH SCIENCES

20. Where should the fulcrum be placed on a 240-centimeter bar to balance 30 kilograms on one end and 50 kilograms on the other?

★★21. An earthquake produces primary and secondary waves. Near the surface of the earth the primary wave travels at about 8 kilometers per second and the secondary wave at about 5 kilometers per second. If a primary wave is recorded at a station 15 seconds before the arrival of the secondary wave, how long did each wave travel and how far is the epicenter of the quake from the station? [*Hint:* If x is the time for the secondary wave and y is the time for the primary wave, then $x - y = 15$. The second equation is obtained from the fact that each wave travels the same distance.]

★★22. Repeat Problem 21 for a time difference of 21 seconds.

MUSIC **23.** If a string on a stringed instrument is divided in the ratio of $4:5$, a major third chord will result. What will be the length of each part if a 36-inch string is used? [*Hint:* Use the proportion $x/y = \frac{4}{5}$ for one of the equations.]

24. If a string on a stringed instrument is divided in the ratio of $5:8$, a minor sixth chord will result. How would you divide a 39-inch string to produce a minor sixth?

PUZZLES **25.** A vending machine takes only nickels and dimes. If it contains 50 coins with a total value of $3.20, how many of each type of coin are in the machine?

26. A vending machine takes only dimes and quarters. If it contains 100 coins worth $14.50, how many of each type of coin are in the machine?

★27. A packing carton contains 144 small packages, some weighing $\frac{1}{4}$ pound each and the others $\frac{1}{2}$ pound each. How many of each type are in the carton if the total contents of the carton weigh 51 pounds?

★28. Repeat Problem 27 if the small packages weigh $\frac{1}{3}$ pound and $\frac{3}{4}$ pound, respectively, and the total contents weigh 73 pounds.

★★29. If 1 flask and 4 mixing dishes balance 16 test tubes and 2 mixing dishes, and if 2 flasks balance 2 test tubes and 6 mixing dishes, how many test tubes will balance 1 flask, and how many test tubes will balance 1 mixing dish?

4-10
CHAPTER REVIEW

When numbers are associated with points on a number line, those that cannot be represented in the form a/b, where a and b are integers, are called **irrational numbers**. Rational numbers have decimal representations that repeat; irrational numbers have nonrepeating decimal representations. The rational and irrational numbers together make up the **real numbers**. A **cartesian coordinate system** is formed with two real number lines—one as a **horizontal axis**, the other as a **vertical axis**—intersecting at their origins. These axes divide the plane into four **quadrants**. Every point in the plane corresponds to its **coordinates**, a pair (a, b) where a is the coordinate of the point projected to the horizontal axis and b is the coordinate of the point projected to the vertical axis. The point $(0, 0)$ is the **origin**.   *(4-1)*

The **solution to an equation in two variables** is an ordered pair of numbers that satisfy the equation. The **graph of an equation** is the graph of its solution set. The graph of an equation of the form $Ax + By = C$ is a straight line; conversely, *every straight line is the graph of such an equation*, called a **linear equation**. *(4-2)*

The **slope** of a nonvertical line is given by

$$\frac{y_1 - y_2}{x_1 - x_2}$$

where (x_1, y_1) and (x_2, y_2) are any two distinct points on the line. The equation $y = mx + b$ represents a line in **slope–intercept form**; m is the slope of the line and b is the **y intercept**, the y coordinate of the point where the line crosses the y axis. A **vertical line** has equation of the form $x = c$ and no slope. A **horizontal line** has equation of the form $y = c$ and slope 0. Two nonvertical lines are parallel when their slopes are the same; they are perpendicular when the product of their slopes is -1. *(4-3)*

To **solve a system of two linear equations in two unknowns** is to find all ordered pairs of real numbers that satisfy both equations. An approximate solution can be found by **graphing**. The system will have one solution (intersecting lines), no solution (parallel lines), or an infinite number of solutions (one line). *(4-4)*

The system also can be solved using **elimination by substitution**: solve one equation for one variable in terms of the other and then substitute into the other equation. *(4-5)*

Equivalent systems are systems with the same solution set. These operations produce equivalent systems:

1. Multiplying an equation by a nonzero constant
2. Adding one equation to another

The method of **elimination by addition** uses these operations to produce an equivalent system with an obvious solution. A system with no solution is called **inconsistent**; a system with an infinite number of solutions is called **dependent**. *(4-6)*

A variety of word problems can be solved by two-variable methods that include solving a system of equations. *(4-7, 4-8, 4-9)*

REVIEW EXERCISE 4-10

Work through all the problems in this chapter review and check answers in the back of the book. (Answers to all problems are there, and following each answer is a number in italics indicating the section in which that type of problem is discussed.) Where weaknesses show up, review appropriate sections in the text.

A *Graph in a rectangular coordinate system.*

1. $y = 2x - 3$

2. $y = \dfrac{x}{2} + 2$

3. $2x + y = 6$ **4.** $4x - 3y = 12$

5. What is the slope of the line having equation $3x + 5y = 8$?

6. Write the equation of the line through $(1, 3)$ having slope -2.

7. Write the equation of the line with slope 3 and y intercept -1.

8. Write the equation of the line through $(3, 0)$ and $(5, 6)$.

9. Solve graphically:

$$x - y = 5$$

$$x + y = 7$$

Solve by an elimination method.

10. $2x + 3y = 7$ **11.** $3x + 2y = 1$
      $3x - \ \ y = 5$ $5x + 6y = 7$

12. Solve using two equations and two unknowns: if you have 30 nickels and dimes in your pocket worth $2.30, how many of each do you have?

B **13.** Indicate true (T) or false (F):
     (A) $\ \sqrt{2}$ is a real number.   **(B)** $\ -5$ is a real number.
     (C) $\ 3.47$ is a real number.   **(D)** $\ -\frac{3}{5}$ is a real number.

14. Indicate true (T) or false (F):
     (A) $\ -\frac{3}{4}$ is a rational number.   **(B)** 5 is an integer.
     (C) $\ -4$ is a real number.   **(D)** $\ \sqrt{3}$ is an irrational number.

Graph in a rectangular coordinate system.

15. $y = \frac{1}{3}x - 2$ **16.** $4x - 3y = 10$

17. Write the equation of the line through $(-1, -4)$ and $(2, 1)$.

18. Write the equation of the line through $(1, -3)$ and parallel to $y = 4x - 2$.

19. Solve graphically:

$$2x - 3y = -3$$

$$3x + \ y = 12$$

Solve by an elimination method.

20. $6u + 4v = -2$ **21.** $5m - 3n = 4$
      $5u + 3v = -1$ $-2m + 4n = -10$

22. Two boats leave from opposite ports along the same shipping route, which is 2,800 miles long. If one boat travels at 22 miles per hour and the other at 13 miles per hour, how long will it take them to meet? Set up an equation and solve.

23. If one car leaves town traveling 48 miles per hour, how long will it take a second car traveling at 54 miles per hour to catch up to the first car, if the second car leaves 1 hour later? Set up an equation and solve.

24. Part of $6,000 is to be invested at 10% and the rest at 6%. How much should be invested at each rate if the total annual return from both investments is to be $440? Set up two equations with two unknowns and solve.

25. A chemical storeroom contains a 50% alcohol solution and a 70% solution. How much of each should be used to obtain 100 milliliters of a 66% solution? Set up two equations with two unknowns and solve.

C   **26.** Solve graphically:

$$2x - 6y = -3$$
$$-\tfrac{2}{3}x + 2y = 1$$

27. Solve by an elimination method:

$$x - 4y = 12$$
$$-\frac{x}{4} + y = 4$$

28. If one printing press can print 90 leaflets per minute and a newer press can print 110, how long will it take to print 6,000 leaflets if the newer press is brought on the job 20 minutes after the first press starts and both continue until finished? Set up an equation and solve.

29. A radiator with a capacity of 12 liters contains a 40% solution of anti-freeze in distilled water. How much should be drained and replaced with pure antifreeze to bring the level up to 50%? Set up an equation and solve.

30. Wishing to log some flying time, you have rented an airplane for 2 hours. You decide to fly due east until you have to turn around in order to be back at the airport at the end of the 2 hours. The cruising speed of the plane is 120 miles per hour in still air. Solve (A) and (B) using the two-equation–two-unknown method.

(A) If there is a wind blowing from the east at 30 miles per hour, how long should you head east before you turn around, and how long will it take you to get back?

(B) How far from the airport were you when you turned back?

5

INEQUALITIES IN ONE AND TWO VARIABLES

We have already observed that there is a natural order among the real numbers: one number is greater than another if it is to the right of the other on the number line. In this chapter we will explore further this inequality relationship. In particular, we will take three concepts we have considered for equations, namely,

   i. Solving an equation in one variable
  ii. Graphing an equation in two variables
 iii. Solving a system of equations in two variables

and develop the same ideas for inequalities.

5-1
INEQUALITY STATEMENTS AND LINE GRAPHS

- Inequality and Notation
- Inequality Statements and Line Graphs

To begin our treatment of inequalities, we will review what we already know about the inequality relation $a < b$ in the various number systems, and consider the solution of inequalities in terms of points on the number line.

INEQUALITY AND NOTATION

We have assumed since Chapter 1 that for any two natural numbers the larger one is easily recognized. We routinely extended this to the integers in Chapter 2 so that one number is larger than another if it is to the right of the other on the number line. The same idea extended to the rational numbers (Chapter 3) but in practice it may be harder to recognize when one rational number is to the right of another. For example, which of $\frac{4}{7}$ and $\frac{6}{11}$ is larger? For this reason, we developed a more formal definition of $<$ and $>$ that applied to all real numbers:

Definition of $<$ and $>$

If a and b are real numbers, then we write

$a < b$

if there exists a positive real number p such that $a + p = b$. We write

$c > d$

if there exists a positive real number q such that $c - q = d$.

Thus to compare $\frac{4}{7}$ and $\frac{6}{11}$, we subtract:

$$\frac{4}{7} - \frac{6}{11} = \frac{2}{77}$$

Since $\frac{2}{77}$ is positive, $\frac{4}{7} > \frac{6}{11}$. If the difference had been negative, we would have concluded the opposite. We could also have compared $\frac{4}{7}$ and $\frac{6}{11}$ by considering their decimal approximations:

$\frac{4}{7} = 0.57 \ldots$ $\frac{6}{11} = 0.54 \ldots$

Understanding the formal definition of $<$ and $>$ given above is necessary, however, for developing properties of inequalities.

We can also use decimal representations to compare irrational numbers or to compare a rational and an irrational number. For example, to compare π and $\sqrt{10}$, we find

$$\pi = 3.14 \ldots \qquad \sqrt{10} = 3.16 \ldots$$

so $\sqrt{10} > \pi$.

Example 1   Which of the two numbers is larger?

(A) $\dfrac{4}{5}, \dfrac{14}{17}$ (B) $\dfrac{13}{19}, \dfrac{15}{23}$

(C) $\dfrac{\pi}{2}, \sqrt{2.5}$ (D) $2\pi, \sqrt{40}$

Solution   (A) $\dfrac{4}{5} - \dfrac{14}{17} = \dfrac{4 \cdot 17}{5 \cdot 17} - \dfrac{5 \cdot 14}{5 \cdot 17} = \dfrac{68}{85} - \dfrac{70}{85} = -\dfrac{2}{85}$

Therefore, $\frac{14}{17} - \frac{4}{5} = \frac{2}{85}$ is positive so $\frac{14}{17} > \frac{4}{5}$.

(B) $\dfrac{13}{19} - \dfrac{15}{23} = \dfrac{13 \cdot 23}{19 \cdot 23} - \dfrac{19 \cdot 15}{19 \cdot 23} = \dfrac{299}{437} - \dfrac{285}{437} = \dfrac{14}{437}$

is positive so $\frac{13}{19} > \frac{15}{23}$.

(C) $\dfrac{\pi}{2} = 1.57 \ldots$

$\sqrt{2.5} = 1.58 \ldots$

Therefore $\sqrt{2.5} > \pi/2$.

(D) $2\pi = 6.28 \ldots$

$\sqrt{40} = 6.32 \ldots$

Therefore $\sqrt{40} > 2\pi$.

Problem 1   Which of the two numbers is larger?

(A) $\dfrac{3}{8}, \dfrac{7}{19}$ (B) $\dfrac{2}{7}, \dfrac{3}{11}$

(C) $3\pi, \sqrt{89}$ (D) $\dfrac{\pi}{4}, \dfrac{15}{19}$

The inequality symbols $<$ and $>$ may be combined with the equality symbol = to form statements such as $a \leq b$ and $a \geq b$, so we have four basic inequality statements:

$a < b$	a is less than b
$a > b$	a is greater than b
$a \leq b$	a is less than or equal to b
$a \geq b$	a is greater than or equal to b

INEQUALITY STATEMENTS AND LINE GRAPHS

The inequality symbols have a very clear geometric interpretation on the real number line. If $a < b$, then a is to the left of b; if $c > d$, then c is to the right of d (Figure 1).

FIGURE 1 $a < b, c > d$

Now let us turn to inequality statements of the form

$$x \geq -3 \qquad -2 < x \leq 3$$

To solve such inequality statements is to find the set of all replacements of the variable x (from some specified set of numbers) that makes the inequality true. This set is called the **solution set** for the inequality. To **graph** an inequality statement on a real number line is to graph its solution set.

Example 2   Graph each inequality statement on a real number line:

(A) $x < 2$ **(B)** $x \geq -3$

Solution   **(A)** The solution set for

$$x < 2$$

is the set of all real numbers less than 2. Graphically, the solution can be represented as follows:

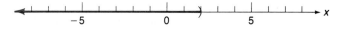

The parenthesis at the point 2 is used to indicate that 2 is not included in the solution set.

(B) The solution set for

$$x \geq -3$$

is the set of all real numbers greater than or equal to -3. Graphically, the solution can be represented as follows:

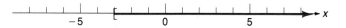

The bracket at the point -3 is used to indicate that -3 is included in the solution set.

Problem 2 Graph each inequality statement on a real number line:

(A) $x > -3$ **(B)** $x \leq 2$

Example 3 Graph each inequality statement on a real number line:

(A) $-2 < x \leq 3$ **(B)** $-2 \leq x < 3$

Solution **(A)** The double inequality

$$-2 < x \leq 3$$

is a short way of writing

$$-2 < x \qquad \text{and} \qquad x \leq 3$$

which means that x is greater than -2 and at the same time x is less than or equal to 3. In other words, x can be any real number between -2 and 3, excluding -2 but including 3.† This set is graphed as follows:

(B) The solution set for

$$-2 \leq x < 3$$

---

† We do not use double inequality forms where the inequality symbols point away from each other or toward each other. Study the following forms carefully to see why:

$$2 < x > -1 \qquad -2 < x > 5 \qquad 5 > x < 8$$

INEQUALITY PROPERTIES

When solving equations we made considerable use of the addition, subtraction, multiplication, and division properties of equality. We can use similar properties to help us solve inequalities. We will start with several numerical examples and generalize from these.

1. Add the same quantity to each side of an inequality:

<table>
<tr><td align="center">Add a positive quantity
to each side.</td><td align="center">Add a negative quantity
to each side.</td></tr>
<tr><td align="center">$-2 < 4$</td><td align="center">$-2 < 4$</td></tr>
<tr><td align="center">$-2 + \mathbf{3} \qquad 4 + \mathbf{3}$</td><td align="center">$-2 + \mathbf{(-3)} \qquad 4 + \mathbf{(-3)}$</td></tr>
<tr><td align="center">$1 < 7$</td><td align="center">$-5 < 1$</td></tr>
<tr><td align="center">Sense of inequality
remains the same.</td><td align="center">Sense of inequality
remains the same.</td></tr>
</table>

2. Subtract the same quantity from each side of an inequality:

<table>
<tr><td align="center">Subtract a positive
quantity from each side.</td><td align="center">Subtract a negative
quantity from each side.</td></tr>
<tr><td align="center">$-2 < 4$</td><td align="center">$-2 < 4$</td></tr>
<tr><td align="center">$-2 - \mathbf{5} \qquad 4 - \mathbf{5}$</td><td align="center">$-2 - \mathbf{(-7)} \qquad 4 - \mathbf{(-7)}$</td></tr>
<tr><td align="center">$-7 < -1$</td><td align="center">$5 < 11$</td></tr>
<tr><td align="center">Sense of inequality
remains the same.</td><td align="center">Sense of inequality
remains the same.</td></tr>
</table>

3. Multiply each side of an inequality by the same nonzero quantity:

<table>
<tr><td align="center">Multiply both sides by
a positive quantity.</td><td align="center">Multiply both sides by
a negative quantity.</td></tr>
<tr><td align="center">$-2 < 4$</td><td align="center">$-2 < 4$</td></tr>
<tr><td align="center">$\mathbf{2}(-2) \qquad \mathbf{2}(4)$</td><td align="center">$\mathbf{(-2)}(-2) \qquad \mathbf{(-2)}(4)$</td></tr>
<tr><td align="center">$-4 < 8$</td><td align="center">$4 > -8$</td></tr>
<tr><td align="center">Sense of inequality
remains the same.</td><td align="center">Sense of inequality
reverses.</td></tr>
</table>

Note difference

4. Divide each side of an inequality by the same nonzero quantity:

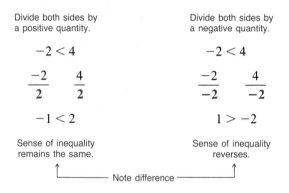

Divide both sides by a positive quantity.

$$-2 < 4$$

$$\frac{-2}{2} \qquad \frac{4}{2}$$

$$-1 < 2$$

Sense of inequality remains the same.

Divide both sides by a negative quantity.

$$-2 < 4$$

$$\frac{-2}{-2} \qquad \frac{4}{-2}$$

$$1 > -2$$

Sense of inequality reverses.

Note difference

These descriptions generalize completely and are summarized as follows without proof:

Inequality Properties

For a, b, and c any real numbers:

1. If $a < b$, then $a + c < b + c$.

$\quad -2 < 4 \qquad\qquad -2 + 3 < 4 + 3$

ADDITION PROPERTY

2. If $a < b$, then $a - c < b - c$.

$\quad -2 < 4 \qquad\qquad -2 - 3 < 4 - 3$

SUBTRACTION PROPERTY

3. If $a < b$ and c is positive, then $ca < cb$.

$\quad -2 < 4 \qquad\qquad\qquad 3(-2) < 3(4)$

4. If $a < b$ and c is negative, then $ca > cb$.

$\quad -2 < 4 \qquad\qquad\qquad (-3)(-2) > (-3)(4)$

MULTIPLICATION PROPERTY

(Note the difference between **3** and **4**.)

5. If $a < b$ and c is positive, then $\dfrac{a}{c} < \dfrac{b}{c}$.

$\quad -2 < 4 \qquad\qquad\qquad \dfrac{-2}{2} < \dfrac{4}{2}$

6. If $a < b$ and c is negative, then $\dfrac{a}{c} > \dfrac{b}{c}$.

$\quad -2 < 4 \qquad\qquad\qquad \dfrac{-2}{-2} > \dfrac{4}{-2}$

DIVISION PROPERTY

(Note the difference between **5** and **6**.)

Similar properties hold if each inequality sign is reversed or if $>$ is replaced with $\geq$ and $<$ is replaced with $\leq$. Thus, we find that we can perform essentially the same operations on inequality statements to produce equivalent statements that we perform on equations to produce equivalent equations with this exception:

The inequality sign reverses if we multiply or divide both sides of an inequality by a negative number.

SOLVING INEQUALITIES

We will now solve some inequalities using the properties presented above. Unless otherwise stated, in **solving an inequality** we find *all* real number solutions.

Example 4   Solve each inequality;

(A) $x + 3 < -2$ **(B)** $5x \geq 10$

(C) $-3x - 2 < 7$ **(D)** $-\dfrac{x}{2} > -3$

Solution   **(A)** $x + 3 < -2$ Subtract 3 from each side.

$$x + 3 - 3 < -2 - 3$$ Inequality sign does not reverse.

$$x < -5$$ Solution set is set of all real numbers less than -5.

(B) $5x \geq 10$ Divide each side by 5.

$$\frac{5x}{5} \geq \frac{10}{5}$$ Inequality sign does not reverse, since we divided by a positive number.

$$x \geq 2$$ Solution set is set of all real numbers greater than or equal to 2.

(C) $-3x - 2 < 7$ Add 2 to each side.

$$-3x - 2 + 2 < 7 + 2$$ Inequality sign does not reverse.

$$-3x < 9$$ Divide each side by -3.

$$\frac{-3x}{-3} > \frac{9}{-3}$$ Inequality sign reverses, since we divided by a negative number.

$$x > -3$$ Solution set is set of all real numbers greater than -3.

(D) $\qquad -\dfrac{x}{2} > -3$ Multiply each side by -2.

$$(-2)\left(-\dfrac{x}{2}\right) < (-2)(-3)$$ Inequality sign reverses, since we multiplied by a negative number.

$$x < 6$$ Solution set is set of all real numbers less than 6.

Problem 4   Solve each inequality:

(A) $x - 3 \geq -5$ (B) $-6x < 18$

(C) $3x + 5 \leq -1$ (D) $-\dfrac{x}{3} > -4$

Example 5   Solve and graph:

(A) $3(x - 1) + 5 \leq 5(x + 2)$ (B) $\dfrac{3x - 2}{2} - 5 > 1 - \dfrac{x}{4}$

Solution   **(A)** $\quad 3(x - 1) + 5 \leq 5(x + 2)$ Simplify left and right sides.
$$3x - 3 + 5 \leq 5x + 10$$ Isolate x on the left side.
$$3x + 2 \leq 5x + 10$$
$$3x \leq 5x + 8$$
$$-2x \leq 8$$
$$x \geq -4$$ Inequality sign reverses. (Why?)

(B) $\qquad \dfrac{3x - 2}{2} - 5 > 1 - \dfrac{x}{4}$ Multiply both sides by 4, the LCM of the denominators.

$$4\left(\dfrac{3x - 2}{2} - 5\right) > 4\left(1 - \dfrac{x}{4}\right)$$ Inequality sign does not reverse. (Why?)

$$2(3x - 2) - 20 > 4 - x$$ Simplify left side.
$$6x - 4 - 20 > 4 - x$$
$$6x - 24 > 4 - x$$ Isolate x on the left side.
$$6x > 28 - x$$
$$7x > 28$$
$$x > 4$$ Inequality sign does not reverse. (Why?)

Problem 5   Solve and graph:

(A) $2(2x + 3) \geq 6(x - 2) + 10$ **(B)** $\dfrac{2x - 3}{3} - 2 > \dfrac{x}{6} - 1$

Example 6   Solve and graph:

(A) $-8 \leq 3x - 5 < 7$ **(B)** $-1 < 1 - 2x < 5$

Solution   **(A)** We proceed as above, except that we try to isolate x in the middle:

$$-8 \leq 3x - 5 < 7 \qquad \text{Add 5 to each member.}$$

$$\boxed{-8 + 5 \leq 3x - 5 + 5 < 7 + 5}$$

$$-3 \leq 3x < 12 \qquad \text{Divide each member by 3.}$$

$$\boxed{\frac{-3}{3} \leq \frac{3x}{3} < \frac{12}{3}} \qquad \text{Inequality signs do not reverse.}$$

$$-1 \leq x < 4$$

(B) $-1 < 1 - 2x < 5 \qquad \text{Subtract 1 from each member.}$

$$\boxed{-1 - 1 < 1 - 2x - 1 < 5 - 1}$$

$$-2 < -2x < 4 \qquad \text{Divide each member by } -2.$$

$$\boxed{\frac{-2}{-2} > \frac{-2x}{-2} > \frac{4}{-2}} \qquad \text{Inequality signs reverse.}$$

$$1 > x > -2$$
or
$$-2 < x < 1$$

Problem 6   Solve and graph:

(A) $-3 < 2x + 3 \leq 9$ **(B)** $-2 \leq 4 - 3x < 1$

APPLICATIONS

We conclude this section with a word problem and an application.

Example 7   What numbers satisfy the condition "4 more than twice a number is less than or equal to that number"?

Solution   Let x = the number. Then

$$2x + 4 \leq x$$
$$x \leq -4$$

Problem 7   What numbers satisfy the condition "6 less than 3 times a number is greater than or equal to 9"?

Example 8   If the temperature for a 24-hour period in Antarctica ranged between $-49°F$ and $14°F$ (that is, $-49 \leq F \leq 14$), what was the range in Celsius degrees? (Recall that $F = \frac{9}{5}C + 32$.)

Solution   Since $F = \frac{9}{5}C + 32$, we replace F in $-49 \leq F \leq 14$ with $\frac{9}{5}C + 32$ and solve the double inequality:

$$-49 \leq \tfrac{9}{5}C + 32 \leq 14$$

$$\boxed{-49 - 32 \leq \tfrac{9}{5}C + 32 - 32 \leq 14 - 32}$$

$$-81 \leq \tfrac{9}{5}C \leq -18$$

$$\boxed{(\tfrac{5}{9})(-81) \leq (\tfrac{5}{9})(\tfrac{9}{5}C) \leq (\tfrac{5}{9})(-18)}$$

$$-45 \leq C \leq -10$$

Problem 8   Repeat Example 8 for $-31 \leq F \leq 5$.

ANSWERS TO
MATCHED PROBLEMS

4. **(A)** $x \geq -2$ **(B)** $x > -3$ **(C)** $x \leq -2$ **(D)** $x < 12$

5. **(A)** $x \leq 4$

(B) $x > 4$

6. **(A)** $-3 < x \leq 3$

(B) $1 < x \leq 2$

7. $x \geq 5$

8. $-35 \leq C \leq -15$

EXERCISE 5-2   A   *Graph on a real number line.*

1. $x < 2$ **2.** $x > 3$ **3.** $x > -2$

4. $x < -3$ **5.** $x \leq 3$ **6.** $x \geq 2$

7. $x \geq -2$ **8.** $x \leq -1$

Write in inequality notation.

9.

10.

11.

12.

13.

14.

15.

16.

Solve and graph.

17. $x - 2 > 5$ **18.** $x - 4 < -1$ **19.** $x + 5 < -2$

20. $x + 3 > -4$ **21.** $2x > 8$ **22.** $3x < 6$

23. $-2x \geq 8$ **24.** $-3x \leq 6$ **25.** $\dfrac{x}{3} < -7$

26. $\dfrac{x}{5} > -2$ **27.** $\dfrac{x}{-3} \leq -7$ **28.** $\dfrac{x}{-5} \geq -2$

29. $3x + 7 < 13$ **30.** $2x - 3 > 5$

31. $-2x + 8 < 4$ **32.** $-4x - 7 > 5$

33. $7x - 8 \leq 4x + 7$ **34.** $6m + 2 \leq 4m + 6$

35. $4y - 7 \geq 9y + 3$ **36.** $x - 1 \leq 4x + 8$

B   *Solve and graph.*

37. $3 - (2 + x) > -9$ **38.** $2(1 - x) \geq 5x$

39. $3 - x \geq 5(3 - x)$ **40.** $2(x - 3) + 5 < 5 - x$

41. $3(u - 5) - 2(u + 1) \geq 2(u - 3)$

42. $4(2u - 3) < 2(3u + 1) - (5 - 3u)$

43. $\dfrac{m}{6} - \dfrac{1}{2} > \dfrac{2}{3} + m$ **44.** $\dfrac{x}{5} - 3 < \dfrac{3}{5} - x$

45. $-2 - \dfrac{1 + x}{3} < \dfrac{x}{4}$ **46.** $\dfrac{x}{4} - \dfrac{2x + 1}{6} < -1$

47. $2 < x + 3 < 5$ **48.** $-3 \leq x - 5 \leq 8$

49. $-4 \leq 5x + 6 \leq 21$ **50.** $2 < 3x - 7 < 14$

51. $-4 \leq \frac{9}{5}C + 32 \leq 68$ **52.** $-1 \leq \frac{2}{3}m + 5 \leq 11$

C   **53.** $-10 \leq \frac{5}{9}(F - 32) \leq 25$ **54.** $-5 \leq \frac{5}{9}(F - 32) \leq 10$

55. $-3 \leq 3 - 2x < 7$ **56.** $-5 < 7 - 4x \leq 15$

APPLICATIONS   *In Problems 57 to 64 set up appropriate inequality statements and solve. The most difficult problems are marked with two stars (★★) and the moderately difficult problems with one star (★). The easier problems are not marked.*

57. *Number*   What numbers satisfy the condition ''3 less than twice the number is greater than or equal to -6''?

58. *Number*   What numbers satisfy the condition ''5 less than 3 times the number is less than or equal to 4 times the number''?

59. *Geometry*   If the perimeter of a rectangle with a length of 10 centimeters must be smaller than 30 centimeters, how small must the width be?

60. *Geometry*   If the area of a rectangle of length 10 inches must be greater than 65 square inches, how large must the width be?

★**61.** *Photography*   A photographic developer is to be kept so that its temperature is not below 68°F or above 77°F. What is the range of temperature in Celsius degrees? (Recall that F = $\frac{9}{5}$C + 32.)

★**62.** *Chemistry*   In a chemistry experiment the solution of hydrochloric acid is to be kept so that its temperature is not below 30°C or above 35°C. What would the range of temperature be in Fahrenheit degrees? [Recall that C = $\frac{5}{9}$(F − 32).]

*63. **Psychology** A person's IQ is found by dividing mental age, as indicated by standard tests, by chronological age and then multiplying this ratio by 100. In terms of a formula,

$$IQ = \frac{MA \cdot 100}{CA}$$

If the IQ range of a group of 12-year-olds is $70 \le IQ \le 120$, what is the mental-age range of this group?

*64. **Business** For a business to make a profit it is clear that revenue R must be greater than costs C; in short, a profit will result only if $R > C$. If a company manufactures records and its cost equation for a week is $C = 300 + 1.5x$, where x is the number of records manufactured in a week, and its revenue equation is $R = 2x$, where x is the number of records sold in a week, how many records must be sold for the company to realize a profit?

5-3

GRAPHING LINEAR INEQUALITIES IN TWO VARIABLES

- Half-Planes and Boundary Lines
- Graphing Linear Inequalities

Linear equations in one variable, such as $3x - 2 = 7$, were introduced in Chapters 2 and 3. The solution of such an equation is generally a single point on the real number line, in this case $x = 3$. Linear inequalities in one variable, such as $3x - 2 < 7$, were introduced in Sections 5-1 and 5-2. The solution for these inequalities is generally an interval on the real number line, in this case the interval $x < 3$.

Linear equations in two variables were introduced in Section 4-2. An equation such as $2x + y = 6$ has as its solution the set of all points on a straight line in the plane (Figure 2).

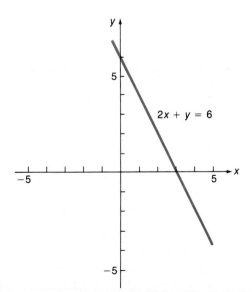

FIGURE 2

In this section, we will consider linear inequalities in two variables, such as $2x + y < 6$.

HALF-PLANES AND BOUNDARY LINES

A line divides the plane into two halves called **half-planes**. A vertical line divides it into right and left half-planes; a nonvertical line divides it into upper and lower half-planes (Figure 3).

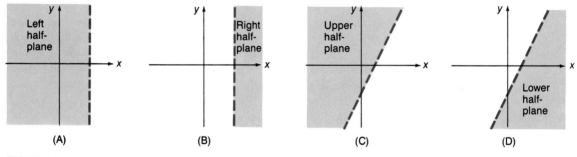

(A)   (B)   (C)   (D)

FIGURE 3

To investigate the half-planes determined by $2x + y = 6$ rewrite the equation as $y = -2x + 6$. For any given value of x, there is exactly one value for y such that (x, y) lies on the line. For example, for $x = 1$, $y = (-2) \cdot 1 + 6 = 4$. For the same value of x and smaller values of y, the point (x, y) will lie below the line, since $y < -2x + 6$. For example, if x still equals 1 and $y < 4$, then $y < -2x + 6$. Thus the lower half-plane corresponds to the solution to the inequality $y < -2x + 6$. Similarly, the upper half-plane corresponds to $y > -2x + 6$ (Figure 4).

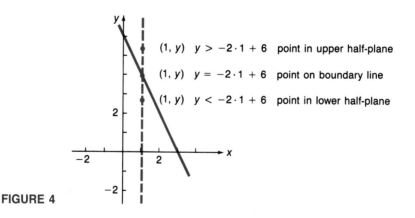

$(1, y)$ $y > -2 \cdot 1 + 6$ point in upper half-plane

$(1, y)$ $y = -2 \cdot 1 + 6$ point on boundary line

$(1, y)$ $y < -2 \cdot 1 + 6$ point in lower half-plane

FIGURE 4

The four inequalities formed from $y = -2x + 6$ by replacing the $=$ sign by $<, >, \leq$, or $\geq$ are

$$y < -2x + 6$$
$$y > -2x + 6$$
$$y \le -2x + 6$$
$$y \ge -2x + 6$$

The graph of each is a half-plane, excluding the boundary line for $<$ and $>$, and including it for $\le$ and $\ge$. The half-planes are graphed as shaded regions in Figure 5. Excluded boundary lines are shown as broken lines, included boundaries as solid lines.

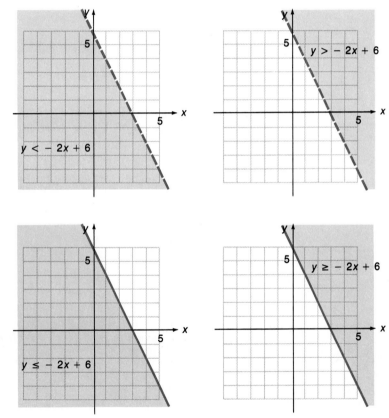

FIGURE 5

GRAPHING LINEAR INEQUALITIES

The preceding discussion suggests the following important result, which we state without proof.

Graphing Linear Inequalities

The graph of a linear inequality

$$Ax + By < C \qquad \text{or} \qquad Ax + By > C$$

with $B \neq 0$ is either the upper half-plane or the lower half-plane (but not both) determined by the line $Ax + By = C$. If $B = 0$, the graph of

$$Ax < C \qquad \text{or} \qquad Ax > C$$

is either the left half-plane or the right half-plane (but not both) determined by the line $Ax = C$.

This result leads to a simple, fast procedure for graphing linear inequalities in two variables:

Steps in Graphing Linear Inequalities

1. First graph the corresponding equation $Ax + By = C$—as a broken line if equality is not included in original statement, as a solid line if equality is included in original statement.
2. Choose a test point in the plane not on the line—the origin is the best choice if it is not on the line—and substitute the coordinates into the inequality.
3. The graph of the original inequality includes:
   (A) The half-plane containing the test point, if the inequality is satisfied by that point
   (B) The half-plane not containing the test point, if the inequality is not satisfied by that point
4. Shade the half-plane to show the graph of the solution set.

Example 9   Graph $2x + 5y \leq 10$

Solution   *Step 1*   Graph the boundary line $2x + 5y = 10$. The line should be solid, since equality is included in

$$2x + 5y \leq 10$$

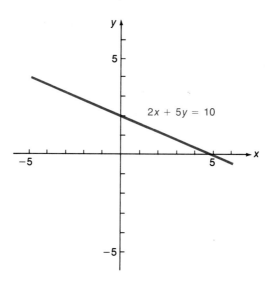

Step 2 Choose a test point. Here the origin will work, since it is not on the boundary.

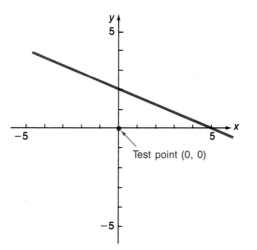

Step 3 The origin (0, 0) satisfies the original inequality:

$$2x + 5y \leq 10$$
$$2 \cdot 0 + 5 \cdot 0 \leq 10$$
$$0 \leq 10$$

Therefore, the origin lies in the half-plane that is the solution to the inequality. The graph is the lower half-plane.

Step 4 The final graph is the lower half-plane including the boundary line:

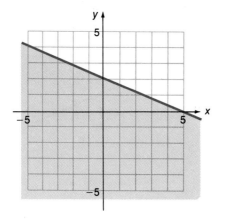

Problem 9 Graph $3x - 4y \geq 12$

Example 10 Graph:

(A) $x < 5$ (B) $2y > 3$ (C) $-2 < y \leq 3$

Solution

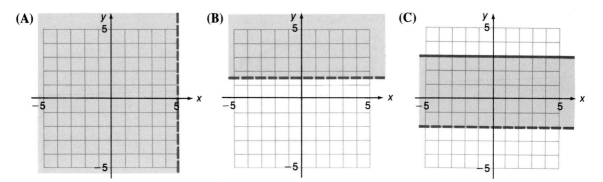

The graph of an inequality such as $x < 5$ depends on the context in which we are working. If we are dealing with only one variable, the graph is a line graph:

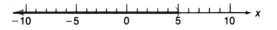

However, if we are dealing with two variables and the second one is simply missing from the inequality, then the graph is the half-plane shown in Example 10(A).

Problem 10   Graph:

(A) $y > -2$ **(B)** $3x < 8$ **(C)** $2 \le x < 5$

ANSWERS TO
MATCHED PROBLEMS

9. $3x - 4y \ge 12$

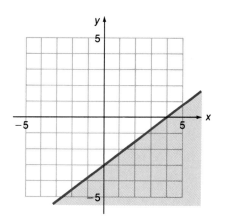

10.

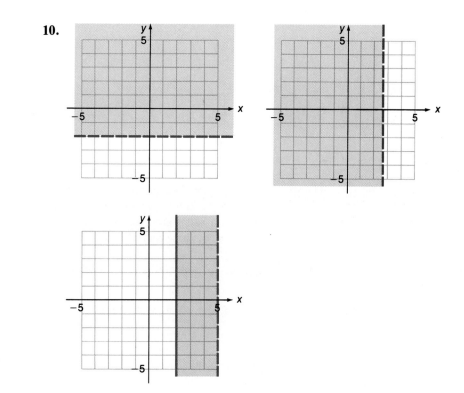

EXERCISE 5-3   *Graph each inequality in a rectangular coordinate system:*

A **1.** $x \leq -1$ **2.** $y \geq 3$ **3.** $x + y \leq 2$

   4. $x + y \leq 3$ **5.** $x - y > 1$ **6.** $x - y < 3$

   7. $y \leq x + 3$ **8.** $y \geq x - 2$ **9.** $x < 0$

B **10.** $3x + y \geq 6$ **11.** $x + 2y \leq 4$ **12.** $2x - 5y < 10$

   13. $-4x + 3y > 12$ **14.** $y \leq \dfrac{1}{2}x + 3$ **15.** $y < \dfrac{1}{2}x - 1$

   16. $y > \dfrac{5}{3}x - 2$ **17.** $y \geq \dfrac{3}{5}x + 1$ **18.** $y < x$

C **19.** $\dfrac{1}{2}x + \dfrac{2}{3}y \leq 1$ **20.** $\dfrac{1}{3}x - \dfrac{1}{2}y \geq 3$ **21.** $\dfrac{1}{3}x - \dfrac{1}{5}y > 1$

   22. $3x - \dfrac{1}{2}y < 4$ **23.** $\dfrac{1}{2}x - \dfrac{1}{2}y < 0$ **24.** $-2x + y \leq \dfrac{1}{3}$

   25. $x + \dfrac{2}{3}y > 0$ **26.** $3x - \dfrac{1}{2}y \geq 0$ **27.** $2x + \dfrac{1}{3}y \leq 0$

5-4
SYSTEMS OF LINEAR INEQUALITIES IN TWO VARIABLES

Systems of linear equations were introduced in Chapter 4. The solution of a system is the intersection of the solutions of all the equations in the system— graphically, the solution is the intersection of the straight lines the equations represent. We now consider systems of linear inequalities. Each inequality represents a half-plane (see Section 5-3). The solution of the system is the intersection of these half-planes.

Example 11   Solve the following system graphically:

$$x \geq 0$$
$$y \geq 0$$
$$2x + 5y \leq 10$$

Solution   The half-planes for $x \geq 0$ and $y \geq 0$ are

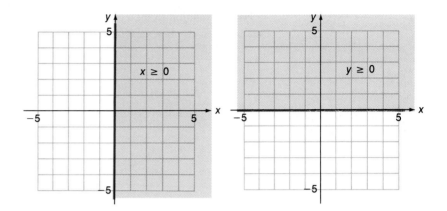

so together these two inequalities determine the first quadrant:

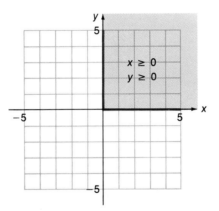

We graphed the third inequality in Example 9:

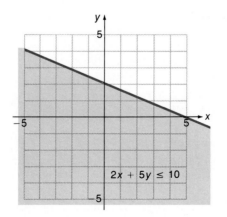

For the solution to the system we need the points in this last half-plane that also lie in the first quadrant:

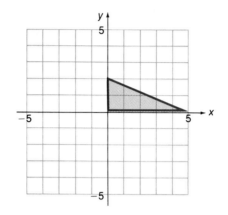

Problem 11   Solve the following system graphically:

$$x \le 0$$
$$y \le 0$$
$$2x + y > -4$$

Example 12   Solve the following system graphically:

$$-2 \le x \le 0$$
$$0 \le y \le 3$$

Solution   Here there are actually four inequalities, each of which is easily graphed individually:

$$-2 \le x \qquad\qquad\qquad x \le 0$$

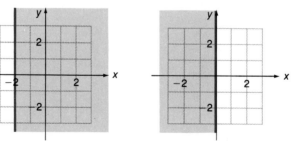

$$0 \le y \qquad\qquad\qquad y < 3$$

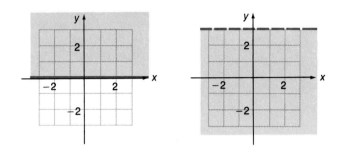

To see the intersection it is helpful to draw all four boundary lines, broken or solid as needed, on the same graph and mark the appropriate side of the line with arrows to indicate the half-plane each inequality determines:

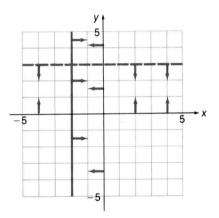

The solution can then be graphed:

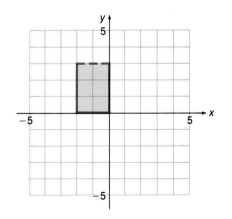

Problem 12   Solve the following system graphically:

$$1 < x < 4$$
$$0 \le y \le 3$$

Example 13   Solve the following system graphically:

$$x \ge 0$$
$$y \ge 0$$
$$2x + 5y \le 10$$
$$3x + 4y \le 12$$

Solution   Although the boundary lines are not all vertical or horizontal, we can still apply the same procedure used in Example 12:

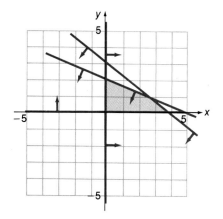

Problem 13   Solve the following system graphically:

$$x \le 0$$
$$y \ge 0$$
$$2x + 5y \le 10$$
$$-3x + 4y \le 12$$

ANSWERS TO   **11.**
MATCHED PROBLEMS

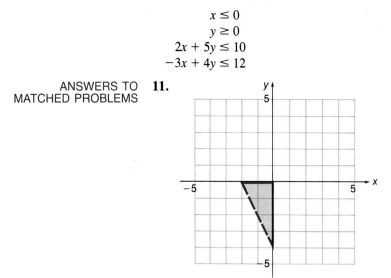

12.

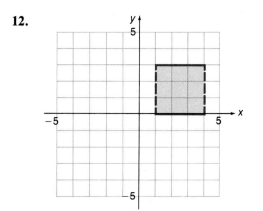

13.

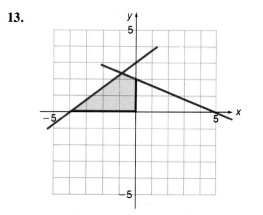

EXERCISE 5-4   *Solve each system graphically:*

A **1.** $x \geq 0$
           $y \geq 0$
        $2x + 3y < 6$

   2. $x \leq 0$
           $y \geq 0$
        $x - 2y \geq 4$

   3. $x \leq 0$
           $y \geq 0$
        $x + y \geq -2$

   4. $x \geq 0$
           $y \leq 0$
        $1 \leq y \leq 3$

   5. $x \geq 0$
        $1 \leq y \leq 3$

   6. $y \leq 3$
        $0 \leq x \leq 2$

B **7.** $1 \leq x \leq 4$
        $y \leq 2x + 3$

   8. $0 \leq x \leq 3$
        $y > x - 1$

   9. $0 \leq y \leq 5$
        $x \leq y + 2$

   10. $-2 \leq y \leq 2$
         $x < y$

   11. $x \leq y + 1$
         $x \geq y$

   12. $-x \leq y$
         $x \leq y + 2$

C **13.** $x + y \leq 4$
            $y \geq 2x - 4$
            $x \geq 0$

14. $x + y > -3$
         $x - y > -2$
         $x \leq 0$

15. $x + y \geq -4$
         $x \leq y + 4$
         $y \leq 0$

16. $x + y \leq 5$
         $y - x \geq 0$
         $x \geq 0$

17. $x - y \leq 4$
         $x + y \leq 4$
         $y \geq -4x - 4$

18. $2x + 3y \leq 6$
         $3x + 2y \leq 6$
         $x + y \geq 2$

5-5

CHAPTER REVIEW

The inequality $a < b$ means there exists a positive real number p such that $a + p = b$, or equivalently that a is to the left of b on the number line. When graphing an inequality statement, a bracket, [or], is used to indicate an endpoint that is included; a parenthesis, (or), indicates an endpoint that is not included.   *(5-1)*

Inequality relations satisfy these **inequality properties**:

1. If $a < b$, then $a + c < b + c$.
2. If $a < b$, then $a - c < b - c$.
3. If $a < b$ and c is positive, then $ac < bc$.
4. If $a < b$ and c is negative, then $ac > bc$.
5. If $a < b$ and c is positive, then $\dfrac{a}{c} < \dfrac{b}{c}$.
6. If $a < b$ and c is negative, then $\dfrac{a}{c} > \dfrac{b}{c}$.

Solving an inequality means finding all real number solutions.   *(5-2)*

A line divides the plane into two halves called **half-planes**. The graph of a linear inequality in two variables is a half-plane. The boundary line is included in the graph if equality is included in the original statement; otherwise it is not.   *(5-3)*

The **solution of a system of linear inequalities** in two variables is the intersection of the half-planes representing each inequality.   *(5-4)*

REVIEW EXERCISE 5-5

Work through all the problems in this chapter review and check answers in the back of the book. (Answers to all problems are there, and following each answer is a number in italics indicating the section in which that type of problem is discussed.) Where weaknesses show up, review appropriate sections in the text.

A   **1.** Select the larger of the two numbers:

(A) $\dfrac{3}{11}, \dfrac{5}{18}$ (B) $\dfrac{\pi}{4}, \dfrac{19}{24}$ (C) $\sqrt{7}, \dfrac{13}{5}$

2. Graph on a real number line:
(A) $-3 < x \le 2$ (B) $-3 \le x < 2$

Solve.

3. $\dfrac{x}{-3} > -2$ **4.** $-4x \le 12$

5. $3x + 9 \le -3 - x$ **6.** $-14 \le 3x - 2 \le 7$

7. What numbers satisfy the condition "5 less than 5 times the number is less than or equal to 10"? Write an inequality and solve.

B   *Solve and graph on a real number line.*

8. $3x - 9 < 7x - 5$ **9.** $2x - (3x + 2) > 5 - 2(3 - 2x)$

10. $\dfrac{x}{2} - \dfrac{x-1}{3} \ge -1$ **11.** $-9 \le \frac{2}{3}x - 5 < 7$

Graph in a rectangular coordinate system.

12. $x + y \le 5$ **13.** $2x + 3y > 6$

14. $y \ge \dfrac{1}{2}x + 2$

15. A chemical is to be kept between 59 and 86°F (that is, $59 \le F \le 86$). What is the temperature range in Celsius degrees? (Recall that $F = \frac{9}{5}C + 32$.) Set up a double inequality and solve.

C   *Find the solution set of the system of inequalities graphically.*

16. $-1 \le x \le 3$
$0 \le y \le 2$

17. $3x + y \le 6$
$x \ge 0$
$y \ge 3$

18. $2x - y \ge -1$
$y + 3x \le 1$
$y \ge 0$

19. $x + y \le 8$
$3x - 2y \le 6$
$x \ge 1$
$1 \le y \le 5$

20. To develop a certain roll of photographic film, the temperature of the solution must be kept between 20 and 25°C (that is, $20 \le C \le 25$). Find the temperature range in Fahrenheit degrees. [Recall that $C = \frac{5}{9}(F - 32)$.] Set up a double inequality and solve.

6

POLYNOMIALS AND FACTORING

The equations we have solved and graphed thus far have been linear, involving no powers of the variables higher than one. The algebraic expressions we have used have, for the most part, been similarly restricted. To be able to deal with more complicated equations, graphs, or word problems, we will have to extend our ability to manipulate more complex algebraic expressions. In this chapter, we consider in more detail the same kinds of expressions we have worked with thus far but allowing higher powers of the variables. This leads us to define a particular kind of algebraic expression, a *polynomial*.

6-1
POLYNOMIALS—
TERMINOLOGY AND
BASIC OPERATIONS

- Terminology
- Addition and Subtraction
- Multiplication

Algebraic expressions can be classified in a variety of ways for more efficient study. We will start with the important class of expressions called polynomials.

TERMINOLOGY

A **polynomial** is an algebraic expression built up from constants and variables by adding, subtracting, or multiplying. If one or two variables are involved, then, in addition to constants, the polynomial will consist of terms of the form ax^n or $bx^m y^n$, where a and b are real-number coefficients and m and n are natural number exponents. In a polynomial a variable cannot appear in a denominator, as an exponent, or within a radical sign. Here are some examples of polynomials and nonpolynomials:

POLYNOMIALS

$$2x^2 - 5x + 8 \qquad 2x - 1 \qquad x \qquad 5 \qquad 0$$
$$x^2 - \tfrac{1}{3}xy + \sqrt{2}y^2 \qquad 2x^3 - 3x^2y - 4xy^2 + y^3$$

NONPOLYNOMIALS

$$\frac{3x - 1}{2x^2 + 3x - 5} \qquad 2^x \qquad x^3 - \frac{2\sqrt{x}}{y} + 3y^4 \qquad \frac{1}{x}$$

Note that the constants in the polynomials may occur as fractions, radicals, or exponents, but the variables never do. You should be sure you recognize why each of the nonpolynomials listed above is not a polynomial.

The polynomial form, particularly in one and two variables, is encountered with great frequency at all levels in mathematics and science. As a consequence, it is a form that receives a great deal of attention in beginning and intermediate algebra.

It is convenient to identify certain types of polynomials. The concept of degree is used for this purpose. The **degree of a term** in a polynomial is the power of the variable present in the term. If more than one variable is present as a factor, then the sum of the powers of the variables in the term is the degree of the term. The **degree of a nonzero constant** is defined to be 0. The **degree of a polynomial** is the degree of the term with the highest degree in the polynomial.

Example 1 (A) What is the degree of $3x^5$? Of $7x^2y^3$?
(B) What is the degree of $4x^7 - 3x^5 + 2x^3 - 1$?

Solution   **(A)** $3x^5$ is of degree 5; $7x^2y^3$ is of degree 5.

(B) In $4x^7 - 3x^5 + 2x^3 - 1$, the highest-degree term is the first, with degree 7; thus the degree of the polynomial is 7.

Problem 1   **(A)** What is the degree of $5x^3$? Of $2x^3y^4$?

(B) What is the degree of the polynomial $6x^3 - 2x^2 + x - 1$? Of $2x^2 - 3xy + y^2 + x - y + 1$?

Any nonzero real constant is defined to be a polynomial of degree 0. Thus 5 is a polynomial of degree 0. The number 0 is also a polynomial, but it is not assigned a degree.

We also call a one-term polynomial a **monomial**, a two-termed polynomial a **binomial**, and a three-termed polynomial a **trinomial**.

$3x^2 - 2x + 1$	$2x - 3y$	$3x^4y^2$	8
Trinomial	Binomial	Monomial	Monomial
Degree 2	Degree 1	Degree 6	Degree 0

ADDITION AND SUBTRACTION

For polynomials to be useful, we must know how to add, subtract, multiply, divide, and factor them. We have already spent some time on these operations with simpler polynomials. In this chapter we will review and extend these processes to more complex forms. We start with addition and subtraction.

Example 2   Add:

$$x^2 + 1 \qquad -x^3 + 2x - 3 \qquad \text{and} \qquad x^3 - 2x^2 + x$$

Solution   *Method 1*   Add horizontally:

$$(x^2 + 1) + (-x^3 + 2x - 3) + (x^3 - 2x^2 + x)$$

$= x^2 + 1 - x^3 + 2x - 3 + x^3 - 2x^2 + x$ Clear parentheses—be careful of signs.

$= -x^2 + 3x - 2$ Combine like terms.

Method 2   Add vertically. Line up like terms and add coefficients. This method is generally preferred when you have several polynomials to add:

$$
\begin{array}{l}
 \; x^2 + 1 \\
-x^3 + 2x - 3 \\
\underline{ x^3 - 2x^2 + x } \\
 - \; x^2 + 3x - 2
\end{array}
$$

Note the spaces for missing powers; for example, think of the first polynomial as $0 \cdot x^3 + x^2 + 0 \cdot x + 1$.

Problem 2   Add horizontally and vertically:

$$2x^3 - x^2 + 4 \qquad x^3 - 3x^2 - x + 1 \qquad \text{and} \qquad x^2 - 6$$

Example 3   Subtract $2x^2 - x + 2$ from $x^2 + 3x + 5$.

Solution   *Method 1*   Work horizontally. This method is often preferred for subtraction.

$$(x^2 + 3x + 5) - (2x^2 - x + 2)$$ Notice which polynomial goes on the right. We are subtracting $2x^2 - x + 2$ from $x^2 + 3x + 5$.

$$= x^2 + 3x + 5 - 2x^2 + x - 2$$ Clear parentheses— be careful of signs.

$$= -x^2 + 4x + 3$$ Combine like terms.

Method 2   Work vertically. Notice which polynomial goes on the bottom.

$$
\begin{array}{l}
x^2 + 3x + 5 \\
\underline{2x^2 - x + 2}
\end{array}
\quad\text{Change signs and add.}\longrightarrow
\begin{array}{l}
x^2 + 3x + 5 \\
\underline{-2x^2 + x - 2} \\
-x^2 + 4x + 3
\end{array}
$$

Extra care should be taken when working subtraction problems vertically, since sign errors here are common. This is why the horizontal method is usually preferred.

Check   Subtraction can be checked by adding the difference to the quantity subtracted to see if the result is the quantity we subtracted from:

$$(-x^2 + 4x + 3) + (2x^2 - x + 2) = -x^2 + 4x + 3 + 2x^2 - x + 2$$
$$= x^2 + 3x + 5$$

Problem 3   Subtract $3x^2 + 2x - 4$ from $2x^2 + 3x + 2$.

MULTIPLICATION

The distributive property is the important principle behind multiplying polynomials. This property leads directly to the mechanical rule:

Mechanics of Multiplying Polynomials

To multiply two polynomials, multiply each term of the first one by each term of the second one; then add like terms.

Example 4   Multiply $(x - 3)(x^2 - 2x + 3)$.

Solution   *Method 1* Horizontal arrangement:

$$(x - 3)(x^2 - 2x + 3)$$

Use distributive property from right to left.

$$= x(x^2 - 2x + 3) - 3(x^2 - 2x + 3)$$

Use distributive property from left to right.

$$= x^3 - 2x^2 + 3x - 3x^2 + 6x - 9$$

Combine like terms.

$$= x^3 - 5x^2 + 9x - 9$$

Method 2 Vertical arrangement. This method is probably preferred by most students for this type of problem:

$$
\begin{array}{r}
x^2 - 2x\; + 3 \\
x\; - 3 \\
\hline
x^3 - 2x^2 + 3x \\
-\, 3x^2 + 6x - 9 \\
\hline
x^3 - 5x^2 + 9x - 9
\end{array}
$$

Notice that we start multiplying from the left first; that is, by x. Then multiply by -3, line up like terms, and add.

Notice that the product of a first-degree polynomial and second-degree polynomial produces a third-degree polynomial. What do you think the product of two second-degree polynomials would produce? Two first-degree polynomials? [*Answer:* Fourth-degree polynomial; second-degree polynomial.]

Problem 4   Multiply $(3x^2 - 2x + 1)(2x^2 + 3x - 2)$ vertically.

ANSWERS TO   **1.** **(A)** 3, 7   **(B)** 3, 2   **2.** $3x^3 - 3x^2 - x - 1$
MATCHED PROBLEMS **3.** $-x^2 + x + 6$ **4.** $6x^4 + 5x^3 - 10x^2 + 7x - 2$

EXERCISE 6-1 A   *Add.*

1. $2x + 1$ and $5x - 3$ **2.** $4x - 3$ and $x + 4$

3. $2x + 3$, $x - 4$, and $5x + 1$ **4.** $6x - 4$, $3x + 5$, and $2x - 1$

5. $x^2 + 3x + 2$, $x + 4$, and $3x - 5$

6. $3x^2 - x + 4$, $2x - 1$, and $x - 6$

Subtract.

7. $3x + 1$ from $6x + 5$ **8.** $4x + 3$ from $5x + 8$

9. $2x - 5$ from $3x + 1$ **10.** $3x - 2$ from $5x + 3$

11. $x^2 - 2x + 3$ from $3x^2 + x + 4$

12. $x^2 + 3x - 2$ from $2x^2 + x - 4$

Multiply.

13. $(2x - 3)(x + 2)$ **14.** $(3x - 5)(2x + 1)$

15. $(2x - 1)(x^2 - 3x + 5)$ **16.** $(3y + 2)(2y^2 + 5y - 3)$

17. $(x - 3y)(x^2 - 3xy + y^2)$ **18.** $(m + 2n)(m^2 - 4mn - n^2)$

B   *Name the degree of each polynomial.*

19. $2x - 3$ **20.** $4x^2 - 2x + 3$

21. $3x^3 - x + 7$ **22.** $2x - y$

23. $x^2 - 3xy + y^2$ **24.** $x^3 - 2x^2y + xy^2 - 3y^3$

25. $2x^6 - 3x^5 + x^2 - x + 1$ **26.** $x^5 - 2x^2 + 5$

Add.

27. $4x^3 + 3x^2 + 2,\ -x^2 + 2x + 3$, and $x - 5$

28. $2x^3 + x - 1,\ x^3 + x^2 + 1$, and $x^2 + x$

29. $3x + 4y$ and $x - 5y$

30. $x^2 + xy + y^2$ and $2x^2 - xy - 2y^2$

31. $2x - 2y + z$ and $-x + y - 2z$

32. $a^2 - b^2$ and $a^2 + 2ab + b^2$

Subtract.

33. $2x^3 - x^2 + 4$ from $x^3 + 3x^2 + 2x + 1$

34. $4x^3 + x^2 - x + 2$ from $5x^3 - 2x^2 + x - 3$

35. $2a - 3b$ from $a - b$

36. $x^2 + xy - y^2$ from $x^2 - 2xy - y^2$

37. $3a - 2b + c$ from $a - b + c$

38. $2x^2 + y^2$ from $x^2 - xy - y^2$

C   *Let P, Q, R, and S be these polynomials:*

$$P = x^2 + 2x + 3$$
$$Q = -2x^2 + 3x - 4$$
$$R = -x^2 - 2x + 1$$
$$S = 2x^2 - x + 2$$

Find the polynomial indicated.

39. $(P + Q) - (R + S)$ **40.** $(P + S) - (R + Q)$

Multiply.

41. $(a + b)(a^2 - ab + b^2)$ **42.** $(a - b)(a^2 + ab + b^2)$

43. $(x + 2y)^3$ **44.** $(2m - n)^3$

45. $(x^2 - 3x + 5)(2x^2 + x - 2)$

46. $(2m^2 + 2m - 1)(3m^2 - 2m + 1)$

47. $(2x^2 - 3xy + y^2)(x^2 + 2xy - y^2)$

48. $(a^2 - 2ab + b^2)(a^2 + 2ab + b^2)$

Simplify.

49. $(3x - 1)(x + 2) - (2x - 3)^2$ **50.** $(2x + 3)(x - 5) - (3x - 1)^2$

51. $2(x - 2)^3 - (x - 2)^2 - 3(x - 2) - 4$

52. $(2x - 1)^3 - 2(2x - 1)^2 + 3(2x - 1) + 7$

6-2
SPECIAL PRODUCTS OF THE FORM $(ax + b)(cx + d)$

- Multiplying Special Binomials
- Squaring a Binomial

The multiplication of certain binomials can be done very quickly. In this section we consider two such situations: first the product of two binomials of degree one $(ax + b)(cx + d)$, and then the square of any binomial $(A + B)^2$.

MULTIPLYING SPECIAL BINOMIALS

Let us multiply $(3x + 2)$ and $(2x - 1)$, using a vertical arrangement:

$$
\begin{array}{r}
3x + 2 \\
2x - 1 \\
\hline
6x^2 + 4x \\
-3x - 2 \\
\hline
6x^2 + x - 2
\end{array}
$$

Now let us use a horizontal arrangement and try to discover a method that will enable us to carry out the multiplication mentally. We start by multiplying each term in the first binomial times each term in the second binomial:

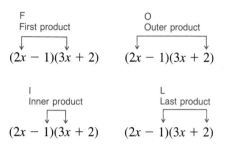

Performing these four operations on one line, we obtain:

$$
\begin{array}{ccccc}
& \text{F} & \text{O} & \text{I} & \text{L} \\
& \text{First} & \text{Outer} & \text{Inner} & \text{Last} \\
& \text{product} & \text{product} & \text{product} & \text{product} \\
& \downarrow & \downarrow & \downarrow & \downarrow \\
(2x - 1)(3x + 2) = & 6x^2 & + 4x & - 3x & - 2
\end{array}
$$

The inner and outer products are like terms and hence combine into one term. Thus,

$$(2x - 1)(3x + 2) = 6x^2 + x - 2$$

With practice we can speed up the process and combine the inner and outer products mentally. The procedure just described is called the **FOIL method**.

   This method provides a simple way to multiply two binomials mentally. It is only applicable, however, to this particular kind of product. Term-by-term multiplication must still be used in general.

   A simple three-step process for carrying out the FOIL method is illustrated in Example 5.

Example 5   Multiply by the FOIL method:

(A) $(2x - 1)(3x + 2)$
(B) $(2a - b)(a + 3b)$
(C) $(2x - 3y)(2x + 3y)$

Solution

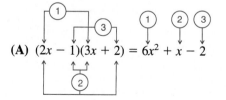

The like terms are picked up in step 2 and combined mentally.

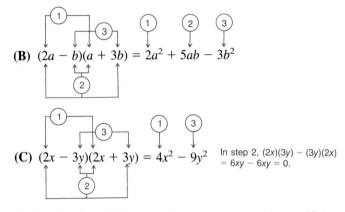

(B) $(2a - b)(a + 3b) = 2a^2 + 5ab - 3b^2$

(C) $(2x - 3y)(2x + 3y) = 4x^2 - 9y^2$

In step 2, $(2x)(3y) - (3y)(2x)$
$= 6xy - 6xy = 0.$

Notice that the middle term dropped out, since its coefficient is 0.

Problem 5 Multiply by the FOIL method:

(A) $(2x + 3)(x - 1)$ **(B)** $(a - 2b)(2a + 3b)$ **(C)** $(x - 2y)(x + 2y)$

In Section 6-4, we will consider the reverse problem: Given a second-degree polynomial, such as $2x^2 - 5x - 3$ or $3m^2 - 7mn + 2n^2$, find first-degree factors with integer coefficients that will produce these second-degree polynomials as products. To be able to factor second-degree polynomial forms with any degree of efficiency, it is important that you know how to mentally multiply first-degree factors of the types illustrated in this section quickly and accurately.

SQUARING A BINOMIAL

Since from the FOIL method

$$(A + B)^2 = (A + B)(A + B) = A^2 + 2AB + B^2$$

we can formulate a simple mechanical rule for squaring a binomial directly from $(A + B)^2$ without having to write $(A + B)(A + B)$ first.

Step 1   Square the first term.
Step 2   Take twice the product of the first and second terms.
Step 3   Square the second term.

Schematically:

Square of first term   Square of second term

$(A + B)^2 = A^2 + 2AB + B^2$ $(A - B)^2 = A^2 - 2AB + B^2$

Twice the product of
first and second terms

$2A(-B)^2 = -2AB$

$A^2 + 2AB + B^2$ and $A^2 - 2AB + B^2$ are **perfect square** trinomials.

Example 6 Square each binomial, using the mechanical rule:

      (A) $(2x + 3)^2$ **(B)** $(3x - 2)^2$ **(C)** $(3x - 2y)^2$

Solution   **(A)** $(2x + 3)^2 \;\vert = (2x)^2 + 2(2x)(3) + 3^2 \vert = 4x^2 + 12x + 9$

        (B) $(3x - 2)^2 \;\vert = (3x)^2 + 2(3x)(-2) + (-2)^2 \vert = 9x^2 - 12x + 4$

        (C) $(3x - 2y)^2 \;\vert = (3x)^2 + 2(3x)(-2y) + (-2y)^2 \vert = 9x^2 - 12xy + 4y^2$

Problem 6 Square each binomial, using the mechanical rule:

      (A) $(2x + 1)^2$ **(B)** $(3x - 4)^2$ **(C)** $(5x - 2y)^2$

ANSWERS TO
MATCHED PROBLEMS

  5. **(A)** $2x^2 + x - 3$ **(B)** $2a^2 - ab - 6b^2$ **(C)** $x^2 - 4y^2$
  6. **(A)** $4x^2 + 4x + 1$ **(B)** $9x^2 - 24x + 16$
        (C) $25x^2 - 20xy + 4y^2$

EXERCISE 6-2   *In Problems 1–46, multiply mentally.*

A   **1.** $(x + 1)(x + 2)$ **2.** $(y + 3)(y + 1)$

        3. $(y + 3)(y + 4)$ **4.** $(x + 3)(x + 2)$

        5. $(x - 5)(x - 4)$ **6.** $(m - 2)(m - 3)$

        7. $(n - 4)(n - 3)$ **8.** $(u - 5)(u - 3)$

        9. $(s + 7)(s - 2)$ **10.** $(t - 6)(t + 4)$

      11. $(m - 12)(m + 5)$ **12.** $(a + 8)(a - 4)$

      13. $(u - 3)(u + 3)$ **14.** $(t + 4)(t - 4)$

      15. $(x + 8)(x - 8)$ **16.** $(m - 7)(m + 7)$

      17. $(y + 7)(y + 9)$ **18.** $(x + 8)(x + 11)$

      19. $(c - 9)(c - 6)$ **20.** $(u - 8)(u - 7)$

      21. $(x - 12)(x + 4)$ **22.** $(y - 11)(y + 7)$

      23. $(a + b)(a - b)$ **24.** $(m - n)(m + n)$

      25. $(x + y)(x + 3y)$ **26.** $(m + 2n)(m + n)$

B **27.** $(x + 2)(3x + 1)$ **28.** $(x + 3)(2x + 3)$

      29. $(4t - 3)(t - 2)$ **30.** $(2x - 1)(x - 4)$

31. $(3y + 7)(y - 3)$　　　　　　**32.** $(t + 4)(2t - 3)$

33. $(2x - 3y)(x + 2y)$　　　　**34.** $(3x + 2y)(x - 3y)$

35. $(2x - 1)(3x + 2)$　　　　　**36.** $(3y - 2)(3y - 1)$

37. $(3y + 2)(3y - 2)$　　　　　**38.** $(2m - 7)(2m + 7)$

39. $(5s - 1)(s + 7)$　　　　　　**40.** $(a - 6)(5a + 6)$

41. $(3m + 7n)(2m - 5n)$　　　**42.** $(6x - 4y)(5x + 3y)$

43. $(4n - 7)(3n + 2)$　　　　　**44.** $(5x - 6)(2x + 7)$

45. $(2x - 3y)(3x - 2y)$　　　　**46.** $(2s - 3t)(3s - t)$

Square each binomial, using the mechanical rule.

47. $(x + 3)^2$　　　　**48.** $(x - 4)^2$　　　　**49.** $(2x - 3)^2$

50. $(3x + 2)^2$　　　**51.** $(2x - 5y)^2$　　**52.** $(3x + 4y)^2$

53. $(4a + 3b)^2$　　**54.** $(5m - 3n)^2$

C *Multiply.*

55. $(x - 1)(x^2 + 2x - 1)$　　　　**56.** $(x + 2)(x^2 - 3x + 2)$

57. $(2x - 3)(3x^2 - 2x + 4)$　　**58.** $(3x + 2)(2x^2 - 3x - 2)$

59. $(x^2 - 3x + 2)(x^2 + x - 3)$　**60.** $(x^2 + 2x - 3)(x^2 - 3x - 2)$

6-3

FACTORING OUT COMMON FACTORS

- Factoring Out Common Monomial Factors
- Factoring Out Common Binomial Factors
- Factoring by Grouping

You have already had some experience in Chapter 1 in factoring out common factors. The distributive property of real numbers in the form

$$ab + ac = a(b + c)$$

Sum of　　　Product of
two terms　　two factors

is the important property behind the process. In rewriting $ab + ac$ as $a(b + c)$, we have converted a sum of two terms to a product with two factors, a and $(b + c)$, by factoring out the common factor a. The process of rewriting polynomials as products is called **factoring**. In this section, we begin to look at factoring polynomials by considering the most direct application of the distributive law, factoring out common factors. Factoring is further developed in the next three sections.

FACTORING OUT COMMON MONOMIAL FACTORS

We begin our discussion of factoring by factoring out common monomial factors.

Example 7   Factor out factors common to all terms:

(A) $6x^2 + 15x$
(B) $2u^3v - 6u^2v^2 + 8uv^3$

Solution   (A) $6x^2 + 15x \boxed{= 3x \cdot 2x + 3x \cdot 5} = 3x(2x + 5)$

(B) $2u^3v - 6u^2v^2 + 8uv^3 \boxed{= 2uv \cdot u^2 - 2uv \cdot 3uv + 2uv \cdot 4v^2}$

$$= 2uv(u^2 - 3uv + 4v^2)$$

Problem 7   Factor out factors common to all terms:

(A) $12y^2 - 28y$ (B) $6m^4 - 15m^3n + 9m^2n^2$

FACTORING OUT COMMON BINOMIAL FACTORS

We also can factor out common factors that are not monomials. Look closely at the following four examples and try to see what they all have in common:

$$2xy + 3y = y(2x + 3)$$
$$2xA + 3A = A(2x + 3)$$
$$2x(x - 4) + 3(x - 4) = (x - 4)(2x + 3)$$
$$2x(3x + 1) + 3(3x + 1) = (3x + 1)(2x + 3)$$

Because of the commutative property, a common factor may be taken out on either the left or the right.

The factoring involved in each example is essentially the same. The only difference is the nature of the common factors being taken out. In the first two examples common monomial factors are taken out. In the last two examples common binomial factors are taken out. In the last two examples think of $(x - 4)$ and $(3x + 1)$ as single numbers, just as A represents a single number in the second example.

Example 8   Remove factors common to all terms:

(A) $5x(x - 1) - (x - 1)$
(B) $3x(2x - y) - 2y(2x - y)$

Solution   (A) $5x(x - 1) - (x - 1) \boxed{= 5x(x - 1) - 1(x - 1)} = (x - 1)(5x - 1)$

(B) $3x(2x - y) - 2y(2x - y) = (2x - \quad (3x - 2y)$

Problem 8 Remove factors common to all terms:

(A) $3m(m + 2) - (m + 2)$ **(B)** $2u(u + 3v) - 3v(u + 3v)$

FACTORING BY GROUPING

Some polynomials can be factored by grouping terms in such a way that we obtain results that look like Example 8. We can then complete the factoring following the procedures used there. This process will prove useful in Section 6-5, where an efficient method is developed for factoring a second-degree polynomial into the product of two first-degree polynomials.

Example 9 Factor by grouping:

(A) $2x^2 - 8x + 3x - 12$ **(B)** $5x^2 - 5x - x + 1$
(C) $6x^2 - 3xy - 4xy + 2y^2$

Solution **(A)** $2x^2 - 8x + 3x - 12$ Group the first two and last two terms.

$\qquad = (2x^2 - 8x) + (3x - 12)$ Remove common factors from each group.

$\qquad = 2x(x - 4) + 3(x - 4)$ The common factor $(x - 4)$ can be taken out.

$\qquad = (x - 4)(2x + 3)$ The factoring is complete.

(B) $5x^2 - 5x - x + 1$ Group the first two and last two terms. Notice what happens to the signs in the second grouping. (When we clear parentheses we must get back to where we started.)

$\qquad = (5x^2 - 5x) - (x - 1)$ Remove common factors from each group.

$\qquad = 5x(x - 1) - 1(x - 1)$ The common factor $(x - 1)$ can be taken out of both terms.

$\qquad = (x - 1)(5x - 1)$ The factoring is complete.

(C) $6x^2 - 3xy - 4xy + 2y^2$ Group the first two and last two terms.

$\qquad = (6x^2 - 3xy) - (4xy - 2y^2)$ Signs change inside second parentheses.

$\qquad = 3x(2x - y) - 2y(2x - y)$ The common factor $(2x - y)$ can be taken out.

$\qquad = (2x - y)(3x - 2y)$ The factoring is complete.

9. **(A)** $(3x + 1)(2x + 3)$ **(B)** $(m + 2)(3m - 1)$

   (C) $(u + 3v)(2u - 3v)$

10. $(a + b)(c + d)$

EXERCISE 6-3

In Problems 1–30, write the expression in factored form by removing factors common to all terms.

A   **1.** $2xA + 3A$ **2.** $xM - 4M$ **3.** $10x^2 + 15x$

    4. $9y^2 - 6y$ **5.** $14u^2 - 6u$ **6.** $20m^2 + 12m$

    7. $6u^2 - 10uv$ **8.** $14x^2 - 21xy$

    9. $10m^2n - 15mn^2$ **10.** $9u^2v + 6uv^2$

   11. $2x^3y - 6x^2y^2$ **12.** $6x^2y^2 - 3xy^3$

   13. $3x(x + 2) + 5(x + 2)$ **14.** $4y(y + 3) + 7(y + 3)$

   15. $3m(m - 4) - 2(m - 4)$ **16.** $x(x - 1) - 4(x - 1)$

   17. $x(x + y) - y(x + y)$ **18.** $m(m - n) + n(m - n)$

B **19.** $6x^4 - 9x^3 + 3x^2$ **20.** $6m^4 - 8m^3 - 2m^2$

   21. $8x^3y - 6x^2y^2 + 4xy^3$ **22.** $10u^3v + 20u^2v^2 - 15uv^3$

   23. $8x^4 - 12x^3y + 4x^2y^2$ **24.** $9m^4 - 6m^3n - 6m^2n^2$

   25. $3x(2x + 3) - 5(2x + 3)$ **26.** $2u(3u - 8) - 3(3u - 8)$

   27. $x(x + 1) - (x + 1)$ **28.** $3u(u - 1) - (u - 1)$

   29. $4x(2x - 3) - (2x - 3)$ **30.** $3y(4y - 5) - (4y - 5)$

Replace question marks with algebraic expressions that will make both sides equal.

   31. $3x^2 - 3x + 2x - 2 = (3x^2 - 3x) + (?)$

   32. $2x^2 + 4x + 3x + 6 = (2x^2 + 4x) + (?)$

   33. $3x^2 - 12x - 2x + 8 = (3x^2 - 12x) - (?)$

   34. $2y^2 - 10y - 3y + 15 = (2y^2 - 10y) - (?)$

   35. $8u^2 + 4u - 2u - 1 = (8u^2 + 4u) - (?)$

   36. $6x^2 + 10x - 3x - 5 = (6x^2 + 10x) - (?)$

Factor out common factors from each group, then complete the factoring if possible.

   37. $(3x^2 - 3x) + (2x - 2)$ **38.** $(2x^2 + 4x) + (3x + 6)$

Problem 9   Factor by grouping:

(A) $6x^2 + 2x + 9x + 3$ (B) $3m^2 + 6m - m - 2$
(C) $2u^2 + 6uv - 3uv - 9v^2$

In Example 9, the polynomials were arranged in such a way that grouping the first two terms and the last two terms led to common factors. The process is not always this neat, however, and you will sometimes have to rearrange terms in order to group them profitably for factoring.

Example 10   Factor $y^2 + xz + xy + yz$ by grouping.

Solution $y^2 + xz + xy + yz$ If we proceed as in Example 9, no common factor can be factored out to complete the factoring.

$= (y^2 + xz) + (xy + yz)$

$= (y^2 + xz) + y(x + z)$

$y^2 + xz + xy + yz$ Rearrange the terms and proceed again as in Example 9.

$= y^2 + xy + xz + yz$

$= y(y + x) + (x + y)z$

$= y(x + y) + z(x + y)$

$= (y + z)(x + y)$

Problem 10   Factor $ac + bd + bc + ad$ by grouping.

It is important to note that many polynomials of the forms considered in Examples 9 and 10 do not have polynomial factors with integer coefficients (excluding 1). Consider the following two polynomials:

$2x^2 + 2x + x - 4$ $y^2 - xz + xy + yz$

No matter how we group the terms, we will not find a factoring of either polynomial using integer coefficients. Try factoring these polynomials by grouping to see what happens.

ANSWERS TO   **7.** (A) $4y(3y - 7)$ (B) $3m^2(2m^2 - 5mn + 3n^2)$
MATCHED PROBLEMS   **8.** (A) $(m + 2)(3m - 1)$ (B) $(u + 3v)(2u - 3v)$

39. $(3x^2 - 12x) - (2x - 8)$ **40.** $(2y^2 - 10y) - (3y - 15)$

41. $(8u^2 + 4u) - (2u + 1)$ **42.** $(6x^2 + 10x) - (3x + 5)$

Factor as the product of two first-degree factors using grouping. (These problems are related to Problems 37–42.)

43. $3x^2 - 3x + 2x - 2$ **44.** $2x^2 + 4x + 3x + 6$

45. $3x^2 - 12x - 2x + 8$ **46.** $2y^2 - 10y - 3y + 15$

47. $8u^2 + 4u - 2u - 1$ **48.** $6x^2 + 10x - 3x - 5$

Factor as the product of two first-degree factors using grouping.

49. $2m^2 - 8m + 5m - 20$ **50.** $5x^2 - 10x + 2x - 4$

51. $6x^2 - 9x - 4x + 6$ **52.** $12x^2 + 8x - 9x - 6$

C **53.** $3u^2 - 12u - u + 4$ **54.** $6m^2 + 4m - 3m - 2$

55. $6u^2 + 3uv - 4uv - 2v^2$ **56.** $2x^2 - 4xy - xy + 2y^2$

57. $6x^2 + 3xy - 10xy - 5y^2$ **58.** $4u^2 - 16uv - 3uv + 12v^2$

59. $3u^2 + 4 - 12u - u$ **60.** $6m^2 - 2 + 4m - 3m$

61. $6u^2 - 2v^2 + 3uv - 4uv$ **62.** $2x^2 + 2y^2 - 4xy - xy$

63. $6x^2 - 5y^2 + 3xy - 10xy$ **64.** $4u^2 + 12v^2 - 3uv - 16uv$

65. $3a^2 + 3b^2 + 9ab + ab$ **66.** $a^2 + b^2 + ab + ab$

67. $uw + vx - vw - ux$ **68.** $2ab + 12 + 6b + 4a$

6-4
FACTORING SECOND-DEGREE POLYNOMIALS

- Recognizing Perfect Squares
- Factoring by Trial and Error

We now turn our attention to factoring second-degree polynomials such as

$$2x^2 - 5x - 3 \quad \text{or} \quad 2x^2 + 3xy - 2y^2 \quad \text{or} \quad x^2 + 14x + 49$$

into the product of two first-degree polynomials with integer coefficients. Using the techniques of Section 6-2, we can see that

$$(x - 3)(x + 2) = x^2 - x - 6 \qquad (x + 3)(x + 3) = x^2 + 6x + 9$$

But can you reverse the process? Can you, for example, find integers a, b, c, and d so that

$$2x^2 - 5x - 3 = (ax + b)(cx + d)$$

and can you recognize that $x^2 + 14x + 49$ is a perfect square and find integers a and b such that

$$x^2 + 14x + 49 = (ax + b)^2$$

Factoring second-degree polynomials with integer coefficients as the product of two first-degree polynomials with integer coefficients is not as easy as multiplying first-degree polynomials. In this section we will reverse the multiplication techniques introduced in Section 6-2. We first consider perfect squares. Then for more general second-degree polynomials we develop a method of attack that is relatively easy to understand, but not always easy to apply. In the next section we will develop an approach that builds on the method of factoring by grouping discussed in the preceding section. The second approach is a little more difficult to understand, but once the method is understood, it is fairly easy to apply.

RECOGNIZING PERFECT SQUARES

The formula $(A + B)^2 = A^2 + 2AB + B^2$ applied to $(x + b)^2$ yields

$$(x + b)^2 = x^2 + 2bx + b^2$$

Note that the last term b^2 is the square of one-half the coefficient of x. Whenever this is the case, we can factor the trinomial as a perfect square.

Example 11   Which of the following trinomials are perfect squares? Factor those that are.

(A) $x^2 + 4x + 2$ **(B)** $x^2 + 4x + 4$
(C) $x^2 - 6x + 9$ **(D)** $x^2 + 9x + 6$

Solution   **(A)** The last term 2 is not the square of one-half the coefficient of x. The coefficient of x is 4; the square of $\frac{1}{2}$ of 4 is $2^2 = 4$. The polynomial is not a perfect square.

(B) The last term 4 is the square of one-half the coefficient of x, that is, 4 is 2^2. Thus, the polynomial is a perfect square, $(x + b)^2$ with $b = 2$:

$$x^2 + 4x + 4 = (x + 2)^2$$

(C) $x^2 - 6x + 9 = (x - 3)^2$
(D) This is not a perfect square.

Problem 11   Which of the following trinomials are perfect squares? Factor those that are.

(A) $x^2 + 14x + 49$ **(B)** $x^2 - 5x + 25$

(C) $x^2 - 8x + 16$ **(D)** $x^2 + 16x + 16$

The polynomial $4x^2 - 12x + 9$ is also a perfect square, since

$$(2x - 3)^2 = 4x^2 - 12x + 9$$

but it is not so easily recognizable because of the coefficient of x^2. The more general factoring method considered next will, however, handle this sort of problem.

FACTORING BY TRIAL AND ERROR

Let us start with a very simple polynomial whose factors you may be able to guess:

$$x^2 + 6x + 8$$

Our problem is to find two first-degree factors with integer coefficients, if they exist. To start we write

$$x^2 + 6x + 8 = (x \quad)(x \quad)$$

The coefficients of x on the right are both 1, since the coefficient of x^2 on the left is 1.† Since the constant terms in each factor must be factors of $+8$, they are either both positive or both negative. They both must be positive, since the middle term on the left is positive. (If the middle term were negative, they would both have to be negative.) Think this through. We always place within the parentheses what we can easily determine first. In this case:

The coefficients of x are both 1.

The signs of both constant terms are $+$.

Thus, we are able to write

_____ Must be factors of 8

$$x^2 + 6x + 8 = (x + \quad)(x + \quad)$$

Now, what are the constant terms? Since they are positive-integer factors of 8, we list the possibilities:

$$\frac{8}{\begin{matrix} 1 \cdot 8 \\ 2 \cdot 4 \end{matrix}\bigg\}}$$ Possible factors of 8

† We could use -1 for both coefficients, but we make the simpler choice of 1.

If we try 1 and 8 (mentally), we obtain

$$(x + 1)(x + 8) = x^2 + 9x + 8$$

which gives us the first and last terms in $x^2 + 6x + 8$, but not the middle term. We now try 2 and 4 (mentally) to obtain

$$(x + 2)(x + 4) = x^2 + 6x + 8$$

We have thus found factors of $x^2 + 6x + 8$ and can write

$$x^2 + 6x + 8 = (x + 2)(x + 4)$$

Example 12   Factor $x^2 - 8x + 12$, using integer coefficients.

Solution

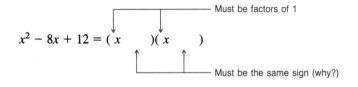

Must be factors of 1

$$x^2 - 8x + 12 = (\,x \qquad)(\,x \qquad)$$

Must be the same sign (why?)

What do we know for certain?

The coefficients of x (on the right) are both 1.

The signs of both constant terms are $-$, since their product is positive (12) and their sum is negative (-8).

Thus,

Must be factors of 12

$$x^2 - 8x + 12 = (x - \quad)(x - \quad)$$

$$\frac{12}{\begin{array}{l} 3 \cdot 4 \\ 2 \cdot 6 \\ 1 \cdot 12 \end{array}} \quad \text{Factors of 12}$$

Testing each pair of factors mentally, we find that the second choice not only gives us the first and last terms in $x^2 - 8x + 12$ but also gives us the middle term. Thus,

$$x^2 - 8x + 12 = (x - 2)(x - 6) \qquad \text{or} \qquad (x - 6)(x - 2)$$

Note: The order of the factors doesn't matter, since (because of the commutative property) $(x - 2)(x - 6) = (x - 6)(x - 2)$.

Problem 12 Factor $x^2 - 11x + 24$, using integer coefficients.

Let us try another polynomial. Find first-degree factors with integer coefficients for

$$2x^2 - 7x + 6$$

Again, we write

```
                              ┌──────────── Must be factors of 2
                              │       │
2x² − 7x + 6 = ( x      )( x      )
```

leaving space for the coefficients of x and the constant terms, and then insert what we know for certain:

The coefficient of one x is 2 and the other is 1.
The signs of both constant terms are $-$. (Why?)

Thus,

```
                          ┌──────────── Must be factors of 6
                          │        │
2x² − 7x + 6 = (2x −    )(x −    )
```

The constant terms both must be factors of 6. The possibilities are

6
$1 \cdot 6$
$6 \cdot 1$
$2 \cdot 3$
$3 \cdot 2$

All pairs result in the first and last terms of $2x^2 - 7x + 6$, but will any give the middle term, $-7x$?

Testing each pair (this is why you need to do binomial multiplication mentally), we find that the last pair gives the middle term. Thus,

$$2x^2 - 7x + 6 = (2x - 3)(x - 2)$$

Before you conclude that all second-degree polynomials with integer coefficients have first-degree factors with integer coefficients, consider the following simple polynomial:

$$x^2 + x + 2$$

Proceeding as above, we write

Must be factors of 2

$$x^2 + x + 2 = (x + \quad)(x + \quad)$$

$$\dfrac{2}{\left.\begin{array}{l} 1 \cdot 2 \\ 2 \cdot 1 \end{array}\right\}} \quad \text{Factors of 2}$$

and find that neither combination produces the middle term x. Hence, we conclude that

$$x^2 + x + 2$$

has no first-degree factors with integer coefficients, and we say the polynomial is not factorable using integer coefficients.

Factor each polynomial, if possible, using integer coefficients:

(A) $2x^2 + 3xy - 2y^2$ **(B)** $x^2 - 3x + 4$ **(C)** $6x^2 + 5xy - 4y^2$

(A) $2x^2 + 3xy - 2y^2$

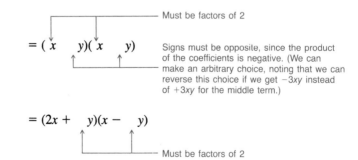

Must be factors of 2

$$= (x \quad y)(x \quad y)$$

Signs must be opposite, since the product of the coefficients is negative. (We can make an arbitrary choice, noting that we can reverse this choice if we get $-3xy$ instead of $+3xy$ for the middle term.)

$$= (2x + \quad y)(x - \quad y)$$

Must be factors of 2

Now what are the factors of 2 (the coefficient of y^2)?

$$\dfrac{2}{\begin{array}{l} 1 \cdot 2 \\ 2 \cdot 1 \end{array}}$$

The first choice gives us $-3xy$ for the middle term—close, but not quite—so we reverse our choice of signs to obtain

$$2x^2 + 3xy - 2y^2 = (2x - y)(x + 2y)$$

(B) $x^2 - 3x + 4 = (x -\quad)(x -\quad)$

$$\frac{4}{}$$
$2 \cdot 2$
$1 \cdot 4$
$4 \cdot 1$

No choice produces the middle term; hence,

$$x^2 - 3x + 4$$

is not factorable using integer coefficients.

```
                                    ┌──────────────── Must be factors of 6
                                    ↓        ↓
(C)  6x² + 5xy - 4y² = (   x +    y)(   x -    y)
                          ↑              ↑
                          └──────────────┴──── Must be factors of 4
```

The signs must be opposite in the factors, since the third term is negative. (We can reverse our choice of signs later, if necessary.)
We now write all factors of 6 and of 4:

6	4
$2 \cdot 3$	$2 \cdot 2$
$3 \cdot 2$	$1 \cdot 4$
$1 \cdot 6$	$4 \cdot 1$
$6 \cdot 1$	

and try each choice on the left with each on the right—a total of 24 combinations (if we count reversing the signs) that give us the first and last terms in $6x^2 + 5xy - 4y^2$. The question is, does any combination also give us the middle term, $5xy$? After trial and error and, perhaps, some educated guessing among the choices, we find that $3 \cdot 2$ matched with $4 \cdot 1$ gives us the middle term. Thus,

$$6x^2 + 5xy - 4y^2 = (3x + 4y)(2x - y)$$

If none of the 24 combinations (including reversing our sign choice) produced the middle term, then we would conclude that the polynomial is not factorable using integer coefficients.

Problem 13 Factor each polynomial, if possible, using integer coefficients:

(A) $x^2 - 8x + 12$ **(B)** $x^2 + 2x + 5$
(C) $2x^2 + 7xy - 4y^2$ **(D)** $4x^2 - 15xy - 4y^2$

It is about here that many students begin to lose interest in factoring, particularly with problems like that found in Example 13(C). It is quickly observed that as the integers a and c in $ax^2 + bx + c$ get larger and larger with more and more factors, the number of combinations that need to be checked increases very rapidly. And it is quite possible in most practical situations that none of the combinations will work. It is important, however, that you understand the approach presented above, since it is effective for most of the simpler factoring problems you will encounter. In the next section we will present a systematic approach to the problem of factoring that will substantially reduce the amount of trial and error and even tell you whether the polynomial can be factored before you proceed too far.

In conclusion, we point out that if a, b, and c are selected at random out of the integers, the probability that

$$ax^2 + bx + c$$

is not factorable using integer coefficients is much greater than the probability that it is. But even being able to factor some second-degree polynomials leads to marked simplification of algebraic expressions and an easy way to solve certain second-degree equations, as we will see later.

ANSWERS TO
MATCHED PROBLEMS

11.   **(A)** $(x + 7)(x + 7) = (x + 7)^2$ **(B)**   Not a perfect square
         (C) $(x - 4)(x - 4) = (x - 4)^2$ **(D)**   Not a perfect square
12. $(x - 3)(x - 8)$
13.   **(A)** $(x - 2)(x - 6)$
         (B)   Not factorable using integer coefficients
         (C) $(2x - y)(x + 4y)$ **(D)** $(4x + y)(x - 4y)$

EXERCISE 6-4   *Factor in the integers, if possible. If not factorable, say so.*

A   **1.** $x^2 + 5x + 4$ **2.** $x^2 + 4x + 3$ **3.** $x^2 + 5x + 6$

4. $x^2 + 7x + 10$ **5.** $x^2 - 4x + 3$ **6.** $x^2 - 5x + 4$

7. $x^2 - 7x + 10$ **8.** $x^2 - 5x + 6$ **9.** $y^2 + 3y + 3$

10. $y^2 + 2y + 2$ **11.** $y^2 - 2y + 6$ **12.** $x^2 - 3x + 5$

13. $x^2 + 8xy + 15y^2$ **14.** $x^2 + 9xy + 20y^2$ **15.** $x^2 - 8x + 16$

16. $x^2 - 8x - 16$ **17.** $x^2 - 10x - 25$ **18.** $x^2 - 10x + 25$

19. $x^2 - 10xy + 21y^2$ **20.** $x^2 - 10xy + 16y^2$ **21.** $u^2 + 4uv + v^2$

22. $u^2 + 5uv + 3v^2$ **23.** $3x^2 + 7x + 2$ **24.** $2x^2 + 7x + 3$

25. $3x^2 - 7x + 4$ **26.** $2x^2 - 7x + 6$

B   **27.** $x^2 + 2x - 1$ **28.** $x^2 - 2x + 1$ **29.** $x^2 + 2x + 1$

30. $x^2 - 2x - 1$ **31.** $3x^2 - 14x + 8$ **32.** $2y^2 - 13y + 15$

33. $3x^2 - 11xy + 6y^2$ **34.** $2x^2 - 7xy + 6y^2$ **35.** $n^2 - 2n - 8$

36. $n^2 + 2n - 8$ **37.** $x^2 - 4x - 6$ **38.** $x^2 - 3x - 8$

39. $3x^2 - x - 2$ **40.** $6m^2 + m - 2$ **41.** $x^2 + 4xy - 12y^2$

42. $2x^2 - 3xy - 2y^2$ **43.** $3u^2 - 11u - 4$ **44.** $8u^2 + 2u - 1$

45. $6x^2 + 7x - 5$ **46.** $2m^2 - 3m - 20$ **47.** $3s^2 - 5s - 2$

48. $2s^2 + 5s - 3$ **49.** $3x^2 + 2xy - 3y^2$ **50.** $2x^2 - 3xy - 4y^2$

51. $5x^2 - 8x - 4$ **52.** $12x^2 + 16x - 3$ **53.** $6u^2 - uv - 2v^2$

54. $6x^2 - 7xy - 5y^2$ **55.** $8x^2 + 6x - 9$ **56.** $6x^2 - 13x + 6$

57. $3u^2 + 7uv - 6v^2$ **58.** $4m^2 + 10mn - 6n^2$

59. $4u^2 - 19uv + 12v^2$ **60.** $12x^2 - xy - 6y^2$

C   **61.** $12x^2 - 40xy - 7y^2$ **62.** $15x^2 + 17xy - 4y^2$

63. $12x^2 + 19xy - 10y^2$ **64.** $24x^2 - 31xy - 15y^2$

6-5

ac TEST AND FACTORING SECOND-DEGREE POLYNOMIALS

We continue our discussion of factoring second-degree polynomials of the type

$$ax^2 + bx + c$$
$$ax^2 + bxy + cy^2 \tag{1}$$

with integer coefficients into the product of two first-degree factors with integer coefficients. In the last section we found that the number of cases that had to be tested tended to increase very rapidly as the coefficients a and c increased in size. And then, in realistic situations, it turns out that it is quite unlikely that any of the combinations tested will work. It would be useful to know ahead of time if the polynomials shown above are, in fact, factorable before we start looking for the factors. We now provide a test, called the *ac test for factorability*, that not only tells us if these polynomials can be factored using integer coefficients but, in addition, leads to a direct way of factoring those that are factorable.

> If in polynomials of type (1) the product ac has two integer factors p and q whose sum is the coefficient b of the middle term; that is, if integers p and q exist so that
>
> $$pq = ac \quad \text{and} \quad p + q = b \tag{2}$$
>
> then the polynomials have first-degree factors with integer coefficients. If no integers p and q exist that satisfy (2), then the polynomials will not have first-degree factors with integer coefficients.

Once we find integers p and q in the *ac* test, if they exist, our work is almost finished. We can write polynomials of type (1), splitting the middle term, in the form

$$
\begin{aligned}
&ax^2 + px + qx + c\\
&ax^2 + pxy + qxy + cy^2
\end{aligned} \tag{3}
$$

and the factoring can be completed in a couple of steps using factoring by grouping discussed at the end of Section 6-3.

We now make the discussion concrete through several detailed examples.

Example 14   Factor, if possible, using integer coefficients:

    (A) $2x^2 + 11x - 6$ **(B)** $4x^2 - 7x + 4$ **(C)** $6x^2 + 5xy - 4y^2$

Solution   **(A)** $2x^2 + 11x - 6$

    Step 1 Test for factorability, using the *ac* test:

$$
\left.
\begin{aligned}
&ax^2 + bx + c\\
&2x^2 + 11x - 6
\end{aligned}
\right\}
\quad
\begin{aligned}
a &= 2\\
b &= 11\\
c &= -6
\end{aligned}
$$

    Multiply a and c to obtain

                        — Don't forget the negative sign.

$$ac = (2)(-6) = -12$$

Now try to find two integer factors of -12 with a sum of $b = 11$. We write (or think) all two-integer factors of -12:

$$\frac{pq}{}$$

$(1)(-12)$
$(-1)(12)$
$(2)(-6)$
$(-2)(6)$
$(3)(-4)$
$(-3)(4)$

Each pair produces -12 as a product, but does any pair add up to 11, the coefficient of the middle term in $2x^2 + 11x - 6$? We see that the second pair works. That is,

$$\begin{array}{ccc} p & q & ac \\ (-1)(12) = -12 \end{array} \quad \text{and} \quad \begin{array}{ccc} p & q & b \\ (-1) + (12) = 11 \end{array}$$

We now conclude, because of the *ac* test, that $2x^2 + 11x - 6$ can be factored using integer coefficients.

Step 2   Since the *ac* test is satisfied, we can factor the polynomial by grouping. Split the middle term in $2x^2 + 11x - 6$, using $p = -1$ and $q = 12$ found in step 1. This is possible since $p + q = (-1) + (12) = 11 = b$.

Use p and q found in step 1.

$$\begin{array}{ccc} b & & p \quad q \\ 2x^2 + 11x - 6 = 2x^2 - 1x + 12x - 6 \end{array}$$

We can now complete the factoring by grouping. (This will always work if the *ac* test is satisfied. Moreover, it doesn't matter if we reverse the values for p and q.)

$2x^2 - x + 12x - 6$ Group the first two and last two terms.

$= (2x^2 - x) + (12x - 6)$ Factor out common factors.

$= x(2x - 1) + 6(2x - 1)$ Factor out the common factor $(2x - 1)$.

$= (2x - 1)(x + 6)$ The factoring is complete.

Thus,

$$2x^2 + 11x - 6 = (2x - 1)(x + 6)$$

This process can be reduced to a few key operational steps when all the commentary is eliminated and some of the steps are done mentally. The only trial and error occurs in step 1, and with a little practice that step often can be done mentally and will go fairly fast.

(B) $4x^2 - 7x + 4$

Compute ac: $ac = (4)(4) = 16$

Write (or think) all two-integer factors of 16, and try to find a pair whose sum is -7, the coefficient of the middle term:

$$\underline{pq}$$

(4)(4)
$(-4)(-4)$
(2)(8)
$(-2)(-8)$
(1)(16)
$(-1)(-16)$

None of these adds up to $-7 = b$; thus, according to the ac test,

$$4x^2 - 7x + 4$$

is not factorable using integer coefficients.

(C) $6x^2 + 5xy - 4y^2$

Don't forget the negative sign.

Compute ac: $ac = (6)(-4) = -24$

Does -24 have two integer factors whose sum is $5 = b$? A little trial and error (either mentally or by listing) gives us

| p | q | ac | | p | q | b |

$$(8)(-3) = -24 \quad \text{and} \quad 8 + (-3) = 5$$

Now we split the middle term $5xy$ into $8xy - 3xy$ (using the p and q just found) and write

$$6x^2 + \overset{b}{5xy} - 4y^2 = 6x^2 + \overset{p}{8xy} - \overset{q}{3xy} - 4y^2$$

We then complete the factoring by grouping:

$$6x^2 + 8xy - 3xy - 4y^2 = (6x^2 + 8xy) - (3xy + 4y^2)$$
$$= 2x(3x + 4y) - y(3x + 4y)$$
$$= (3x + 4y)(2x - y)$$

Thus,

$$6x^2 + 5xy - 4y^2 = (3x + 4y)(2x - y)$$

Problem 14   Factor, if possible, using integer coefficients:

(A) $4x^2 + 4x - 3$ **(B)** $6x^2 - 3x - 4$ **(C)** $6x^2 - 25xy + 4y^2$

Which Factoring Method?   When do we use the *ac* test and when do we use the trial-and-error method described in the preceding section? Generally, if *a* in $ax^2 + bx + c$ is larger than 1, then the *ac* test will prove effective; otherwise, use the trial-and-error method.

ANSWERS TO
MATCHED PROBLEM
14.   **(A)** $(2x - 1)(2x + 3)$ **(B)**   Not factorable
          (C) $(6x - y)(x - 4y)$

EXERCISE 6-5   *In Problems 1–34, factor, if possible, using integer coefficients. Use the ac test and proceed as in Example 14.*

A   **1.** $3x^2 - 7x + 4$ **2.** $2x^2 - 7x + 6$ **3.** $x^2 + 4x - 6$

   4. $x^2 - 3x - 8$ **5.** $2x^2 + 5x - 3$ **6.** $3x^2 - 5x - 2$

   7. $3x^2 - 5x + 4$ **8.** $2x^2 - 11x + 6$

B   **9.** $3x^2 - 14x + 8$ **10.** $2y^2 - 13y + 15$ **11.** $6x^2 + 7x - 5$

   12. $5x^2 - 8x - 4$ **13.** $6x^2 - 4x - 5$ **14.** $5x^2 - 7x - 4$

   15. $2m^2 - 3m - 20$ **16.** $12x^2 + 16x - 3$

   17. $3u^2 - 11u - 4$ **18.** $8u^2 + 2u - 1$

   19. $6u^2 - uv - 2v^2$ **20.** $6x^2 - 7xy - 5y^2$

   21. $3x^2 + 2xy - 3y^2$ **22.** $2x^2 - 3xy - 4y^2$

   23. $8x^2 + 6x - 9$ **24.** $6x^2 - 5x - 6$

   25. $4m^2 + 10mn - 6n^2$ **26.** $3u^2 + 7uv - 6v^2$

   27. $3u^2 - 8uv - 6v^2$ **28.** $4m^2 - 9mn - 6n^2$

   29. $4u^2 - 19uv + 12v^2$ **30.** $12x^2 - xy - 6y^2$

C   **31.** $12x^2 - 40xy - 7y^2$ **32.** $15x^2 + 17xy - 4y^2$

33. $18x^2 - 9xy - 20y^2$ **34.** $15m^2 + 2mn - 24n^2$

35. Find all integers b such that $x^2 + bx + 12$ can be factored.

36. Find all positive integers c under 15 so that $x^2 - 7x + c$ can be factored.

6-6
MORE FACTORING

■ Sum and Difference of Two Squares
■ Sum and Difference of Two Cubes
■ Combined Factoring Processes
■ Factoring by Grouping
■ A Factoring Strategy

In this last section on factoring we will consider several additional basic factoring forms as well as problems that require a combination of the processes we have considered.

SUM AND DIFFERENCE OF TWO SQUARES

Look at the following products and try to determine what they all have in common:

$$(x - 3)(x + 3) = x^2 - 9 \qquad (x - 2y)(x + 2y) = x^2 - 4y^2$$

$$(2x + 4)(2x - 4) = 4x^2 - 16 \qquad (A - B)(A + B) = A^2 - B^2$$

We note that the binomial factors on the left side of each equation are the same except for the signs. When each pair is multiplied, the middle term drops out. Looking at the expressions on the right, we see that each is the difference of two squares. Writing the last equation in reverse order, we obtain a **factoring formula for the difference of two squares**: $A^2 - B^2 = (A - B)(A + B)$. If we try to factor the sum of two squares, $A^2 + B^2$, we find that it cannot be factored using integer coefficients. (Try it to see why.)

Sum and Difference of Two Squares

$A^2 + B^2$ cannot be factored using integer coefficients (unless A and B have common factors).

$A^2 - B^2 = (A - B)(A + B)$ Memorize this factoring formula and use it for difference-of-two-squares forms.

In words, a first number squared minus a second number squared is the first number minus the second number, times the first number plus the second number.

Example 15   Factor, if possible, using integer coefficients:

(A) $x^2 - y^2$ (B) $4x^2 - 9$
(C) $U^2 + V^2$ (D) $9m^2 - 25n^2$

Solution   (A) $x^2 - y^2 = (x - y)(x + y)$

(B) $4x^2 - 9 \;\boxed{= (2x)^2 - (3)^2}\; = (2x - 3)(2x + 3)$

(C) $U^2 + V^2$ is not factorable using integer coefficients.

(D) $9m^2 - 25n^2 \;\boxed{= (3m)^2 - (5n)^2}\; = (3m - 5n)(3m + 5n)$

Problem 15   Factor, if possible, using integer coefficients:

(A) $x^2 - 4$ (B) $4x^2 - 9y^2$ (C) $4m^2 + n^2$ (D) $16x^2 - 5$

SUM AND DIFFERENCE OF TWO CUBES

We can verify, by direct multiplication of the right sides, the following factoring formulas for the sum and difference of two cubes:

Sum and Difference of Two Cubes
$A^3 + B^3 = (A + B)(A^2 - AB + B^2)$ $A^3 - B^3 = (A - B)(A^2 + AB + B^2)$

These formulas are used in the same way as the factoring formula for the difference of two squares. (Notice that neither $A^2 - AB + B^2$ nor $A^2 + AB + B^2$ factor further using integer coefficients.) Both formulas should be memorized.

Notice that in each formula the linear factor $A + B$ or $A - B$ has the same addition or subtraction sign as the original sum or difference. The term AB in the other factor has the opposite sign.

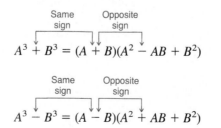

To factor

$$x^3 - 8$$

we recognize that $8 = 2^3$ so the polynomial can be rewritten as the difference of two cubes

$$x^3 - 2^3$$

Now we can apply the formula from the box with $A = x$, $B = 2$ to obtain

$$x^3 - 8 = x^3 - 2^3 = (x - 2)(x^2 + 2x + 4)$$

Example 16   Factor as far as possible, using integer coefficients:

(A) $x^3 - 27$
(B) $8x^3 + 1$

Solution   **(A)** $x^3 - 27 = x^3 - 3^3 = (x - 3)(x^2 + 3x + 9)$
(B) $8x^3 + 1 = (2x)^3 + 1^3 = (2x + 1)[(2x)^2 - 2x + 1]$
$\qquad\qquad = (2x + 1)(4x^2 - 2x + 1)$

Problem 16   Factor as far as possible, using integer coefficients:

(A) $x^3 + 8$
(B) $27x^3 - 1$

COMBINED FACTORING PROCESSES

We now consider several examples that involve the removal of common factors as well as other factoring processes considered earlier. The factoring process generally will be simpler if we **remove common factors first before proceeding to other methods**.

Example 17   Factor as far as possible, using integer coefficients:

(A) $4x^3 - 14x^2 + 6x$ **(B)** $18x^3 - 8x$
(C) $8x^3y + 20x^2y^2 - 12xy^3$ **(D)** $3y^3 + 6y^2 + 6y$

Solution   **(A)** $4x^3 - 14x^2 + 6x$
$\qquad\qquad = 2x(2x^2 - 7x + 3)$
$\qquad\qquad = 2x(2x - 1)(x - 3)$

(B) $18x^3 - 8x$ Remove common factors.

$= 2x(9x^2 - 4)$ Factor the difference of two squares.

$= 2x(3x - 2)(3x + 2)$ Factoring is complete.

(C) $8x^3y + 20x^2y^2 - 12xy^3$

$= 4xy(2x^2 + 5xy - 3y^2)$

$= 4xy(2x - y)(x + 3y)$

(D) $3y^3 + 6y^2 + 6y$

$= 3y(y^2 + 2y + 2)$ Cannot be factored further using integer coefficients.

Problem 17   Factor as far as possible, using integer coefficients:

(A) $3x^3 - 15x^2y + 18xy^2$ **(B)** $3x^3 - 48x$
(C) $3x^3y + 3x^2y - 36xy$ **(D)** $4x^3 + 12x^2 + 12x$

FACTORING BY GROUPING

Occasionally, polynomial forms of a different nature than we considered in Section 6-3 can be factored by appropriate grouping of terms. The following example illustrates the process.

Example 18   **(A)** $x^2 + xy + 2x + 2y$ Group the first two and last two terms.

$= (x^2 + xy) + (2x + 2y)$ Remove common factors.

$= x(x + y) + 2(x + y)$ Since each term has the common factor $(x + y)$, we can complete the factoring.

$= (x + y)(x + 2)$ Notice that the factors are not first-degree polynomials of the same type.

(B) $x^2 - 2x - xy + 2y$

$= (x^2 - 2x) - (xy - 2y)$ Be careful of signs here.

$= x(x - 2) - y(x - 2)$

$= (x - 2)(x - y)$

Problem 18   Factor by grouping terms:

(A) $x^2 - xy + 5x - 5y$ **(B)** $x^2 + 4x - xy - 4y$

A FACTORING STRATEGY

There is no general procedure (**algorithm**) for factoring all polynomials having factors with integer coefficients. However, the following strategy may be helpful.

General Strategy for Factoring Polynomials

1. Remove common factors (Section 6-3).
2. If the polynomial has two terms, look for a difference of two squares or a sum or difference of two cubes (Section 6-6).
3. If the polynomial has three terms:
   (A) See if it is a perfect square (Section 6-4).
   (B) Try trial and error (Section 6-4).
   (C) Or use the *ac* test (Section 6-5).
4. If the polynomial has more than three terms, try grouping (Sections 6-3 and 6-6).

Factoring requires skill, creativity, and perseverance. Often the appropriate technique is not apparent immediately and practice is necessary to develop your recognition of what might work on a given problem. Exercises 6-6 and 6-8 contain numerous problems for this purpose.

ANSWERS TO MATCHED PROBLEMS

15.   **(A)** $(x - 2)(x + 2)$ **(B)** $(2x - 3y)(2x + 3y)$
     (C)   Not factorable using integers
     (D)   Not factorable using integers
16.   **(A)** $(x + 2)(x^2 - 2x + 4)$ **(B)** $(3x - 1)(9x^2 + 3x + 1)$
17.   **(A)** $3x(x - 2y)(x - 3y)$ **(B)** $3x(x - 4)(x + 4)$
     (C) $3xy(x - 3)(x + 4)$ **(D)** $4x(x^2 + 3x + 3)$
18.   **(A)** $(x - y)(x + 5)$ **(B)** $(x + 4)(x - y)$

EXERCISE 6-6

In Problems 1–62, factor as far as possible using integer coefficients.

A

1. $6x^3 + 9x^2$ **2.** $8x^2 + 2x$

3. $u^4 + 6u^3 + 8u^2$ **4.** $m^5 + 8m^4 + 15m^3$

5. $x^3 - 5x^2 + 6x$ **6.** $x^3 - 7x^2 + 12x$

7. $x^2 - 4$ **8.** $x^2 - 1$

9. $4x^2 - 1$ **10.** $9x^2 - 4$

11. $u^2 + v^2$ **12.** $m^2 + 64$

13. $2x^2 - 8$ **14.** $3x^2 - 3$

B

15. $9x^2 - 16y^2$ **16.** $25x^2 - 1$

17. $6u^2v^2 - 3uv^3$ **18.** $2x^3y - 6x^2y^3$

19. $4x^3y - xy^3$ **20.** $x^3y - 9xy^3$

21. $3x^4 + 27x^2$ **22.** $2x^3 + 8x$

23. $6x^2 + 36x + 48$ **24.** $4x^2 - 28x + 48$

25. $3x^3 - 6x^2 + 15x$ **26.** $2x^3 - 2x^2 + 8x$

27. $9u^2 + 4v^2$ **28.** $x^2 + 16y^2$

29. $12x^3 + 16x^2y - 16xy^2$ **30.** $9x^2y + 3xy^2 - 30y^3$

31. $x^2 + 3x + xy + 3y$ **32.** $xy + 2x + y^2 + 2y$

33. $x^2 - 3x - xy + 3y$ **34.** $x^2 - 5x + xy - 5y$

35. $2ac + bc - 6ad - 3bd$ **36.** $2ac + 4bc - ad - 2bd$

37. $2mu + 2nu - mv - nv$ **38.** $3wx + 6wy - xz - 2yz$

C **39.** $4x^3y + 14x^2y^2 + 6xy^3$ **40.** $3x^3y - 15x^2y^2 + 18xy^3$

41. $60x^2y^2 - 200xy^3 - 35y^4$ **42.** $60x^4 + 68x^3y - 16x^2y^2$

43. $x^3 - 8$ **44.** $x^3 + 1$

45. $x^3 + 27$ **46.** $8y^3 - 1$

47. $3m^4 + 12m^2$ **48.** $3x(2x - y) - 2y(2x - y)$

49. $x^2 - 7x + 6$ **50.** $u^2 - 4u + 6$

51. $4y^2 - 1$ **52.** $4x^2 - 20x + 25$

53. $6x^3 - 8x^2 - 8x$ **54.** $3x^2 + 10xy - 8y^2$

55. $6x^2y^2 - 3xy^3 + 3xy^2$ **56.** $18x^4y - 9x^3y - 3x^2y$

57. $u^2 - 5u - uv + 5v$ **58.** $x^4 + x^2 + 4x + 4$

59. $x^3 - 8y^3$ **60.** $27a^3 + b^3$

61. $16xy^3 + 2x^4$ **62.** $54 - 2x^3y^3$

Some higher-degree polynomials may be "disguised" variations of lower-degree polynomials that can be factored. For example,

$$x^4 + 3x^2 + 2 = (x^2 + 1)(x^2 + 2)$$

as can be verified by multiplication. Recognizing the factorization may be made easier with a substitution: let $u = x^2$, so $x^4 + 3x^2 + 2$ becomes $u^2 + 3u + 2$. This last is factored easily.

$$u^2 + 3u + 2 = (u + 1)(u + 2)$$
$$= (x^2 + 1)(x^2 + 2)$$

Factor as far as possible using integer coefficients.

63. $x^4 + 4x^2 + 4$ **64.** $x^6 + 3x^3 + 2$

65. $x^6 - 3x^3 - 4$ **66.** $x^4 + 8x^2 + 16$

67. $x^4 - 16$ **68.** $x^6 - 8$

69. $x^6 + 27$ **70.** $x^6 - 25$

71. $x^4 - 1$ **72.** $x^6 - 64$

73. $x^4 - y^4$ **74.** $x^6 - y^3$

6-7

SOLVING EQUATIONS BY FACTORING

The real numbers have the property that if a product of two or more numbers is zero, then at least one of the factors must be zero. That is, the product of nonzero numbers cannot be zero. More formally we have the following:

> **Zero Property**
>
> $ab = 0$ if and only if $a = 0$ or $b = 0$

The zero property can be used to solve certain types of equations. If an expression which can be factored is set equal to zero, we can solve the given equation by setting each factor equal to zero.

Example 19   Solve $x^2 + 2x - 15 = 0$ by factoring.

Solution $x^2 + 2x - 15 = 0$ Factor the left side.
                  $(x - 3)(x + 5) = 0$ $(x - 3)(x + 5) = 0$ if and only if $(x - 3) = 0$ or $(x + 5) = 0$

$x - 3 = 0$ or $x + 5 = 0$
$\boxed{x = 3}$ or $\boxed{x = -5}$

Check $x = 3$: $3^2 + 2(3) - 15 = 9 + 6 - 15 = 0$
            $x = -5$: $(-5)^2 + 2(-5) - 15 = 25 - 10 - 15 = 0$

Problem 19   Solve $x^2 - 2x - 8 = 0$ by factoring.

CAUTION

It is important to recognize that this method depends on a particular property of 0 and that to use it we must have a product equal to 0. The method cannot be applied directly to a product like $ab = 12$. Many equations can be rewritten in the form of a product equal to 0, however, and then this method applies.

Example 20   Solve $2x^2 = 3x$.

Solution

$$2x^2 = 3x$$

Since x might be 0, we cannot divide by x.

$$2x^2 - 3x = 0$$

Write as a polynomial set equal to 0 and factor.

$$x(2x - 3) = 0$$

$x(2x - 3) = 0$ if and only if $x = 0$ or $2x - 3 = 0$

$$x = 0 \quad \text{or} \quad 2x - 3 = 0$$
$$\boxed{x = 0} \quad \text{or} \quad \boxed{x = \tfrac{3}{2}}$$

Check $\quad x = 0: \quad 2(0)^2 \overset{?}{=} 3(0) \qquad x = \tfrac{3}{2}: \quad 2(\tfrac{3}{2})^2 \overset{?}{=} 3(\tfrac{3}{2})$
$$0 \overset{\checkmark}{=} 0 \qquad\qquad\qquad \tfrac{9}{2} \overset{\checkmark}{=} \tfrac{9}{2}$$

Problem 20 Solve $3t^2 = 2t$.

Example 21 Solve $2x^2 - 8x + 3 = 0$ by factoring, if possible, using integer coefficients.

Solution $2x^2 - 8x + 3$ cannot be factored using integer coefficients; hence, another method, which we will consider later, must be used.

Problem 21 Solve $x^2 - 3x - 3 = 0$ by factoring, if possible, using integer coefficients.

Example 22 Solve $3x + \dfrac{21}{2} = \dfrac{6}{x}$.

Solution

$$3x + \frac{21}{2} = \frac{6}{x}$$

If 0 turns up later as an apparent solution, it must be rejected, since we cannot substitute 0 for x in $\frac{6}{x}$. Multiply both sides by $2x$, the LCM of the denominators.

$$2x \cdot 3x + 2x \cdot \frac{21}{2} = 2x \cdot \frac{6}{x}$$

Eliminate denominators by reducing fractions.

$$6x^2 + 21x = 12$$

Write as a polynomial set equal to 0.

$$6x^2 + 21x - 12 = 0$$

Since the coefficient of each term is divisible by 3, multiply each side by $\frac{1}{3}$ to simplify further.

$$\frac{1}{3} \cdot 6x^2 + \frac{1}{3} \cdot 21x - \frac{1}{3} \cdot 12 = \frac{1}{3} \cdot 0$$

Eliminate denominators by reducing fractions.

$$2x^2 + 7x - 4 = 0$$

Factor, if possible.

$$(2x - 1)(x + 4) = 0$$

Solve as in Example 19.

$$2x - 1 = 0 \quad \text{or} \quad x + 4 = 0$$
$$2x = 1 \qquad\qquad \boxed{x = -4}$$
$$\boxed{x = \tfrac{1}{2}}$$

Checking the solution is left to you.

Problem 22 Solve $5x = \dfrac{5}{2} + \dfrac{15}{x}$.

Example 23 Find the dimensions of a rectangle with area 36 square inches and length 5 inches more than its width.

Solution Let x be the width; then $x + 5$ is the length.

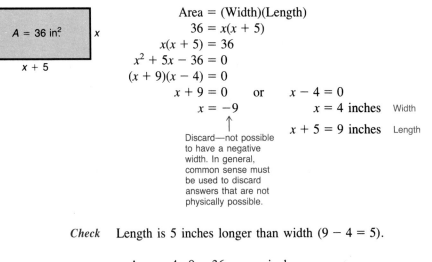

$$\text{Area} = (\text{Width})(\text{Length})$$
$$36 = x(x + 5)$$
$$x(x + 5) = 36$$
$$x^2 + 5x - 36 = 0$$
$$(x + 9)(x - 4) = 0$$
$$x + 9 = 0 \quad \text{or} \quad x - 4 = 0$$
$$x = -9 \qquad\qquad x = 4 \text{ inches} \quad \text{Width}$$

Discard—not possible to have a negative width. In general, common sense must be used to discard answers that are not physically possible.

$$x + 5 = 9 \text{ inches} \quad \text{Length}$$

Check Length is 5 inches longer than width $(9 - 4 = 5)$.

$$\text{Area} = 4 \cdot 9 = 36 \text{ square inches}$$

Problem 23 Find the dimensions of a rectangle with area 24 square inches if its width is 2 inches less than its length.

ANSWERS TO MATCHED PROBLEMS
19. $x = -2, 4$ **20.** $t = 0, \frac{2}{3}$
21. Cannot be solved by factoring using integer coefficients.
22. $x = -\frac{3}{2}, 2$
23. Width = 4 inches, Length = 6 inches

EXERCISE 6-7   **A**   *Solve.*

1. $(x - 3)(x - 4) = 0$ **2.** $(x - 9)(x - 4) = 0$

3. $(x + 6)(x - 5) = 0$ **4.** $(x - 9)(x + 3) = 0$

5. $(x + 4)(3x - 2) = 0$ **6.** $(2x - 1)(x + 2) = 0$

7. $(4t + 3)(5t - 2) = 0$ **8.** $(2m + 3)(3m - 2) = 0$

9. $u(4u - 1) = 0$ **10.** $z(3z + 5) = 0$

Solve by factoring.

11. $x^2 - 6x + 5 = 0$

12. $x^2 - 5x + 6 = 0$

13. $x^2 - 4x + 3 = 0$

14. $x^2 - 8x + 15 = 0$

15. $x^2 - 4x - 12 = 0$

16. $x^2 + 4x - 5 = 0$

17. $x^2 - 3x = 0$

18. $x^2 + 5x = 0$

19. $4t^2 - 8t = 0$

20. $3m^2 + 12m = 0$

21. $x^2 - 25 = 0$

22. $x^2 - 36 = 0$

B *Solve each equation by factoring. If an equation cannot be solved by factoring, state this as your answer.*

Note: First clear the equation of fractions (if they are present) by multiplying through by the least common multiple of all the denominators. Then write the equation in the form of a polynomial set equal to 0. Then, if all numerical coefficients contain a common factor, divide it out. Then test for factorability. Finally, if factorable, solve.

23. $2x^2 = 3 - 5x$

24. $3x^2 = x + 2$

25. $3x(x - 2) = 2(x - 2)$

26. $2x(x - 1) = 3(x + 1)$

27. $4n^2 = 16n + 128$

28. $3m^2 + 12m = 36$

29. $3z^2 - 10z = 8$

30. $2y^2 + 15y = 8$

31. $3 = t^2 + 7t$

32. $y^2 = 5y - 2$

33. $\dfrac{u}{4}(u + 1) = 3$

34. $\dfrac{x^2}{2} = x + 4$

35. $y = \dfrac{9}{y}$

36. $\dfrac{t}{2} = \dfrac{2}{t}$

37. The width of a rectangle is 8 inches less than its length. If its area is 33 square inches, find its dimensions.

38. Find the base and height of a triangle with area 2 square feet if its base is 3 feet longer than its height ($A = \frac{1}{2}bh$).

C *Solve.*

39. $y = \dfrac{15}{y - 2}$

40. $2x - 3 = \dfrac{2}{x}$

41. $2 + \dfrac{2}{x^2} = \dfrac{5}{x}$

42. $1 - \dfrac{3}{x} = \dfrac{10}{x^2}$

43. $(x - 4)(x - 3) = 2$ **44.** $(x + 3)(x - 3) = 7$

45. $(x - 1)(x + 3) = 5$ **46.** $(x - 2)(x - 1) = 6$

47. The sum of a number and its reciprocal is $\frac{13}{6}$. Find the number or numbers.

48. The difference between a number and its reciprocal is $\frac{7}{12}$. Find the number or numbers.

49. A flag has a white cross of uniform width centered on a colored background (see the figure). Find the width of the cross so that it takes up exactly half of the total area of a 4- by 3-foot flag.

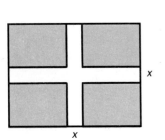

6-8

ALGEBRAIC LONG DIVISION

There are times when it is useful to find quotients of polynomials by a long-division process similar to that used in arithmetic. Several examples will illustrate the process.

Example 24   Divide: $2x^2 + 5x - 12$ by $x + 4$.

Solution

$$x + 4 \overline{)2x^2 + 5x - 12}$$

Both polynomials are to be arranged in descending powers of the variable if this is not already done.

$$\begin{array}{r} 2x \\ x + 4 \overline{)2x^2 + 5x - 12} \end{array}$$

Divide the first term of the divisor into the first term of the dividend. That is, what must x be multiplied by so that the product is exactly $2x^2$? Answer: $2x$.

$$\begin{array}{r} \boxed{2x} \\ x + 4 \overline{)2x^2 + 5x - 12} \\ 2x^2 + 8x \\ \hline -3x - 12 \end{array}$$

Multiply the divisor by $2x$, line up like terms, subtract, and bring down -12 from above.

$$\begin{array}{r} 2x - 3 \\ x + 4 \overline{)2x^2 + 5x - 12} \\ 2x^2 + 8x \\ \hline -3x - 12 \\ -3x - 12 \\ \hline 0 \end{array}$$

Repeat the process until the degree of the remainder is less than that of the divisor or the remainder is 0.

Check $(x + 4)(2x - 3) = 2x^2 + 5x - 12$

Problem 24   Divide $2x^2 + 7x + 3$ by $x + 3$ and check.

Example 25   Divide $x^3 + 8$ by $x + 2$.

Solution

$$
\begin{array}{r}
x^2 - 2x + 4 \\
x + 2{\overline{\smash{\big)}\,x^3 + 0x^2 + 0x + 8}} \\
\underline{x^3 + 2x^2} \\
-2x^2 + 0x \\
\underline{-2x^2 - 4x} \\
4x + 8 \\
\underline{4x + 8} \\
0
\end{array}
$$

Insert, with 0 coefficients, any missing terms of lower degree than 3, and proceed as in Example 24.

To check, note that as the sum of two cubes,

$$x^3 + 8 = (x + 2)(x^2 - 2x + 4)$$

Problem 25   Divide and check: $(x^3 - 8)/(x - 2)$.

Example 26   Divide and check: $(3 - 7x + 6x^2)/(3x + 1)$.

Solution

$$
\begin{array}{r}
2x - 3 \\
3x + 1{\overline{\smash{\big)}\,6x^2 - 7x + 3}} \\
\underline{6x^2 + 2x} \\
-9x + 3 \\
\underline{-9x - 3} \\
6 = \text{R}
\end{array}
$$
   (Remainder)

Arrange $3 - 7x + 6x^2$ in descending powers of x; then proceed as above until the degree of the remainder is less than the degree of the divisor.

Check   Just as in arithmetic, when there is a remainder we check by adding the remainder to the product of the divisor and quotient. Thus,

$$
\begin{aligned}
(3x + 1)(2x - 3) + 6 &\overset{?}{=} 6x^2 - 7x + 3 \\
6x^2 - 7x - 3 + 6 &\overset{?}{=} 6x^2 - 7x + 3 \\
6x^2 - 7x + 3 &\overset{\checkmark}{=} 6x^2 - 7x + 3
\end{aligned}
$$

Problem 26   Divide and check: $(2 + 6x^2 - x)/(3x - 2)$.

If we know, or could guess, one solution to a third-degree, or *cubic,* equation, long division can help us find the others as shown in the next example.

Example 27   Solve $x^3 - 4x^2 + 5x - 2 = 0$

Solution   With the constant term in the expression being 2, we might guess 1 or 2 as a possible solution. Substituting $x = 2$ into $x^3 - 4x^2 + 5x - 2$, we obtain

$$2^3 - 4 \cdot 2^2 + 5 \cdot 2 - 2 = 8 - 16 + 10 - 2 = 0$$

so 2 is, in fact, a solution. This means that $x - 2$ is a factor of $x^3 - 4x^2 +$

$5x - 2$, although we will not prove this here. To find the other factors, we divide the cubic by $x - 2$:

$$
\begin{array}{r}
x^2 - 2x + 1 \\
x - 2\overline{)x^3 - 4x^2 + 5x - 2} \\
\underline{x^3 - 2x^2} \\
-2x^2 + 5x \\
\underline{-2x^2 + 4x} \\
x - 2 \\
\underline{x - 2} \\
0
\end{array}
$$

Thus

$$
\begin{aligned}
x^3 - 4x^2 + 5x - 2 &= (x - 2)(x^2 - 2x + 1) \\
&= (x - 2)(x - 1)^2 = (x - 2)(x - 1)(x - 1)
\end{aligned}
$$

The solutions to the equation are found by setting $x - 2 = 0$ and $x - 1 = 0$, and thus are $x = 2$ and $x = 1$.

In the solution to Example 27, 2 was a solution to $x^3 - 4x^2 + 5x - 2 = 0$ and $x - 2$ turned out to be a factor of the polynomial. This is true in general: If r is a real number which, when substituted into the polynomial P, yields 0, then $x - r$ is a factor of P.

Problem 27   Solve $x^3 - 6x^2 + 11x - 6 = 0$, given that $x = 2$ is one solution.

ANSWERS TO
MATCHED PROBLEMS

24. $2x + 1$ **25.** $x^2 + 2x + 4$ **26.** $2x + 1, R = 4$
27. $x = 1, 2, 3$

EXERCISE 6-8

In Problems 1–30, divide, using the long-division process. Check the answers.

A   **1.** $(x^2 + 5x + 6)/(x + 3)$ **2.** $(x^2 + 6x + 8)/(x + 4)$

  3. $(2x^2 + x - 6)/(x + 2)$ **4.** $(3x^2 - 5x - 2)/(x - 2)$

  5. $(2x^2 - 3x - 4)/(x - 3)$ **6.** $(3x^2 - 11x - 1)/(x - 4)$

  7. $(2m^2 + m - 10)/(2m + 5)$ **8.** $(3y^2 + 5y - 12)/(3y - 4)$

  9. $(6x^2 + 5x - 6)/(3x - 2)$ **10.** $(8x^2 - 14x + 3)/(2x - 3)$

  11. $(6x^2 + 11x - 12)/(3x - 2)$ **12.** $(6x^2 + x - 13)/(2x + 3)$

  13. $(3x^2 + 13x - 12)/(3x - 2)$ **14.** $(2x^2 - 7x - 1)/(2x + 1)$

B   **15.** $(x^2 - 4)/(x - 2)$ **16.** $(y^2 - 9)/(y + 3)$

  17. $(m^2 - 7)/(m - 3)$ **18.** $(u^2 - 18)/(u + 4)$

  19. $(8c + 4 + 5c^2)/(c + 2)$ **20.** $(4a^2 - 22 - 7a)/(a - 3)$

21. $(9x^2 - 8)/(3x - 2)$ **22.** $(8x^2 + 7)/(2x - 3)$

23. $(5y^2 - y + 2y^3 - 6)/(y + 2)$ **24.** $(x - 5x^2 + 10 + x^3)/(x + 2)$

25. $(x^3 - 1)/(x - 1)$ **26.** $(x^3 + 27)/(x + 3)$

27. $(x^4 - 16)/(x + 2)$ **28.** $(x^5 + 32)/(x - 2)$

29. $(3y - y^2 + 2y^3 - 1)/(y + 2)$ **30.** $(3 + x^3 - x)/(x - 3)$

C   **31.** $(4x^4 - 10x - 9x^2 - 10)/(2x + 3)$

      32. $(9x^4 - 2 - 6x - x^2)/(3x - 1)$

      33. $(16x - 5x^3 - 4 + 6x^4 - 8x^2)/(2x - 4 + 3x^2)$

      34. $(8x^2 - 7 - 13x + 24x^4)/(3x + 5 + 6x^2)$

Solve the equation using the fact that the number given is one solution.

35. $x^3 - 8x^2 + 19x - 12 = 0; \ x = 4$

36. $x^3 + 5x^2 - x - 5 = 0; \ x = -5$

37. $x^3 + 6x^2 + 11x + 6 = 0; \ x = -3$

38. $x^3 - 7x - 6 = 0; \ x = 3$

6-9
CHAPTER REVIEW

A **polynomial** in one or two variables x and y is an algebraic expression constructed by adding or subtracting constants and terms of the form ax^n or $bx^m y^n$, where a and b are real number coefficients and m and n are positive integers. The **degree of a term** in a polynomial is the sum of the powers of the variable factors in the term; nonzero constants are assigned degree 0. The **degree of a polynomial** is the highest degree of its terms. The number 0 is a polynomial with no assigned degree. Polynomials with one, two, and three terms are called **monomials**, **binomials**, and **trinomials**, respectively. Polynomials are added or subtracted by combining like terms. Polynomials are multiplied by multiplying each term of the first by each term of the second. *(6-1)*

Binomials can be multiplied mentally by the FOIL method:

$$(A + B)(C + D) = AC + AD + BC + BD$$

and squared by $(A + B)^2 = A^2 + 2AB + B^2$. *(6-2)*

Common factors are factored out by using the distributive property. Grouping may lead to factoring out common factors.   *(6-3)*

Second-degree polynomials can be factored by trial and error and sometimes by recognizing perfect squares.   *(6-4)*

Another method for factoring second-degree polynomials is the **ac test**. The *ac* test to factor $ax^2 + bx + c$ or $ax^2 + bxy + cy^2$ involves finding two integers p and q such that $pq = ac$ and $p + q = b$, rewriting the middle term as $px + qx$ or $pxy + qxy$, and grouping.   *(6-5)*

The sum $A^2 + B^2$ of two squares cannot be factored unless there are common factors. The difference of two squares is factored

$$A^2 - B^2 = (A - B)(A + B)$$

The sum and difference of two cubes are factored

$$A^3 + B^3 = (A + B)(A^2 - AB + B^2)$$
$$A^3 - B^3 = (A - B)(A^2 + AB + B^2)$$

A general strategy for factoring is

1. Remove common factors.
2. If the polynomial has two terms, look for a difference of two squares or a sum or difference of two cubes.
3. If the polynomial has three terms:
    (A) See if it is a perfect square.
    (B) Try trial and error.
    (C) Or use the *ac* test.
4. If the polynomial has more than three terms, try grouping.   *(6-6)*

An equation that can be factored can be solved by factoring using the **zero property**:

$$ab = 0 \qquad \text{if and only if} \qquad a = 0 \text{ or } b = 0 \quad (6\text{-}7)$$

Algebraic long division can be used to find the quotient of two polynomials. Just as in arithmetic, if division of polynomial P by divisor D yields quotient Q and remainder R, then $P = DQ + R$.   *(6-8)*

REVIEW EXERCISES 6-9

Work through all the problems in this chapter review and check answers in the back of the book. (Answers to all problems are there, and following each answer is a number in italics indicating the section in which that type of problem is discussed.) Where weaknesses show up, review appropriate sections in the text.

A   **1.**   Add: $2x^2 + x - 3$, $2x - 3$, and $3x^2 + 2$.

2. Subtract: $3x^2 - x - 2$ from $5x^2 - 2x + 5$.

3. Divide using algebraic long division: $(6x^2 + 5x - 2)/(2x - 1)$.

Perform the indicated operations and simplify.

4. $(3x - 2)(2x + 5)$

5. $(2u - 3v)(3u + 4v)$

6. $(2x^2 - 3x + 1) + (3x^3 - x^2 + 5)$

7. $(2x^2 - 3x + 1) - (3x^3 - x^2 + 5)$

Factor, if possible, using integer coefficients.

8. $x^2 - 9x + 14$ **9.** $3x^2 - 10x + 8$

10. $x^2 - 3x - 3$ **11.** $4x^2y - 6xy^2$

12. $x^3 - 5x^2 + 6x$ **13.** $4u^2 - 9$

14. $x(x - 1) + 3(x - 1)$ **15.** $m^2 + 4n^2$

B *Solve.*

16. $(x + 5)(x - 2) = 0$ **17.** $x(3x - 1) = 0$

18. What is the degree of the polynomial $3x^5 - 2x^3 + 7x^2 - x + 2$? What is the degree of the fourth term? Of the fifth term?

19. Subtract $2x^2 - 5x - 6$ from the product $(2x - 1)(2x + 1)$.

Divide using algebraic long division.

20. $(2x^2 - 7x - 1)/(2x + 1)$ **21.** $(2 - 10x + 9x^3)/(3x - 2)$

Perform the indicated operations and simplify.

22. $(2x - 3)(2x^2 - 3x + 2)$ **23.** $(9x^2 - 4)(3x^2 + 7x - 6)$

24. $(a + b)(a^2 - ab + b^2)$

25. $[(3x^2 - x + 1) - (x^2 - 4)] - [(2x - 5)(x + 3)]$

Factor, if possible, using integer coefficients.

26. $3u^2 - 12$ **27.** $2x^2 - xy - 3y^2$

28. $x^2 - xy + y^2$ **29.** $6y^3 + 3y^2 - 45y$

30. $2x^3 - 4x^2y - 10xy^2$ **31.** $12x^3y + 27xy^3$

32. $x^2(x - 1) - 9(x - 1)$

Factor (using integer coefficients) by grouping.

33. $x^2 - xy + 4x - 4y$ **34.** $x^2 + xy - 3x - 3y$

35. $2u^2 - 3u + 6u - 9$ **36.** $6x^2 + 4x - 3x - 2$

Solve by factoring.

37. $x^2 + 3x - 4 = 0$ **38.** $2x^2 + 3x = 2$

C   **39.** Simplify: $[-2xy(x^2 - 4y^2)] - [-2xy(x - 2y)(x + 2y)]$

40. Divide using algebraic long division:

$(20x - 14x^2 + 2x^4 + 4)/(6 + 2x)$

Factor, if possible, using integer coefficients.

41. $36x^3y + 24x^2y^2 - 45xy^3$ **42.** $12u^4 - 12u^3v - 20u^3v^2$

43. $6ac + 4bc - 12ad - 8bd$ **44.** $12ux - 15vx - 4u + 5v$

45. $8x^3 + 1$

46. Find all integers b such that $2x^2 + bx - 4$ can be factored into two first-degree factors using integer coefficients.

47. Solve $x^3 - 4x^2 - 4x + 16 = 0$, given that $x = 4$ is one solution.

7

ALGEBRAIC FRACTIONS

Polynomials involve only the operations of addition, subtraction, and multiplication of variables. In this chapter, we extend the kinds of algebraic expressions we consider to include those in which division may involve variables, that is, expressions which may have variables in a denominator.

7-1

REDUCING TO LOWEST TERMS

- ■ Rational Expressions
- ■ Reducing to Lowest Terms

In this section we will introduce the simplest algebraic expressions that include division involving a variable. These are fractional forms where both the numerator and denominator are polynomials.

RATIONAL EXPRESSIONS

Fractional forms in which the numerator and denominator are polynomials are called **rational expressions**. For example:

$$\frac{1}{x} \qquad \frac{3}{y-5} \qquad \frac{x-2}{2x^2 - 2x + 5} \qquad \frac{x^2 - 3xy + y^2}{x^2 - y^2}$$

are all rational expressions.

In Chapter 3 we worked with simple fractional forms. In this chapter we will use the same basic ideas established there on more complex fractional forms.

The **fundamental principle of real fractions**

$$\frac{ak}{bk} = \frac{a}{b} \qquad b, \, k \neq 0$$

will play an important role in our work.

REDUCING TO LOWEST TERMS

If the numerator and denominator in a quotient of two polynomials (a rational expression) contain a common factor, it may be divided out using the fundamental principle of fractions. The process that converts ak/bk to a/b is usually denoted by

$$\frac{a\!\!\!/k}{b\!\!\!/k} \qquad \text{or} \qquad \frac{\overset{1}{a\!\!\!/k}}{\underset{1}{b\!\!\!/k}} \qquad \text{or} \qquad \frac{\overset{a}{\cancel{ak}}}{\underset{b}{\cancel{bk}}}$$

Recall that removing a common factor from a numerator and denominator is equivalent to dividing the numerator and denominator by this same common factor. If all common factors are removed from the numerator and the denominator, the resulting rational expressions is said to be reduced to **lowest terms**. The language exactly parallels that introduced for fractions in Chapter 3. Several examples should make the process clear. In the examples it is important to keep in mind:

Example 1 Reduce to lowest terms by eliminating all common factors from **numerator** and denominator.

(A) $\dfrac{5(x + 3)}{2x(x + 3)}$ (B) $\dfrac{6x^2 - 3x}{3x}$ (C) $\dfrac{x^2y - xy^2}{x^2 - xy}$

(D) $\dfrac{4x^3 + 10x^2 - 6x}{2x^3 - 18x}$ (E) $\dfrac{2 - x}{x - 2}$

Solution (A) $\dfrac{5(x + 3)}{2x(x + 3)} = \dfrac{5\cancel{(x + 3)}^{\,1}}{2x\cancel{(x + 3)}_{\,1}}$ Divide out common factors.

$$= \dfrac{5}{2x}$$

(B) $\dfrac{6x^2 - 3x}{3x} = \dfrac{\cancel{3x}^{\,1}(2x - 1)}{\cancel{3x}_{\,1}}$ Factor the top; then divide out common factors.

$$= 2x - 1$$ Note the *term* 3x cannot be divided out in $\dfrac{6x^2 - 3x}{3x}$.

(C) $\dfrac{x^2y - xy^2}{x^2 - xy} = \dfrac{\cancel{xy}^{\,1}\cancel{(x - y)}^{\,1}}{\cancel{x}_{\,1}\cancel{(x - y)}_{\,1}}$ Factor the top and bottom, then divide out common factors.

$$= y$$

(D) $\dfrac{4x^3 + 10x^2 - 6x}{2x^3 - 18x} = \dfrac{\cancel{2x}^{\,1}(2x^2 + 5x - 3)}{\cancel{2x}_{\,1}(x^2 - 9)}$

$$= \dfrac{(2x - 1)\cancel{(x + 3)}^{\,1}}{(x - 3)\cancel{(x + 3)}_{\,1}}$$

$$= \dfrac{2x - 1}{x - 3}$$

(E) $\dfrac{2 - x}{x - 2} = \dfrac{\cancel{-(x - 2)}^{\,-1}}{\cancel{x - 2}_{\,1}} = -1$

In Example 1(E), we used the result first introduced in Section 2-6:

$$-(a - b) = -a + b = b - a$$

Problem 1 Reduce to lowest terms by eliminating all common factors from numerator and denominator.

(A) $\dfrac{3x(x^2 + 2)}{2(x^2 + 2)}$ (B) $\dfrac{4m}{8m^2 - 4m}$ (C) $\dfrac{x^2 - 3x}{x^2y - 3xy}$

(D) $\dfrac{2x^3 - 8x}{4x^3 - 14x^2 + 12x}$ (E) $\dfrac{y - x}{x^2 - xy}$

ANSWERS TO
MATCHED PROBLEM   **1.** (A) $\dfrac{3x}{2}$ (B) $\dfrac{1}{2m - 1}$ (C) $\dfrac{1}{y}$ (D) $\dfrac{x + 2}{2x - 3}$

(E) $-\dfrac{1}{x}$

EXERCISE 7-1   *Eliminate all common factors from numerator and denominator.*

A   **1.** $\dfrac{2x^2}{6x}$ **2.** $\dfrac{9y}{3y^3}$ **3.** $\dfrac{A}{A^2}$

4. $\dfrac{B^2}{B}$ **5.** $\dfrac{x + 3}{(x + 3)^2}$ **6.** $\dfrac{(y - 1)^2}{y - 1}$

7. $\dfrac{8(y - 5)^2}{2(y - 5)}$ **8.** $\dfrac{4(x - 1)}{12(x - 1)^3}$ **9.** $\dfrac{2x^2(x + 7)}{6x(x + 7)^3}$

10. $\dfrac{15y^3(x - 9)^3}{5y^4(x - 9)^2}$ **11.** $\dfrac{x^2 - 2x}{2x - 4}$ **12.** $\dfrac{2x^2 - 10x}{4x - 20}$

13. $\dfrac{9y - 3y^2}{3y}$ **14.** $\dfrac{2x^2 - 4x}{2x}$

15. $\dfrac{m^2 - mn}{m^2n - mn^2}$ **16.** $\dfrac{a^2b + ab^2}{ab + b^2}$

17. $\dfrac{(2x - 1)(2x + 1)}{3x(2x + 1)}$ **18.** $\dfrac{(x + 3)(2x + 5)}{2x^2(2x + 5)}$

19. $\dfrac{(2x + 1)(x - 5)}{(3x - 7)(x - 5)}$ **20.** $\dfrac{(3x + 2)(x + 9)}{(2x - 5)(x + 9)}$

B   **21.** $\dfrac{x^2 + 5x + 6}{2x^2 + 6x}$ **22.** $\dfrac{x^2 + 6x + 8}{3x^2 + 12x}$ **23.** $\dfrac{x^2 - 9}{x^2 + 6x + 9}$

24. $\dfrac{x^2 - 4}{x^2 + 4x + 4}$ **25.** $\dfrac{x^2 - 4x + 4}{x^2 - 5x + 6}$ **26.** $\dfrac{x^2 - 6x + 9}{x^2 - 5x + 6}$

27. $\dfrac{2x^2 + 5x - 3}{4x^2 - 1}$ **28.** $\dfrac{9x^2 - 4}{3x^2 + 7x - 6}$ **29.** $\dfrac{9x^2 - 3x + 6}{3}$

30. $\dfrac{2 - 6x - 4x^2}{2}$ **31.** $\dfrac{10 + 5m - 15m^2}{5m}$

32. $\dfrac{12t^2 + 4t - 8}{4t}$ **33.** $\dfrac{4m^3n - 2m^2n^2 + 6mn^3}{2mn}$

34. $\dfrac{6x^3y - 12x^2y^2 - 9xy^3}{3xy}$ **35.** $\dfrac{x^2 - x - 6}{x - 3}$

36. $\dfrac{x^2 + 2x - 8}{x - 2}$ **37.** $\dfrac{4x^2 - 9y^2}{4x^2y + 6xy^2}$ **38.** $\dfrac{a^2 - 16b^2}{4ab - 16b^2}$

39. $\dfrac{8 - y}{y - 8}$ **40.** $\dfrac{5 - m}{m - 5}$ **41.** $\dfrac{y^2 - xy}{x - y}$

42. $\dfrac{n - m}{m^2 - mn}$ **43.** $\dfrac{3 - x}{x^2 - x - 6}$ **44.** $\dfrac{2 - y}{y^2 - 4}$

C **45.** $\dfrac{x^2 - xy + 2x - 2y}{x^2 - y^2}$ **46.** $\dfrac{u^2 + uv - 2u - 2v}{u^2 + 2uv + v^2}$

47. $\dfrac{x^2y - 8xy + 15y}{xy - 3y}$ **48.** $\dfrac{m^3 + 7m^2 + 10m}{m^2 + 5m}$

49. $\dfrac{6x^3 + 28x^2 - 10x}{12x^3 - 4x^2}$ **50.** $\dfrac{12x^3 - 78x^2 - 42x}{16x^4 + 8x^3}$

51. $\dfrac{x^3 - 8}{x^2 - 4}$ **52.** $\dfrac{y^3 + 27}{2y^3 - 6y^2 + 18y}$

7-2
MULTIPLICATION AND DIVISION

- Multiplication
- Division

The earlier treatment of multiplication and division of rational numbers in Chapter 3 extends naturally to real-number fractions and rational forms in general.

MULTIPLICATION

The definition of multiplication for fractions extends to multiplying quotients of real numbers.

> ## Multiplication of Real Fractions
>
> For a, b, c, and d any real numbers (b, $d \neq 0$),
>
> $$\frac{a}{b} \cdot \frac{c}{d} = \frac{a \cdot c}{b \cdot d} \qquad \frac{3}{4} \cdot \frac{\pi}{2} = \frac{3\pi}{8}$$

This definition, coupled with the fundamental principle of real fractions

$$\frac{ak}{bk} = \frac{a}{b} \qquad b, k \neq 0$$

provides the basic tool for multiplying and reducing rational expressions to lowest terms.

Example 2   Multiply and reduce to lowest terms:

(A) $\dfrac{2x^2y}{3z} \cdot \dfrac{3z^2}{4xy}$ **(B)** $(x^2 - 1) \cdot \dfrac{x+2}{x+1}$

(C) $\dfrac{x^2 - 1}{x^2 + 5x + 6} \cdot \dfrac{x+2}{x+1}$

Solution   **(A)** $\dfrac{2x^2y}{3z} \cdot \dfrac{3z^2}{4xy} = \dfrac{(2x^2y)(3z^2)}{(3z)(4xy)} = \dfrac{6x^2yz^2}{12xyz}$ The numerator $6x^2yz^2$ and denominator $12xyz$ have common factor $6xyz$.

$$= \dfrac{(6xyz)xz}{(6xyz)2} = \dfrac{xz}{2}$$

Instead of multiplying out and then removing the common factor $6xyz$, we could have recognized from the original product that both the numerator and the denominator would contain a 2, 3, x, y, and z as factors. Consequently, these common factors could have been eliminated before multiplying:

$$\frac{\overset{1}{\cancel{2}} \cdot \overset{x}{\cancel{x^2}} \cdot \overset{1}{\cancel{y}}}{\underset{1 \cdot 1}{\cancel{3} \cdot \cancel{z}}} \cdot \frac{\overset{1}{\cancel{3}} \cdot \overset{z}{\cancel{z^2}}}{\underset{2 \cdot 1 \cdot 1}{\cancel{4} \cdot \cancel{x} \cdot \cancel{y}}} = \frac{xz}{2}$$

(B) $(x^2 - 1) \cdot \dfrac{x + 2}{x + 1} = \dfrac{(x - 1)\overset{1}{\cancel{(x + 1)}}}{1} \cdot \dfrac{x + 2}{\underset{1}{\cancel{x + 1}}}$ Factor all numerators
and denominators and
divide out common factors.
Then multiply.

$$= \dfrac{(x - 1)(x + 2)}{1}$$

$$= (x - 1)(x + 2)$$

(C) $\dfrac{x^2 - 1}{x^2 + 5x + 6} \cdot \dfrac{x + 2}{x + 1} = \dfrac{(x - 1)\overset{1}{\cancel{(x + 1)}}}{\underset{1}{\cancel{(x + 2)}}(x + 3)} \cdot \dfrac{\overset{1}{\cancel{x + 2}}}{\underset{1}{\cancel{x + 1}}}$

$$= \dfrac{x - 1}{x + 3}$$

Problem 2 Multiply and reduce to lowest terms:

(A) $\dfrac{3a^2b^2}{5c} \cdot \dfrac{10c^2}{9ab}$ **(B)** $\dfrac{x + 2}{x + 3} \cdot (x^2 - 9)$

(C) $\dfrac{x + 2}{x + 3} \cdot \dfrac{x^2 + 7x + 12}{x^2 - 4}$

DIVISION

The definition of division of real fractions is the same as given in Chapter 3 for quotients of integers: $A \div B = Q$ means $B \cdot Q = A$. The same rule of inverting and multiplying then applies.

Division of Real Fractions

For a, b, c, and d any real numbers ($b, d, c \neq 0$),

Divisor   Reciprocal of divisor

$$\dfrac{a}{b} \div \dfrac{c}{d} = \dfrac{a}{b} \cdot \dfrac{d}{c} \qquad \dfrac{\pi}{2} \div \dfrac{4}{3} = \dfrac{\pi}{2} \cdot \dfrac{3}{4} = \dfrac{3\pi}{8}$$

That is, to divide one fraction by another, multiply by the reciprocal of the divisor.

Example 3   Divide and reduce to lowest terms:

(A) $\dfrac{2x^2y}{3z} \div \dfrac{4xy}{3z^2}$ (B) $(x^2 - 4) \div \dfrac{x - 2}{x + 3}$

(C) $\dfrac{x^2 - x}{x + 1} \div \dfrac{x^2 - 2x + 1}{x^2 + 2x + 1}$

Solution   (A) $\dfrac{2x^2y}{3z} \div \dfrac{4xy}{3z^2} = \dfrac{2x^2y}{3z} \cdot \dfrac{3z^2}{4xy}$ Invert and multiply. The product is the same as Example 2(A).

$= \dfrac{xz}{2}$

(B) $(x^2 - 4) \div \dfrac{x - 2}{x + 3} = (x - 2)(x + 2) \cdot \dfrac{x + 3}{x - 2}$

$= (x + 2)(x + 3)$

(C) $\dfrac{x^2 - x}{x + 1} \div \dfrac{x^2 - 2x + 1}{x^2 + 2x + 1} = \dfrac{x(x - 1)}{x + 1} \cdot \dfrac{(x + 1)(x + 1)}{(x - 1)(x - 1)}$

$= \dfrac{x(x + 1)}{x - 1}$

Problem 3   Divide and reduce to lowest terms:

(A) $\dfrac{2a^2b}{3c^2} \div \dfrac{6ab}{5c}$ (B) $\dfrac{x - 1}{x + 2} \div (x^2 - 1)$

(C) $\dfrac{x^2 + 3x + 2}{x^2 - 9} \div \dfrac{x + 2}{x^2 + 4x + 3}$

ANSWERS TO
MATCHED PROBLEMS

2. (A) $\dfrac{2abc}{3}$ (B) $(x + 2)(x - 3)$ (C) $\dfrac{x + 4}{x - 2}$

3. (A) $\dfrac{5a}{9c}$ (B) $\dfrac{1}{(x + 1)(x + 2)}$ (C) $\dfrac{(x + 1)^2}{x - 3}$

EXERCISE 7-2   *In Problems 1–28, perform the indicated operations and simplify.*

A   **1.** $\dfrac{15}{16} \cdot \dfrac{24}{27}$ **2.** $\dfrac{6}{7} \cdot \dfrac{28}{9}$ **3.** $\dfrac{36}{8} \div \dfrac{9}{4}$

4. $\dfrac{4}{6} \div \dfrac{24}{8}$ **5.** $\dfrac{y^4}{3u^5} \cdot \dfrac{2u^3}{3y}$ **6.** $\dfrac{6x^3y}{7u} \cdot \dfrac{14u^3}{12xy}$

7. $\dfrac{uvw}{5xyz} \div \dfrac{5vy}{uwxz}$

8. $\dfrac{3c^2d}{a^3b^3} \div \dfrac{3a^3b^3}{cd}$

9. $\dfrac{x+3}{2x^2} \cdot \dfrac{4x}{x+3}$

10. $\dfrac{3x^2y}{x-y} \cdot \dfrac{x-y}{6xy}$

11. $\dfrac{a^2-a}{a-1} \cdot \dfrac{a+1}{a}$

12. $\dfrac{x+3}{x^3+3x^2} \cdot \dfrac{x^3}{x-3}$

13. $\dfrac{4x}{x-4} \div \dfrac{8x^2}{x^2-6x+8}$

14. $\dfrac{x-2}{4y} \div \dfrac{x^2+x-6}{12y^2}$

B 15. $\dfrac{d^5}{3a} \div \left(\dfrac{d^2}{6a^2} \cdot \dfrac{a}{4d^3} \right)$

16. $\left(\dfrac{d^5}{3a} \div \dfrac{d^2}{6a^2} \right) \cdot \dfrac{a}{4d^3}$

17. $\dfrac{2x^2+4x}{12x^2y} \cdot \dfrac{6x}{x^2+6x+8}$

18. $\dfrac{6x^2}{4x^2y-12xy} \cdot \dfrac{x^2+x-12}{3x^2+12x}$

19. $\dfrac{2y^2+7y+3}{4y^2-1} \div (y+3)$

20. $(t^2-t-12) \div \dfrac{t^2-9}{t^2-3t}$

21. $\dfrac{x^2-6x+9}{x^2-x-6} \div \dfrac{x^2+2x-15}{x^2+2x}$

22. $\dfrac{m+n}{m^2-n^2} \div \dfrac{m^2-mn}{m^2-2mn+n^2}$

23. $-(x^2-4) \cdot \dfrac{3}{x+2}$

24. $-(x^2-3x) \cdot \dfrac{x-2}{x-3}$

C 25. $\dfrac{2-m}{2m-m^2} \cdot \dfrac{m^2+4m+4}{m^2-4}$

26. $\dfrac{x^2-9}{x^2+5x+6} \cdot \dfrac{x+2}{x-3}$

27. $\left(\dfrac{x^2-xy}{xy+y^2} \div \dfrac{x^2-y^2}{x^2+2xy+y^2} \right) \div \dfrac{x^2-2xy+y^2}{x^2y+xy^2}$

28. $\dfrac{x^2-xy}{xy+y^2} \div \left(\dfrac{x^2-y^2}{x^2+2xy+y^2} \div \dfrac{x^2-2xy+y^2}{x^2y+xy^2} \right)$

29. $(x^2-1)/(x-1)$ and $x+1$ name the same real number for (*all, all but one, no*) replacements of x by real numbers.

30. $(x^2-x-6)/(x-3) = x+2$, except for what values of x?

31. Can you evaluate the following arithmetic problem in less than 3 minutes?

$$\dfrac{(108{,}641)^2 - (108{,}643)^2}{(108{,}642)(108{,}646) - (108{,}644)^2}$$

[*Hint:* Let $108{,}641 = x$, $108{,}642 = x+1$, and so on.]

7-3
ADDITION AND SUBTRACTION

- Addition and Subtraction
- Sign Changes and Multiplication by -1

We will add and subtract rational expressions exactly as we did fractions in Chapter 3. You may want to review Section 3-4.

ADDITION AND SUBTRACTION

To add or subtract real fractions, we proceed in the same way we did for rational numbers. If the denominators are the same, we add or subtract the numerators:

Addition and Subtraction of Real Fractions

For a, b, and c any real numbers ($b \neq 0$),

1. $\dfrac{a}{b} + \dfrac{c}{b} = \dfrac{a + c}{b}$ $\dfrac{\pi}{2} + \dfrac{3}{2} = \dfrac{\pi + 3}{2}$

2. $\dfrac{a}{b} - \dfrac{c}{b} = \dfrac{a - c}{b}$ $\dfrac{2\pi}{3} - \dfrac{\pi}{3} = \dfrac{2\pi - \pi}{3} = \dfrac{\pi}{3}$

If the denominators are not the same, we can use the Fundamental Principle of Fractions to change the fractions to equivalent fractions with the same denominator. We can use any common denominator, but the least common denominator (LCD) will save effort in reducing the resulting sum or difference. The **LCD** in this context means the same as it did in Chapter 3, the least common multiple of all the denominators. We may be able to find the LCD by inspection. If not, we can proceed exactly as we did in Section 3-4:

Finding the Least Common Denominator (LCD)

Step 1 Factor each denominator completely, using integer coefficients.
Step 2 The LCD must contain each *different* factor that occurs in all the denominators to the highest power it occurs in any one denominator.

Example 4   Combine into a single fraction and reduce to lowest terms:

(A) $\dfrac{x - 3}{2(x + 1)} + \dfrac{x - 5}{2(x + 1)}$ **(B)** $\dfrac{4x - 5}{x(x - 1)} - \dfrac{x - 2}{x(x - 1)}$

Solution   **(A)** $\dfrac{x-3}{2(x+1)} + \dfrac{x-5}{2(x+1)}$

Since the denominators are equal, we can add using Property 1 from the box on page 310.

$$= \frac{(x-3)+(x-5)}{2(x+1)}$$

$$= \frac{x-3+x-5}{2(x+1)}$$

Simplify the numerator.

$$= \frac{2x-8}{2(x+1)}$$

Factor the numerator to reduce to lowest terms.

$$= \frac{2(x-4)}{2(x+1)}$$

Remove the common factor 2 from numerator and denominator.

$$= \frac{x-4}{x+1}$$

(B) $\dfrac{4x-5}{x(x-1)} - \dfrac{x-2}{x(x-1)}$

$$= \frac{(4x-5) \overset{\downarrow}{-} (x-2)}{x(x-1)}$$

Using parentheses at this stage will minimize sign errors. The arrows indicate where an error commonly occurs.

$$= \frac{4x-5 \overset{\downarrow}{-} x \overset{\downarrow}{+} 2}{x(x-1)}$$

Simplify the numerator. Be careful of the signs!

$$= \frac{3x-3}{x(x-1)}$$

Factor the numerator.

$$= \frac{3(x-1)}{x(x-1)}$$

$$= \frac{3}{x}$$

Problem 4   Combine into a single fraction and reduce to lowest terms:

(A) $\dfrac{x^2-4x+1}{x(x+2)} + \dfrac{x^2-1}{x(x+2)}$

(B) $\dfrac{3x+5}{3(x+4)} - \dfrac{x-3}{3(x+4)}$

Example 5   Combine into a single fraction and then reduce to lowest terms:

$$\frac{1}{4(x + 1)} + \frac{1}{2(x^2 - 1)}$$

Solution   Find the LCD of the denominators:

$$4(x + 1) = 2^2(x + 1) \qquad \text{Factor each denominator completely.}$$

$$2(x^2 - 1) = 2(x + 1)(x - 1)$$

$$\text{LCD} = 2^2(x + 1)(x - 1) \qquad \text{The LCD contains each different} \\ \text{factor to the highest power it} \\ \text{occurs in any denominator.}$$

$$= 4(x^2 - 1)$$

Use the Fundamental Principle of Fractions to change each fraction to one with the LCD as denominator:

$$\frac{1}{4(x + 1)} = \frac{(x - 1)}{4(x + 1)(x - 1)} = \frac{x - 1}{4(x^2 - 1)}$$

$$\frac{1}{2(x^2 - 1)} = \frac{2}{2 \cdot 2(x^2 - 1)} = \frac{2}{4(x^2 - 1)}$$

Now we can add the fractions:

$$\frac{1}{4(x + 1)} + \frac{1}{2(x^2 - 1)} = \frac{x - 1}{4(x^2 - 1)} + \frac{2}{4(x^2 - 1)}$$

$$= \frac{x - 1 + 2}{4(x^2 - 1)} = \frac{x + 1}{4(x^2 - 1)}$$

$$= \frac{x + 1}{4(x + 1)(x - 1)}$$

$$= \frac{1}{4(x - 1)}$$

As we indicated before, we could have used any common denominator to combine the fractions. For example, here we could have used the product $4(x + 1) \cdot 2(x^2 - 1)$. If we had done so, however, more common factors would have had to be removed to reduce the result to lowest terms. Try using $4(x + 1) \cdot 2(x^2 - 1)$ as the common denominator to see what happens.

Problem 5 Combine into a single fraction and reduce to lowest terms:

$$\frac{3x + 1}{5(x^2 - 2x - 3)} - \frac{1}{10(x + 1)}$$

Example 6 Combine into a single fraction and reduce to lowest terms:

$$\frac{3}{(x - 1)(x + 2)} - \frac{5}{(x + 2)(x - 3)}$$

Solution

$$\frac{3}{(x - 1)(x + 2)} - \frac{5}{(x + 2)(x - 3)}$$ The LCD is $(x - 1)(x + 2)(x - 3)$ Use the Fundamental Principle of Fractions to convert each fraction so the denominator is the LCD.

$$= \frac{3(x - 3)}{(x - 1)(x + 2)(x - 3)} - \frac{5(x - 1)}{(x - 1)(x + 2)(x - 3)}$$

$$= \frac{3(x - 3) - 5(x - 1)}{(x - 1)(x + 2)(x - 3)}$$

$$= \frac{3x - 9 - 5x + 5}{(x - 1)(x + 2)(x - 3)}$$

$$= \frac{-2x - 4}{(x - 1)(x + 2)(x - 3)}$$

$$= \frac{-2(x + 2)}{(x - 1)(x + 2)(x - 3)} = \frac{-2}{(x - 1)(x - 3)}$$

Problem 6 Combine into a single fraction and reduce to lowest terms:

$$\frac{2}{(x + 1)(x + 3)} + \frac{3}{(x + 1)(x - 2)}$$

SIGN CHANGES AND MULTIPLICATION BY -1

The relationship

$$-(a - b) = b - a$$

that you were reminded of in Section 6-1, is often useful in combining fractions. Keep in mind that the relation results from multiplying by -1:

$$\begin{aligned}
-(a - b) &= (-1)(a - b) \\
&= (-1)a - (-1)b \\
&= -a - (-b) \\
&= -a + b \\
&= b - a
\end{aligned}$$

Example 7   Replace the question mark with an appropriate algebraic expression.

(A) $x - 3 = -(?)$ **(B)** $2x - 5 = -(?)$
(C) $-(x - 1) = (?) - x$

Solution   **(A)** $x - 3 = -(3 - x)$
(B) $2x - 5 = -(5 - 2x)$
(C) $-(x - 1) = 1 - x$

Problem 7   Replace the question mark with an appropriate algebraic expression.

(A) $a - 2 = -(?)$ **(B)** $3 - a = -(?)$
(C) $-(2a - 3) = (?) - 2a$

Example 8   Combine into a single fraction and reduce to lowest terms:

$$\frac{x}{x - 1} + \frac{2}{1 - x}$$

Solution $\dfrac{x}{x - 1} + \dfrac{2}{1 - x} = \dfrac{x}{x - 1} + \dfrac{2}{-(x - 1)}$ Recognize $1 - x = -(x - 1)$.

$$= \frac{x}{x - 1} - \frac{2}{x - 1}$$ Recall $\dfrac{a}{-b} = -\dfrac{a}{b}$.

$$= \frac{x - 2}{x - 1}$$

We could also have solved this problem by noting that

$$\frac{2}{1 - x} = \frac{-2}{-(1 - x)} = \frac{-2}{x - 1}$$

so that

$$\frac{x}{x - 1} + \frac{2}{1 - x} = \frac{x}{x - 1} + \frac{-2}{x - 1} = \frac{x - 2}{x - 1}$$

Problem 8   Combine into a single fraction and reduce to lowest terms:

$$\frac{3}{y - 3} - \frac{y}{3 - y}$$

ANSWERS TO
MATCHED PROBLEMS

4. (A) $\dfrac{2(x-2)}{x+2}$ (B) $\dfrac{2}{3}$ **5.** $\dfrac{1}{2(x-3)}$ **6.** $\dfrac{5}{(x-2)(x+3)}$

7. (A) $2-a$ (B) $a-3$ (C) 3 **8.** $\dfrac{y+3}{y-3}$

EXERCISE 7-3 *Combine into single fractions and reduce to lowest terms.*

A **1.** $\dfrac{3}{2x}-\dfrac{1}{2x}$ **2.** $\dfrac{2}{3x}+\dfrac{1}{3x}$

3. $\dfrac{5}{3x^2}+\dfrac{1}{3x^2}$ **4.** $\dfrac{5}{2x^2}-\dfrac{1}{2x^2}$

5. $\dfrac{2x}{x+3}+\dfrac{6}{x+3}$ **6.** $\dfrac{4}{x+3}-\dfrac{1}{x+3}$

7. $\dfrac{4}{x-1}-\dfrac{3}{x-1}$ **8.** $\dfrac{2x}{x-1}+\dfrac{-2}{x-1}$

9. $\dfrac{1}{z}+\dfrac{2}{z+3}$ **10.** $\dfrac{1}{z}-\dfrac{2}{z+3}$

11. $\dfrac{3}{y+1}-\dfrac{2}{y+2}$ **12.** $\dfrac{3}{y+1}+\dfrac{2}{y+2}$

B **13.** $\dfrac{3}{x+1}-\dfrac{6}{x^2-1}$ **14.** $\dfrac{3}{x+1}+\dfrac{6}{x^2-1}$

15. $\dfrac{1}{x}+\dfrac{x}{x(x+1)}$ **16.** $\dfrac{1}{x}-\dfrac{x}{x(x+1)}$

17. $1-\dfrac{y}{y-1}$ **18.** $1+\dfrac{y}{y-1}$

19. $\dfrac{1}{(x-1)(x-2)}+\dfrac{2}{(x-1)(x-3)}$

20. $\dfrac{2}{(x-1)(x-2)}-\dfrac{1}{(x-1)(x-3)}$

21. $\dfrac{3}{x(x+1)}-\dfrac{6}{x(x+2)}$ **22.** $\dfrac{1}{x(x+1)}+\dfrac{2}{x(x+2)}$

23. $\dfrac{1}{x^2-4}-\dfrac{2}{x^2-4x+4}$ **24.** $\dfrac{2}{x^2-4}+\dfrac{1}{x^2-4x+4}$

25. $\dfrac{-1}{x^2-5x+6}+\dfrac{6}{x^2-9}$ **26.** $\dfrac{1}{x^2-5x+6}-\dfrac{3}{x^2-9}$

27. $1 + \dfrac{2}{x} + \dfrac{3}{x^2}$

28. $3 + \dfrac{2}{x} + \dfrac{1}{x^2}$

29. $\dfrac{-1}{x^2 + 3x + 2} + \dfrac{7}{x^2 + 5x + 4}$

30. $\dfrac{1}{x^2 + 3x + 2} - \dfrac{3}{x^2 + 5x + 4}$

31. $\dfrac{3}{x - 1} + \dfrac{2}{x + 1} - \dfrac{6}{x^2 - 1}$

32. $\dfrac{2}{x - 1} - \dfrac{3}{x + 1} + \dfrac{x - 5}{x^2 - 1}$

33. $\dfrac{1}{x(x - 1)} + \dfrac{1}{x^2 - 1} + \dfrac{2}{x(x + 1)}$

34. $\dfrac{-3}{x(x + 1)} - \dfrac{2}{x + 1} + \dfrac{3}{x}$

35. $\dfrac{1}{y - 1} + \dfrac{2}{1 - y^2}$

36. $\dfrac{-y}{y^2 - 1} - \dfrac{1}{1 - y}$

37. $\dfrac{-2}{y^2 - 1} + \dfrac{2}{1 - y} - \dfrac{1}{1 + y}$

38. $\dfrac{4}{x^2 - 4} - \dfrac{2}{2 - x} + \dfrac{1}{2 + x}$

7-4
EQUATIONS INVOLVING FRACTIONAL FORMS

- Equations with Constants in Denominators
- Equations with Variables in Denominators
- Application

Equations involving fractional forms are generally solved by eliminating the fractions. Special care must be taken, however, in the case where a variable occurs in a denominator.

EQUATIONS WITH CONSTANTS IN DENOMINATORS

We have already considered equations involving constants in denominators, such as

$$\frac{2}{3} - \frac{x-4}{2} = \frac{5x}{6}$$

(see Section 3-5) and found we could easily convert such an equation into an equivalent equation with integer coefficients by multiplying both sides by the LCM of the denominators—in this case 6:

$$\mathbf{6} \cdot \frac{2}{3} - \mathbf{6} \cdot \frac{(x-4)}{2} = \mathbf{6} \cdot \frac{5x}{6} \quad \text{Multiply each side by 6 to clear fractions.}$$

Since 6 is the LCM of the denominators, each denominator will divide into 6 exactly, leaving

$$4 - 3(x - 4) = 5x$$

and we finish the solution in a few simple steps:

$$4 - 3x + 12 = 5x \quad \text{A sign error frequently occurs where the arrow points.}$$
$$-3x + 16 = 5x$$
$$-8x = -16$$
$$x = 2$$

EQUATIONS WITH VARIABLES IN DENOMINATORS

If an equation involves a variable in one or more denominators, such as

$$\frac{3}{x} - \frac{1}{2} = \frac{4}{x}$$

we may proceed in essentially the same way as above so long as we are careful:

We must avoid any value that makes a denominator in the equation 0.

Example 9   Solve $\dfrac{3}{x} - \dfrac{1}{2} = \dfrac{4}{x}$.

Solution
$$\frac{3}{x} - \frac{1}{2} = \frac{4}{x} \qquad x \neq 0$$

If 0 turns up later as an apparent solution, then it must be discarded, since we cannot divide by 0. Since $x \neq 0$, we can multiply both sides by $2x$, the LCM of the denominators.

$$2x \cdot \frac{3}{x} - 2x \cdot \frac{1}{2} = 2x \cdot \frac{4}{x}$$

All denominators divide out.

$$6 - x = 8$$
$$-x = 2$$
$$x = -2$$

Problem 9   Solve $\dfrac{2}{3} - \dfrac{2}{x} = \dfrac{4}{x}$.

Example 10   Solve $\dfrac{3x}{x-2} - 4 = \dfrac{14 - 4x}{x-2}$.

Solution

$$\frac{3x}{x-2} - 4 = \frac{14 - 4x}{x-2} \qquad x \neq 2$$

If 2 turns up later as an apparent solution, it must be rejected, since we cannot divide by $2 - 2 = 0$. Multiply by $(x - 2)$, the LCM of the denominators. Also, it is a good idea to place all binomial numerators and denominators in parentheses to avoid multiplication errors.

$$(x-2)\frac{3x}{(x-2)} - 4(x-2) = (x-2)\frac{(14-4x)}{(x-2)}$$

$$3x - 4(x - 2) = 14 - 4x$$
$$3x - 4x + 8 = 14 - 4x$$
$$-x + 8 = 14 - 4x$$
$$3x = 6$$
$$x = 2 \qquad\qquad \text{\textit{x} cannot equal 2.}$$

The original equation has no solution. Results such as $x = 2$ in this case are called **extraneous solutions**.

Problem 10   Solve $\dfrac{2x}{x-1} - 3 = \dfrac{7 - 3x}{x-1}$.

APPLICATION

Sometimes even a simple application will lead to an equation with a variable in the denominator.

Example 11   A baseball player begins the week with 31 hits in 100 at bats for a batting average (hits/at bats) of .310. During the week he gets 11 hits and raises his average to exactly .350. How many times did the player bat during the week?

Solution   Let x be the number of at bats during the week. The player's overall average at the end of the week is

$$\frac{\text{Total hits}}{\text{Total at bats}} = \frac{31 + 11}{100 + x} = \frac{42}{100 + x} = .350$$

Thus

$$.35(100 + x) = 42$$
$$35 + .35x = 42$$
$$.35x = 7$$
$$x = \frac{7}{.35} = 20 \text{ at bats}$$

Problem 11   A basketball player has made 18 out of 24 free throws for a free throw percentage of 0.75 (that is, 75%). Several games later she has made 10 more free throws and raised her free throw percentage to 80%. How many more free throws did she attempt?

ANSWERS TO MATCHED PROBLEMS
9. $x = 9$ **10.** $x = 2$ **11.** 11

EXERCISE 7-4   *Solve.*

A   **1.** $\dfrac{2}{x} - \dfrac{1}{3} = \dfrac{5}{x}$

2. $\dfrac{1}{2} - \dfrac{2}{x} = \dfrac{3}{x}$

3. $\dfrac{5}{6} - \dfrac{1}{y} = \dfrac{2}{3y}$

4. $\dfrac{1}{x} + \dfrac{2}{3} = \dfrac{1}{2}$

5. $\dfrac{2}{3x} + \dfrac{1}{2} = \dfrac{4}{x} + \dfrac{4}{3}$

6. $\dfrac{1}{m} - \dfrac{1}{9} = \dfrac{4}{9} - \dfrac{2}{3m}$

7. $\dfrac{1}{2t} + \dfrac{1}{8} = \dfrac{2}{t} - \dfrac{1}{4}$

8. $\dfrac{4}{3k} - 2 = \dfrac{k + 4}{6k}$

B   **9.** $\dfrac{9}{L + 1} - 1 = \dfrac{12}{L + 1}$

10. $\dfrac{7}{y - 2} - \dfrac{1}{2} = 3$

11. $\dfrac{3}{2x - 1} + 4 = \dfrac{6x}{2x - 1}$

12. $\dfrac{5x}{x + 5} = 2 - \dfrac{25}{x + 5}$

13. $\dfrac{3N}{N - 2} - \dfrac{9}{4N} = 3$

14. $\dfrac{2E}{E - 1} = 2 + \dfrac{5}{2E}$

15. $5 + \dfrac{2x}{x - 3} = \dfrac{6}{x - 3}$

16. $\dfrac{6}{x - 2} = 3 + \dfrac{3x}{x - 2}$

17. $\dfrac{5}{x - 3} = \dfrac{33 - x}{x^2 - 6x + 9}$

18. $\dfrac{D^2 + 2}{D^2 - 4} = \dfrac{D}{D - 2}$

19. $\dfrac{n-5}{6n-6} = \dfrac{1}{9} - \dfrac{n-3}{4n-4}$

20. $\dfrac{1}{3} - \dfrac{s-2}{2s+4} = \dfrac{s+2}{3s+6}$

C **21.** $\dfrac{2}{x-2} = 3 - \dfrac{5}{2-x}$

22. $\dfrac{3x}{x-4} - 2 = \dfrac{3}{4-x}$

23. $\dfrac{5x-22}{x^2-6x+9} - \dfrac{11}{x^2-3x} - \dfrac{5}{x} = 0$

24. $\dfrac{1}{x^2-x-2} - \dfrac{3}{x^2-2x-3} = \dfrac{1}{x^2-5x+6}$

25. A baseball player has 118 hits in 412 at bats for a batting average of approximately .286. How many consecutive hits will raise his average to exactly .300?

26. A basketball player has made 35 of 46 free throws for a percentage of approximately .761. How many consecutive free throws made will raise her percentage to exactly .800?

7-5
FORMULAS AND EQUATIONS WITH SEVERAL VARIABLES

Literal equations were introduced in Section 2-7. There we noted that solving for one variable in terms of the others often results in fractional forms. We can now deal more fully with such forms. In the following examples, formulas involving several variables are changed to isolate a particular variable. The remaining variables are treated as constants in the solution process. The process is the same as we have used for single-variable equations: first, remove any fractions by multiplying by the LCM of the denominators as in Sections 3-5 and 7-4; then solve by isolating the variable as in Section 2-7.

Example 12   Solve the formula $c = wrt/1{,}000$ for t. (The formula gives the cost of using an electrical appliance, where $w =$ Power in watts, $r =$ Rate per kilowatt-hour, $t =$ Time in hours.)

Solution

$$c = \frac{wrt}{1{,}000} \qquad \text{Start with the given formula.}$$

$$1{,}000c = wrt \qquad \text{Multiply both sides of the equation by 1,000 to remove fractions.}$$

$$\frac{1{,}000c}{wr} = t \qquad \text{Divide both sides, by } wr, \text{ the coefficient of } t.$$

It is not necessary that the variable t be isolated on the left side of the equation, since the final form is equivalent to $t = 1{,}000c/wr$. If desired, equations can be reversed at any step by using the symmetric property of equality.

Problem 12 Solve the formula in Example 12 for w.

Example 13 Solve the formula $A = P + Prt$ for r (simple interest formula).

Solution
$$A = P + Prt$$
$$P + Prt = A$$ Reverse the equation; then perform operations to isolate r on the left side.†
$$Prt = A - P$$

$$\frac{Prt}{Pt} = \frac{A - P}{Pt}$$

$$r = \frac{A - P}{Pt}$$

Problem 13 Solve the formula $A = P + Prt$ for t.

Example 14 Solve the formula $A = P + Prt$ for P.

Solution
$$A = P + Prt$$
$$P + Prt = A$$

Note: If we write $P = A - Prt$ we have not solved for P. To solve for P is to isolate P on the left side with a coefficient of 1. **In general, if the variable we are solving for appears on both sides of an equation, we have not solved for it!** Since P is a common factor to both terms on the left, we factor P out and complete the problem:

$$P(1 + rt) = A$$ Divide both sides by $(1 + rt)$ to isolate P.

$$\frac{P(1 + rt)}{(1 + rt)} = \frac{A}{(1 + rt)}$$

$$P = \frac{A}{1 + rt}$$ Note that P appears only on the left side.

Problem 14 Solve $A = ac + ab$ for a.

Example 15 Solve $K = \dfrac{3t^2}{s}$ for s.

† Isolating the variable on the left, rather than the right, is only tradition, not a mathematical necessity.

Solution $K = \dfrac{3t^2}{s}$ Multiply both sides by *s* to remove fractions.

$sK = 3t^2$ Divide both sides by *K* to isolate *s*.

$s = \dfrac{3t^2}{K}$

Problem 15   Solve $M = \dfrac{c + d}{e}$ for *e*.

Example 16   Solve $\dfrac{1}{a} = \dfrac{1}{b} + \dfrac{1}{c}$ for *a*.

Solution $\dfrac{1}{a} = \dfrac{1}{b} + \dfrac{1}{c}$ Multiply both sides by *abc* to clear fractions.

$$abc \cdot \dfrac{1}{a} = abc \cdot \dfrac{1}{b} + abc \cdot \dfrac{1}{c}$$

$bc = ac + ab$ Reverse equation.

$ac + ab = bc$ Factor out *a*.

$a(c + b) = bc$ Divide both sides by $(c + b)$.

$a = \dfrac{bc}{c + b}$

Problem 16   Solve $\dfrac{1}{a} = \dfrac{1}{b} + \dfrac{1}{c}$ for *b*.

Example 17   Solve $y = \dfrac{x + 2}{3x - 1}$ for *x* in terms of *y*.

Solution $y = \dfrac{x + 2}{3x - 1}$ Remove fractions by multiplying each side by $3x - 1$.

$y(3x - 1) = x + 2$ Simplify the left side.

$3yx - y = x + 2$ Isolate *x* on the left side.

$3yx - y - x = 2$

$3yx - x = 2 + y$ Factor out *x* on the left side.

$(3y - 1)x = 2 + y$

$x = \dfrac{2 + y}{3y - 1}$

Problem 17   Solve $y = \dfrac{2x - 1}{x + 3}$ for x in terms of y.

ANSWERS TO MATCHED PROBLEMS

12. $w = \dfrac{1{,}000c}{rt}$ **13.** $t = \dfrac{A - P}{Pr}$ **14.** $a = \dfrac{A}{c + b}$

15. $e = \dfrac{c + d}{M}$ **16.** $b = \dfrac{ac}{c - a}$ **17.** $x = \dfrac{3y + 1}{2 - y}$

EXERCISE 7-5   *The following formulas and equations are widely used in science and mathematics.*

A   **1.**   Solve $A = P + I$ for I.   *Simple interest*

    2.   Solve $R = R_1 + R_2$ for R_2.   *Electric circuits—resistance in series*

    3.   Solve $d = rt$ for r.   *Distance–rate–time*

    4.   Solve $d = 1{,}100t$ for t.   *Sound distance in air*

    5.   Solve $I = Prt$ for t.   *Simple interest*

    6.   Solve $C = 2\pi r$ for r.   *Circumference of a circle*

    7.   Solve $C = \pi D$ for π.   *Circumference of a circle*

    8.   Solve $e = mc^2$ for m.   *Mass–energy equation*

    9.   Solve $ax + b = 0$ for x.   *First-degree polynomial equation in one variable*

    10. Solve $p = 2a + 2b$ for a.   *Perimeter of a rectangle*

    11. Solve $s = 2t - 5$ for t.   *Slope–intercept form for a line*

    12. Solve $y = mx + b$ for m.   *Slope–intercept form for a line*

B   **13.** Solve $3x - 4y - 12 = 0$ for y.   *Linear equation in two variables*

    14. Solve $Ax + By + C = 0$ for y.   *Linear equation in two variables*

    15. Solve $I = E/R$ for E.   *Electric circuits—Ohm's law*

    16. Solve $m = b/a$ for b.   *Optics—magnification*

    17. Solve the formula in Problem 15 for R.

    18. Solve the formula in Problem 16 for a.

19. Solve $c = 100B/L$ for B.   *Anthropology—cephalic index*

20. Solve IQ = (100)(MA)/(CA) for (MA).   *Psychology—intelligence quotient*

21. Solve the formula in Problem 19 for L.

22. Solve the formula in Problem 20 for (CA).

23. Solve $F = G(mM/d^2)$ for m.   *Gravitational force between two masses*

24. Solve the formula in Problem 23 for G.

25. Solve $P = M - Mdt$ for d.   *Simple discount*

26. Solve the formula in Problem 25 for t.

27. Solve the formula in Problem 25 for M.

28. Solve $A = \dfrac{ah}{2} + \dfrac{bh}{2}$ for h.   *Area of a trapezoid*

29. Solve $C = \tfrac{5}{9}(F - 32)$ for F.   *Celsius–Fahrenheit*

30. Solve $F = \tfrac{9}{5}C + 32$ for C.   *Fahrenheit–Celsius*

C **31.** Solve $\dfrac{1}{f} = \dfrac{1}{a} + \dfrac{1}{b}$ for f.   *Optics–focal length*

32. Solve $\dfrac{1}{R} = \dfrac{1}{R_1} + \dfrac{1}{R_2}$ for R_1.   *Electrical resistance*

33. Solve $y = \dfrac{3x + 1}{2x - 1}$ for x in terms of y.

34. Solve $y = \dfrac{x - 3}{3x - 2}$ for x in terms of y.

35. Solve $a = \dfrac{b + 2}{2b - 1}$ for b in terms of a.

36. Solve $a = \dfrac{3b - 2}{b + 1}$ for b in terms of a.

37. Solve $x = \dfrac{y - 3z}{2y + z}$ for y.

38. Solve $x = \dfrac{y - 3z}{2y + z}$ for z.

7-6
COMPLEX FRACTIONS

- Simplifying by Using Division
- Simplifying by Using the Fundamental Principle of Fractions

A fraction form with fractions in its numerator or denominator is called a **complex fraction**. It is often necessary to represent a complex fraction as a **simple fraction**—that is (in all cases we will consider), as the quotient of two polynomials or two integers. The process does not involve any new concepts. It is a matter of applying old concepts appropriately.

SIMPLIFYING BY USING DIVISION

All fractions, simple or complex, represent division problems. To simplify, it is often easiest just to divide.

Example 18 Express as a simple fraction:

$$\text{(A)} \quad \frac{\dfrac{3}{5}}{\dfrac{2}{3}} \qquad \text{(B)} \quad \frac{\dfrac{a}{2b}}{\dfrac{a^2}{b}}$$

Solution (A) $\dfrac{\dfrac{3}{5}}{\dfrac{2}{3}} = \dfrac{3}{5} \div \dfrac{2}{3} = \dfrac{3}{5} \cdot \dfrac{3}{2} = \dfrac{9}{10}$

(B) $\dfrac{\dfrac{a}{2b}}{\dfrac{a^2}{b}} = \dfrac{a}{2b} \div \dfrac{a^2}{b} = \dfrac{a}{2b} \cdot \dfrac{b}{a^2} = \dfrac{1}{2a}$

Problem 18 Express as a simple fraction:

$$\text{(A)} \quad \frac{\dfrac{3}{4}}{\dfrac{5}{8}} \qquad \text{(B)} \quad \frac{\dfrac{xy}{z^2}}{\dfrac{x}{yz}}$$

Example 19 Express as a simple fraction:

$$\frac{\dfrac{x}{x^2-1}}{\dfrac{x^2}{x+1}}$$

Solution

$$\frac{\dfrac{x}{x^2-1}}{\dfrac{x^2}{x+1}} = \frac{x}{x^2-1} \div \frac{x^2}{x+1} = \frac{x}{x^2-1} \cdot \frac{x+1}{x^2}$$

$$= \frac{x}{(x+1)(x-1)} \cdot \frac{x+1}{x^2} = \frac{1}{x(x-1)}$$

Problem 19   Express as a simple fraction:

$$\frac{\dfrac{a^2}{a^2-2a-3}}{\dfrac{a}{a^2-9}}$$

SIMPLIFYING BY USING THE FUNDAMENTAL PRINCIPLE OF FRACTIONS

The Fundamental Principle of Fractions

$$\frac{a}{b} = \frac{ka}{kb} \qquad b, k \neq 0$$

can also be used to simplify complex fractions. Consider, for example, the complex fraction simplified in Example 19:

$$\frac{\dfrac{x}{x^2-1}}{\dfrac{x^2}{x+1}}$$

If we multiply the numerator and denominator by $k = x^2 - 1$, the top and bottom fractions will disappear:

$$\frac{(x^2-1)\dfrac{x}{x^2-1}}{(x^2-1)\dfrac{x^2}{x+1}} = \frac{x}{(x-1)x^2} = \frac{1}{(x-1)x}$$

We chose the multiplier $x^2 - 1$ because it is the LCD of the top and bottom fractions.

Example 20 Express as a simple fraction:

$$\text{(A)}\quad \frac{1 - \dfrac{1}{x}}{x - \dfrac{1}{x}} \qquad \text{(B)}\quad \frac{\dfrac{a}{b} - \dfrac{b}{a}}{\dfrac{1}{b} + \dfrac{1}{a}}$$

Solution **(A)** $\dfrac{1 - \dfrac{1}{x}}{x - \dfrac{1}{x}} = \dfrac{x\left(1 - \dfrac{1}{x}\right)}{x\left(x - \dfrac{1}{x}\right)}$

Multiply top and bottom by x, the LCD of the fractions in the numerator and denominator.

$$= \frac{x - 1}{x^2 - 1}$$

Factor the denominator and reduce to lowest terms.

$$= \frac{x - 1}{(x - 1)(x + 1)}$$

$$= \frac{1}{x + 1}$$

(B) $\dfrac{\dfrac{a}{b} - \dfrac{b}{a}}{\dfrac{1}{b} + \dfrac{1}{a}} = \dfrac{ab\left(\dfrac{a}{b} - \dfrac{b}{a}\right)}{ab\left(\dfrac{1}{b} + \dfrac{1}{a}\right)}$

The LCD of the fractions in the numerator and denominator is ab.

$$= \frac{a^2 - b^2}{a + b}$$

Reduce to lowest terms.

$$= a - b$$

Problem 20 Express as a simple fraction:

$$\text{(A)}\quad \frac{4 - \dfrac{1}{x^2}}{1 - \dfrac{1}{2x}} \qquad \text{(B)}\quad \frac{\dfrac{1}{a} - \dfrac{1}{b}}{b - \dfrac{a^2}{b}}$$

Which Method? When internal fractions within a fraction have denominators that contain more than one term (as in Example 19), the division method is usually easier to use. If internal fractions have single-term denominators (as in Example 20), using the fundamental principle of fractions to clear denominators is generally easier.

18.   **(A)** $\dfrac{6}{5}$ **(B)** $\dfrac{y^2}{z}$

19. $\dfrac{a(a + 3)}{a + 1}$

20.   **(A)** $\dfrac{2(2x + 1)}{x}$ **(B)** $\dfrac{1}{a(a + b)}$

EXERCISE 7-6   *Express as simple fractions reduced to lowest terms.*

A   **1.** $\dfrac{\dfrac{2}{3}}{\dfrac{4}{5}}$ **2.** $\dfrac{\dfrac{3}{4}}{\dfrac{3}{8}}$ **3.** $\dfrac{\dfrac{7}{12}}{\dfrac{2}{3}}$ **4.** $\dfrac{\dfrac{4}{5}}{\dfrac{8}{15}}$

5. $\dfrac{\dfrac{x^2 y}{z}}{\dfrac{xy^2}{z^2}}$ **6.** $\dfrac{\dfrac{x^2 y^2}{z^2}}{\dfrac{xy^3}{z}}$ **7.** $\dfrac{\dfrac{a^4}{b^3 c^2}}{\dfrac{a^2}{b^3 c^4}}$ **8.** $\dfrac{\dfrac{a^3}{b^3 c}}{\dfrac{a}{bc}}$

9. $\dfrac{\dfrac{a}{bc}}{\dfrac{b}{ac}}$ **10.** $\dfrac{\dfrac{xy^2}{z^3}}{\dfrac{x}{yz}}$ **11.** $\dfrac{\dfrac{x^2 - y^2}{x}}{\dfrac{x - y}{y}}$ **12.** $\dfrac{\dfrac{a^2 - b^2}{ab}}{\dfrac{a + b}{ab}}$

B   **13.** $\dfrac{x - \dfrac{1}{x}}{x - 1}$ **14.** $\dfrac{\dfrac{x - 1}{x}}{1 - \dfrac{1}{x}}$ **15.** $\dfrac{\dfrac{x^2 - y^2}{xy}}{1 - \dfrac{y}{x}}$ **16.** $\dfrac{\dfrac{1}{a} - \dfrac{1}{b}}{\dfrac{b}{a} - \dfrac{a}{b}}$

17. $\dfrac{1 - \dfrac{1}{a^2}}{1 + \dfrac{1}{a}}$ **18.** $\dfrac{\dfrac{a}{b} - \dfrac{b}{a}}{\dfrac{1}{a} + \dfrac{1}{b}}$ **19.** $\dfrac{\dfrac{1}{x} - \dfrac{1}{y}}{\dfrac{1}{x^2} - \dfrac{1}{y^2}}$ **20.** $\dfrac{a - \dfrac{b^2}{a}}{\dfrac{1}{a} - \dfrac{1}{b}}$

21. $\dfrac{\dfrac{m^2}{m^2 + m - 6}}{\dfrac{m^3}{m^2 - 9}}$ **22.** $\dfrac{\dfrac{2x^2 y}{x^2 + xy - 2y^2}}{\dfrac{4xy^2}{x^2 - 4y^2}}$

23. $\dfrac{\dfrac{n^2 - m^2}{m^2 - mn}}{\dfrac{-m^3}{m^2 + mn}}$

24. $\dfrac{\dfrac{bc - ac}{a^2 - 7a + 12}}{\dfrac{-(a - b)}{a^2 - a - 6}}$

25. $\dfrac{\dfrac{x^2}{x + y} - x}{\dfrac{y^2}{x + y} - y}$

26. $\dfrac{\dfrac{x}{x + y} - 1}{\dfrac{x^3}{x^2 - y^2} - x}$

27. $\dfrac{\dfrac{x^3 - y^3}{x^3 y^3}}{\dfrac{x - y}{x^2 y^2}}$

28. $\dfrac{\dfrac{a^2 - b^2}{a^3 + b^3}}{\dfrac{a^3 - b^3}{a^2 + ab + b^2}}$

29. $\dfrac{\dfrac{x}{x + 1} - \dfrac{x}{x - 1}}{\dfrac{x + 1}{x - 1} - \dfrac{x - 1}{x + 1}}$

30. $\dfrac{\dfrac{a - b}{a} - \dfrac{a + b}{b}}{\dfrac{a + b}{a} + \dfrac{a - b}{b}}$

31. $1 + \dfrac{1}{1 + \dfrac{1}{x}}$

32. $1 - \dfrac{a}{a - \dfrac{1}{a}}$

APPLICATIONS

33. If one pump can empty a pool in r minutes and a second can empty it in s minutes, then the two working together can empty it in

$$t = \frac{1}{\dfrac{1}{r} + \dfrac{1}{s}} \text{ minutes}$$

Express t as a simple fraction.

34. The airspeed indicator on a jet aircraft registers 500 miles per hour. If the plane is traveling with an airstream moving at 100 miles per hour, then the plane's ground speed would be 600 miles per hour—or would it? According to Einstein, velocities must be added according to the following formula:

$$v = \frac{v_1 + v_2}{1 + \dfrac{v_1 v_2}{c^2}}$$

where v is the resultant velocity, c is the speed of light, and v_1 and v_2 are the two velocities to be added. Convert the right side of the equation into a simple fraction.

7-7
CHAPTER REVIEW

A **rational expression** is a fraction form in which the numerator and denominator are polynomials. The **fundamental principle of real fractions**

$$\frac{ak}{bk} = \frac{a}{b}$$

is used with rational expressions to **reduce to lower terms**.   *(7-1)*

Multiplication, division *(7-2)*, addition, and subtraction *(7-3)* are performed as for rational numbers:

$$\frac{a}{b} \cdot \frac{c}{d} = \frac{ac}{bd} \qquad \frac{a}{b} + \frac{c}{b} = \frac{a+c}{b}$$

$$\frac{a}{b} \div \frac{c}{d} = \frac{a}{b} \cdot \frac{d}{c} \qquad \frac{a}{b} - \frac{c}{b} = \frac{a-c}{b}$$

To add or subtract rational expressions with different denominators, the form of the fractions is changed, using the fundamental principle, so that the denominators are the same. The **least common denominator (LCD)** is generally used. To find the LCD, factor each denominator and include each factor to the highest power it occurs in any denominator. In simplifying fractions, the identity $a - b = -(b - a)$ may be useful.   *(7-3)*

Equations with only constants in the denominators are solved by first removing fractions by multiplying both sides by the LCM of the denominators. Equations involving variables in the denominators are solved the same way, but values that make a denominator 0 must be avoided.   *(7-4)*

Formulas involving several variables may be solved for one variable in terms of the other; the process is the same as for one-variable equations. *(7-5)*

A **complex fraction** is a fractional form with fractions in its numerator or denominator. It may be reduced to a **simple fraction**, the quotient of two polynomials, either by using the fundamental principle of fractions or by using division.   *(7-6)*

REVIEW EXERCISE 7-7

Work through all the problems in this chapter review and check answers in the back of the book. (Answers to all problems are there, and following each answer is a number in italics indicating the section in which that type of problem is discussed.) Where weaknesses show up, review appropriate sections in the text.

A *Perform the indicated operations and reduce to lowest terms.*

1. $1 + \dfrac{2}{3x}$

2. $\dfrac{2}{x} - \dfrac{1}{6x} + \dfrac{1}{3}$

3. $\dfrac{3x^2(x - 3)}{6y} \cdot \dfrac{8y^3}{9(x - 3)^2}$

4. $(d - 2)^2 \div \dfrac{d^2 - 4}{d - 2}$

5. $\dfrac{2}{3x - 1} - \dfrac{1}{2x}$

6. $\dfrac{x}{x - 4} - 1$

7. $\dfrac{\frac{1}{4}}{\frac{5}{6}}$

8. $\dfrac{4\frac{2}{3}}{1\frac{1}{2}}$

Solve.

9. $\dfrac{2}{3m} - \dfrac{1}{4m} = \dfrac{1}{12}$

10. $\dfrac{3x}{x - 5} - 8 = \dfrac{15}{x - 5}$

11. Solve $A = bh/2$ for b.   *Area of a triangle*

B *Perform the indicated operations and reduce to lowest terms.*

12. $\dfrac{y - 2}{y^2 - 4y + 4} \div \dfrac{y^2 + 2y}{y^2 + 4y + 4}$

13. $\dfrac{6x^4 - 6x^3}{3xy} \cdot \dfrac{xy + y}{x^4 - x^2}$

14. $\dfrac{x + 1}{x + 2} - \dfrac{x + 2}{x + 3}$

15. $\dfrac{1}{2x^2} + \dfrac{1}{3x(x - 1)}$

16. $\dfrac{m + 2}{m - 2} - \dfrac{m^2 + 4}{m^2 - 4}$

17. $\dfrac{1}{x^2 - y^2} - \dfrac{1}{x^2 - 2xy + y^2}$

18. $\dfrac{x - \dfrac{1}{x}}{1 - \dfrac{1}{x^2}}$

19. $\dfrac{\dfrac{x}{y} - \dfrac{y}{x}}{\dfrac{x}{y} + 1}$

Solve.

20. $\dfrac{5}{2x + 3} - 5 = \dfrac{-5x}{2x + 3}$

21. $\dfrac{3}{x} - \dfrac{2}{x + 1} = \dfrac{1}{2x}$

22. $s = \dfrac{n(a + L)}{2}$ for L

23. $M = xA + A$ for A

24. If $\frac{1}{2}$ is added to the reciprocal of a number, the sum is 2. Find the number by setting up an equation and solving.

C   *Perform the indicated operations and reduce to lowest terms.*

25. $\dfrac{y^2 - y - 6}{y^2 + 4y + 4} \div \dfrac{3 - y}{2 + y}$

26. $\dfrac{2x + 4}{2x - y} + \dfrac{2x - y}{y - 2x}$

27. $\dfrac{\dfrac{3}{x - 1} - 3}{\dfrac{2}{x - 1} + 2}$

28. $2 - \dfrac{2}{2 - \dfrac{2}{x}}$

Solve.

29. $5 - \dfrac{2x}{3 - x} = \dfrac{6}{x - 3}$

30. $y = \dfrac{3x + 1}{2x - 3}$ for x in terms of y

8

EXPONENTS AND RADICALS

Natural number exponents were introduced in Chapter 1. In this chapter, the exponent concept is extended to integers and the rules for manipulating expressions involving exponents are expanded.

We have assumed you have a basic familiarity with the arithmetic concept of square root. For example, $\sqrt{2}$ was used in Chapter 3 as an example of an irrational number. This chapter considers roots more carefully, extends the idea to higher-order roots, and places the topic in an algebraic setting.

8-1
NATURAL NUMBER EXPONENTS

- ■ Five Exponent Laws
- ■ Summary and Use of the Five Laws

Earlier we defined a number raised to a natural number power. Recall:

Natural Number Exponent

For n a natural number,

$$a^n = a \cdot a \cdot \cdots \cdot a \qquad n \text{ factors of } a \qquad\qquad (1)$$

$2^5 = 2 \cdot 2 \cdot 2 \cdot 2 \cdot 2 = 32 \qquad 5 \text{ factors of } 2$

We then introduced the first law of exponents: If m and n are positive integers and a is a real number, then $a^m a^n = a^{m+n}$. By now you have used this law over and over again. More complicated algebraic forms involving exponents are frequently encountered. Four other exponent laws combined with the first law provide efficient tools for simplifying and changing these forms. In this section we will review the first law and discuss the four additional laws.

FIVE EXPONENT LAWS

In the following discussion, m and n are natural numbers and a and b are real numbers, excluding division by 0, of course.

From the definition of exponent [Equation (1)]

$$\underset{\substack{3 \\ \text{factors}}}{} \qquad \underset{\substack{4 \\ \text{factors}}}{} \qquad \underset{\substack{3+4 \\ \text{factors}}}{}$$

$$a^3 a^4 = (a \cdot a \cdot a)(a \cdot a \cdot a \cdot a) = (a \cdot a \cdot a \cdot a \cdot a \cdot a \cdot a) = a^{3+4} = a^7$$

In general, it can be proved that:

Law 1

$$a^m a^n = a^{m+n} \qquad 2^3 \cdot 2^2 \;\; \overbrace{}^{2^3}\,\overbrace{}^{2^2}\; = 2 \cdot 2 \cdot 2 \cdot 2 \cdot 2 = 2^{3+2} \;\; = 2^5$$

$$a^5 a^2 = a^{5+2} = a^7$$

Example 1   Rewrite, using Law 1: $x^7 x^4$

Solution $x^7 x^4 \;\; \boxed{= x^{7+4}} \; = x^{11}$

Problem 1 Rewrite, using Law 1:

(A) a^6a^3 **(B)** $x^{10}x^8$

From the definition of exponent [Equation (1)]

$$
(a^3)^4 = \overset{\substack{\text{4 groups of} \\ \text{3 factors each}}}{a^3 \cdot a^3 \cdot a^3 \cdot a^3} = (a \cdot a \cdot a)(a \cdot a \cdot a)(a \cdot a \cdot a)(a \cdot a \cdot a)
$$

$$
= \underset{\substack{4 \cdot 3 \\ \text{factors of } a}}{(a \cdot a \cdot a \cdot a \cdot a \cdot a \cdot a \cdot a \cdot a \cdot a \cdot a \cdot a)} = a^{4 \cdot 3} = a^{12}
$$

In general, it can be proved that:

Law 2

$(a^n)^m = a^{mn}$ $(2^3)^2 \; \left[= (2 \cdot 2 \cdot 2)(2 \cdot 2 \cdot 2) \right] \; = 2^6$

$(a^5)^3 = a^{3 \cdot 5} = a^{15}$

Example 2 Rewrite, using Law 2: $(x^4)^7$

Solution $(x^4)^7 \; \left[= x^{7 \cdot 4} \right] \; = x^{28}$

Problem 2 Rewrite, using Law 2:

(A) $(y^2)^5$ **(B)** $(u^4)^6$

From the definition of exponent [Equation (1)]

$$
(ab)^4 = \overset{\substack{4 \\ \text{factors of } (ab)}}{(ab)(ab)(ab)(ab)} = \overset{\substack{4 \\ \text{factors of } a}}{(a \cdot a \cdot a \cdot a)} \overset{\substack{4 \\ \text{factors of } b}}{(b \cdot b \cdot b \cdot b)} = a^4 b^4
$$

In general, it can be proved that:

Law 3

$(ab)^m = a^m b^m$ $(2 \cdot 3)^3 \; \left[= (2 \cdot 3)(2 \cdot 3)(2 \cdot 3) \right] \; = 2^3 \cdot 3^3$

$(ab)^3 = a^3 b^3$

Example 3 Rewrite, using Law 3:

(A) $(xy)^4$ (B) $(2x^2y^3)^3$

Solution (A) $(xy)^4 = x^4y^4$

(B) $(2x^2y^3)^3 \; \boxed{= (2^1x^2y^3)^3 = 2^{3\cdot1}x^{3\cdot2}y^{3\cdot3}} \; = 2^3x^6y^9 = 8x^6y^9$

Problem 3 Rewrite, using Law 4:

(A) $(uv)^5$ (B) $(3a^3b^4)^4$

From the definition of exponent [Equation (1)]

$$\left(\frac{a}{b}\right)^5 = \overbrace{\frac{a}{b}\cdot\frac{a}{b}\cdot\frac{a}{b}\cdot\frac{a}{b}\cdot\frac{a}{b}}^{\substack{5 \\ \text{factors of } a/b}} = \frac{\overbrace{a\cdot a\cdot a\cdot a\cdot a}^{5 \text{ factors of } a}}{\underbrace{b\cdot b\cdot b\cdot b\cdot b}_{5 \text{ factors of } b}} = \frac{a^5}{b^5}$$

In general, it can be proved that:

Law 4

$$\left(\frac{a}{b}\right)^m = \frac{a^m}{b^m} \qquad \left(\frac{2}{3}\right)^2 \; \boxed{= \frac{2}{3}\cdot\frac{2}{3} = \frac{2\cdot2}{3\cdot3}} = \frac{2^2}{3^2}$$

$$\left(\frac{a}{b}\right)^3 = \frac{a}{b^3}$$

Example 4 Rewrite, using Law 4:

(A) $\left(\dfrac{x}{y}\right)^5$ (B) $\left(\dfrac{2u^2}{v^3}\right)^3$

Solution (A) $\left(\dfrac{x}{y}\right)^5 = \dfrac{x^5}{y^5}$

(B) $\left(\dfrac{2u^2}{v^3}\right)^3 \; \boxed{= \left(\dfrac{2^1u^2}{v^3}\right)^3 = \dfrac{2^{3\cdot1}u^{3\cdot2}}{v^{3\cdot3}}} \; = \dfrac{2^3u^6}{v^9} = \dfrac{8u^6}{v^9}$

Problem 4   Rewrite, using Law 4:

(A) $\left(\dfrac{w}{z}\right)^7 = ?$ **(B)** $\left(\dfrac{3x^3}{y^2}\right)^4$

We now look at the quotient form a^m/a^n. Consider the following three special cases:

1. $\dfrac{a^7}{a^3} = \dfrac{a \cdot a \cdot a \cdot a \cdot a \cdot a \cdot a}{a \cdot a \cdot a} = \dfrac{(a \cdot a \cdot a)(a \cdot a \cdot a \cdot a)}{(a \cdot a \cdot a)} = a^{7-3} = a^4$

2. $\dfrac{a^3}{a^3} = \dfrac{a \cdot a \cdot a}{a \cdot a \cdot a} = 1$

3. $\dfrac{a^4}{a^7} = \dfrac{a \cdot a \cdot a \cdot a}{a \cdot a \cdot a \cdot a \cdot a \cdot a \cdot a} = \dfrac{(a \cdot a \cdot a \cdot a)}{(a \cdot a \cdot a \cdot a)(a \cdot a \cdot a)} = \dfrac{1}{a^{7-4}} = \dfrac{1}{a^3}$

In general, it can be proved that:

Law 5

$$\dfrac{a^m}{a^n} = \begin{cases} a^{m-n} & \text{if } m > n & \dfrac{2^3}{2^2} \;\boxed{= \dfrac{2 \cdot 2 \cdot 2}{2 \cdot 2}} = 2 = 2^{3-2} \\[2ex] 1 & \text{if } m = n & \dfrac{2^2}{2^2} = 1 \\[2ex] \dfrac{1}{a^{n-m}} & \text{if } n > m & \dfrac{2^2}{2^3} \;\boxed{= \dfrac{2 \cdot 2}{2 \cdot 2 \cdot 2}} = \dfrac{1}{2} = \dfrac{1}{2^{3-2}} \end{cases}$$

$$\dfrac{x^8}{x^3} = x^{8-3} = x^5 \qquad \dfrac{x^8}{x^8} = 1 \qquad \dfrac{x^3}{x^8} = \dfrac{1}{x^{8-3}} = \dfrac{1}{x^5}$$

Example 5   Rewrite, using Law 5:

(A) $\dfrac{u^5}{u}$ **(B)** $\dfrac{d^3}{d^3}$ **(C)** $\dfrac{y^4}{y^6}$

Solution   **(A)** $\dfrac{u^5}{u} \;\boxed{= u^{5-1}} = u^4$ **(B)** $\dfrac{d^3}{d^3} = 1$

(C) $\dfrac{y^4}{y^6} \;\boxed{= \dfrac{1}{y^{6-4}}} = \dfrac{1}{y^2}$

Problem 5   Rewrite, using Law 5:

(A) $\dfrac{x^7}{x^2}$ (B) $\dfrac{c^4}{c^4}$ (C) $\dfrac{w}{w^4}$

SUMMARY AND USE OF THE FIVE LAWS

The laws of exponents are theorems, and as such they require proofs. We have only given plausible arguments for each law. Formal proofs of these laws require a property of the natural numbers, called the inductive property, that is beyond the scope of this course.

It is very important to observe and remember:

The laws of exponents involve products and quotients, not sums and differences.

Many mistakes are made in algebra by people applying a law of exponents to the wrong algebraic form. For example, $(ab)^3 = a^3b^3$, but $(a + b)^3 \neq a^3 + b^3$. The exponent laws are summarized here for convenient reference:

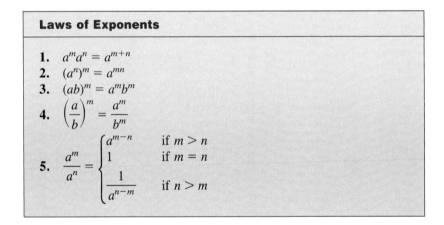

Laws of Exponents

1. $a^m a^n = a^{m+n}$
2. $(a^n)^m = a^{mn}$
3. $(ab)^m = a^m b^m$
4. $\left(\dfrac{a}{b}\right)^m = \dfrac{a^m}{b^m}$
5. $\dfrac{a^m}{a^n} = \begin{cases} a^{m-n} & \text{if } m > n \\ 1 & \text{if } m = n \\ \dfrac{1}{a^{n-m}} & \text{if } n > m \end{cases}$

Example 6   Rewrite, using the laws of exponents:

(A) $x^{11}x^7$ (B) $(y^{10})^3$ (C) $(xy)^8$

(D) $\left(\dfrac{x}{y}\right)^8$ (E) $\dfrac{y^3}{y^9}$ (F) $\dfrac{y^{12}}{y^4}$

Solution   (A) $x^{11}x^7 \; \boxed{= x^{11+7}} \; = x^{18}$

(B) $(y^{10})^3 \; \boxed{= y^{10\cdot3}} \; = y^{30}$

(C) $(xy)^8 = x^8 y^8$

(D) $\left(\dfrac{x}{y}\right)^8 = \dfrac{x^8}{y^8}$

(E) $\dfrac{y^3}{y^9} \boxed{= \dfrac{1}{y^{9-3}}} = \dfrac{1}{y^6}$

(F) $\dfrac{y^{12}}{y^4} \boxed{= y^{12-4}} = y^8$

Problem 6 Rewrite, using the laws of exponents:

(A) $y^6 y^{13}$ **(B)** $(y^4)^{10}$ **(C)** $(xy)^{10}$

(D) $\left(\dfrac{x}{y}\right)^{10}$ **(E)** $\dfrac{x^{10}}{x^5}$ **(F)** $\dfrac{y^5}{y^{15}}$

Example 7 Rewrite, using the laws of exponents:

(A) $(x^3 y^2)^5$ **(B)** $\left(\dfrac{x^3}{y^2}\right)^4$ **(C)** $\dfrac{3x^3 y^2}{6x^4 y}$

Solution   **(A)** $(x^3 y^2)^5 = (x^3)^5 (y^2)^5 = x^{3 \cdot 5} y^{2 \cdot 5} = x^{15} y^{10}$

(B) $\left(\dfrac{x^3}{y^2}\right)^4 \boxed{= \dfrac{(x^3)^4}{(y^2)^4}} = \dfrac{x^{3 \cdot 4}}{y^{2 \cdot 4}} = \dfrac{x^{12}}{y^8}$

(C) $\dfrac{3x^3 y^2}{6x^4 y} \boxed{= \dfrac{3}{6} \cdot \dfrac{x^3}{x^4} \cdot \dfrac{y^2}{y} = \dfrac{1}{2} \cdot \dfrac{1}{x} \cdot y} = \dfrac{y}{2x}$

Problem 7 Rewrite, using the laws of exponents:

(A) $(w^7 z^4)^3$ **(B)** $\left(\dfrac{w^7}{z^4}\right)^5$ **(C)** $\dfrac{8w^3 z^5}{2w^6 z^3}$

    Knowing the rules of the game of chess doesn't make you a good chess player; similarly, memorizing the laws of exponents doesn't necessarily make you good at using them. To acquire skill in their use, you must use these laws in a fairly large variety of problems. Exercise 8-1 should help you acquire this skill.

ANSWERS TO
MATCHED PROBLEMS

1. **(A)** a^9 **(B)** x^{18} **2.** **(A)** y^{10} **(B)** u^{24}

3. **(A)** $u^5 v^5$ **(B)** $81a^{12} b^{16}$ **4.** **(A)** $\dfrac{w^7}{z^7}$ **(B)** $\dfrac{81x^{12}}{y^8}$

5.   **(A)** x^5 **(B)**   1   **(C)** $\dfrac{1}{w^3}$

6.   **(A)** y^{19} **(B)** y^{40} **(C)** $x^{10}y^{10}$ **(D)** $\dfrac{x^{10}}{y^{10}}$ **(E)** x^5

     (F) $\dfrac{1}{y^{10}}$

7.   **(A)** $w^{21}z^{12}$ **(B)** $\dfrac{w^{35}}{z^{20}}$ **(C)** $\dfrac{4z^2}{w^3}$

EXERCISE 8-1   *Rewrite, using the laws of exponents.*

A   **1.** x^5x^8 **2.** $y^{11}y^6$ **3.** y^9y^6

       4. $x^{12}x^3$ **5.** $(x^3)^5$ **6.** $(y^4)^6$

       7. $(y^5)^3$ **8.** $(x^4)^5$ **9.** $(xy)^8$

     10. $(xy)^9$ **11.** x^7y^7 **12.** x^5y^5

     13. $\left(\dfrac{x}{y}\right)^8$ **14.** $\left(\dfrac{x}{y}\right)^9$ **15.** $\dfrac{x^5}{y^5}$

     16. $\dfrac{x^7}{y^7}$ **17.** $\dfrac{x^{10}}{x^4}$ **18.** $\dfrac{y^4}{y^{11}}$

     19. $\dfrac{x^5}{x^{13}}$ **20.** $\dfrac{y^9}{y^2}$ **21.** $\dfrac{y^{10}}{y^{14}}$

     22. $\dfrac{x^{14}}{x^7}$ **23.** $\dfrac{y^9}{y^3}$ **24.** $\dfrac{x^{16}}{x^{24}}$

     25. $10^{13} \times 10^2$ **26.** $10^{11} \times 10^4$ **27.** $(10^3)^4$

     28. $(10^5)^3$ **29.** $(2 \times 10^3)(3 \times 10^8)$

     30. $(4 \times 10^5)(2 \times 10^5)$ **31.** $(4 \times 10^6) \div (2 \times 10^3)$

     32. $(8 \times 10^5) \div (4 \times 10^2)$ **33.** $(6 \times 10^8) \div (4 \times 10^2)$

     34. $(-2)^2$ **35.** $(-2)^3$

     36. $(-3)^3$ **37.** $(-3)^2$

B   **38.** $(a^2b^3)^2$ **39.** $(x^5y^2)^4$ **40.** $(2xy^2)^5$

     41. $(3a^2b)^3$ **42.** $(3a^2)(4a^3)$ **43.** $(2x^4)(3x^3)$

     44. $\dfrac{6x^4}{4x^3}$ **45.** $\dfrac{3a^4}{6a^8}$ **46.** $\dfrac{2x^3y^2}{6xy^3}$

     47. $\dfrac{12a^4b^2}{4ab^3}$ **48.** $(x^2y)^3(xy^3)^2$ **49.** $(ab^4)^2(a^2b)^3$

50. $3(x^2y)^2$ **51.** $5(xy^3)^4$ **52.** $(3x^2y)^2$

53. $(5xy^3)^4$ **54.** $-(x^2y)^3$ **55.** $(-xy^2)^2$

56. $(-x^2y)^3$ **57.** $-(xy^2)^2$ **58.** $(-2)^4$

59. -2^4 **60.** -3^3 **61.** $(-3)^3$

C   **62.** $(3a^4b^2c)^3$ **63.** $(2xy^3z^4)^4$

64. $(2x^3)(x^7)(3x^{11})$ **65.** $(3a^4)(2a^5)(a^6)$

66. $(2x)^3x^7(3x^8)^2$ **67.** $(3a)^4(2a^5)^2a^6$

68. $\dfrac{(3x^2y)^4}{(3xy^2)^3}$ **69.** $\dfrac{(2a^2b^3)^3}{(4ab)^2}$

70. $(-x^2y)^3(-xy^3)^2$ **71.** $(-ab^2)^4(-a^2b)$

72. $\dfrac{(-a^4b)^2}{(a^2b^3)^3}$ **73.** $\dfrac{(a^5b^2)^2}{(-a^4b^3)^3}$

74. $\dfrac{(x^2y)(x^4y^2)}{-x^4y^5}$ **75.** $\dfrac{(-a^4b)^3(ab^5)}{-a^8b^8}$

76. $\dfrac{(xy)^3(-x^2y)^2}{-x^9y^9}$

8-2
INTEGER EXPONENTS

- Zero Exponents
- Negative Exponents
- Summary

The fifth law of exponents suggests the following pattern:

$$\frac{x^3}{x} = x^2 = x^{3-1}$$

$$\frac{x^3}{x^2} = x^1 = x^{3-2}$$

$$\frac{x^3}{x^3} = 1 = x^{3-3} = x^0$$

$$\frac{x^3}{x^4} = \frac{1}{x} = x^{3-4} = x^{-1}$$

In this section, we will extend the exponent concept to 0 and negative integers. The definitions of x^0 and x^{-n} for natural number n will be made in such a way that all five exponent laws still hold.

ZERO EXPONENTS

We will define a^0 to be 1 for any $a \neq 0$. If the laws of exponents are to hold, then this must be true. For example,

$$a^0 a^3 = a^{0+3} = a^3 = 1 \cdot a^3$$

The expression 0^0 is not defined; any possible definition will lead to difficulties with the exponent laws.

Definition of Zero Exponent

For all real numbers $a \neq 0$,

$$a^0 = 1 \qquad 12^0 = 1$$

0^0 is not defined

For example, all the following are equal to 1:

$$7^0 = 1 \qquad 1238^0 = 1 \qquad \pi^0 = 1$$
$$z^0 = 1 \text{ (for } z \neq 0)$$
$$(a^2 b^7 c^{11})^0 = 1 \text{ (for } a,b,c \neq 0)$$

NEGATIVE EXPONENTS

We will define a^{-n} to be $\dfrac{1}{a^n}$ for $a \neq 0$ and n a natural number. Again, this definition is forced upon us if the exponent laws are to hold. For example, if $a \neq 0$, then

$$a^{-3} \cdot a^3 = a^{-3+3} = a^0 = 1$$

so a^{-3} must be $\dfrac{1}{a^3}$.

This kind of reasoning leads us to the following general definition:

Definition of Negative-Integer Exponents

If n is a positive integer and a is a nonzero real number, then

$$a^{-n} = \frac{1}{a^n} \qquad a^{-2} = \frac{1}{a^2}$$

Now since

$$\frac{1}{a^{-3}} = \frac{1}{\dfrac{1}{a^3}} = 1 \cdot \frac{a^3}{1} = a^3$$

both of the following statements are true:

$$a^{-3} = \frac{1}{a^3} \qquad \text{and} \qquad a^3 = \frac{1}{a^{-3}}$$

In other words, we can move a cube back and forth between numerator and denominator simply by changing the sign of the exponent. More generally we have

$$a^{-n} = \frac{1}{a^n} \qquad \text{and} \qquad a^n = \frac{1}{a^{-n}} \qquad \text{for } a \neq 0 \text{ and } n \text{ an integer}$$

CAUTION

Thus we can shift any integer power back and forth between numerator and denominator by changing the sign of the exponent. This is true, however, only for *factors* in the numerator and denominator, not for *terms*. Thus, for example,

$$\frac{1}{x^{-3} + 5} \neq \frac{x^3}{5}$$

Example 8 Rewrite, using positive exponents only:

(A) x^{-4} (B) $\dfrac{1}{x^{-4}}$ (C) 10^{-4} (D) $\dfrac{x^{-4}}{y^{-8}}$

Solution (A) $x^{-4} = \dfrac{1}{x^4}$

(B) $\dfrac{1}{x^{-4}} = x^4$

(C) $10^{-4} = \dfrac{1}{10^4} = 0.0001$

(D) $\dfrac{x^{-4}}{y^{-8}} \left[= x^{-4} \cdot \dfrac{1}{y^{-8}} = \dfrac{1}{x^4} \cdot y^8 \right] = \dfrac{y^8}{x^4}$

Problem 8   Rewrite, using positive exponents only:

(A) x^{-7} (B) $\dfrac{1}{x^{-7}}$ (C) 10^{-7} (D) $\dfrac{x^{-7}}{y^{-4}}$

All five laws of exponents remain true, with the definition of exponent extended to the integers. The fifth law of exponents can now be restated in a more compact form:

Law 5

For real number $a \neq 0$; m and n integers

$$\frac{a^m}{a^n} = a^{m-n} = \frac{1}{a^{n-m}} \qquad \frac{2^3}{2^2} = 2^{3-2} = 2 \qquad \frac{2^2}{2^2} = 2^0 = 1 \qquad \frac{2^2}{2^3} = 2^{-1} = \frac{1}{2}$$

Example 9   Rewrite, using negative exponents only:

(A) $\dfrac{3^3}{3^5}$ (B) $\dfrac{8^{-3}}{8^4}$

Rewrite, using positive exponents only:

(C) $\dfrac{3^3}{3^5}$ (D) $\dfrac{8^{-3}}{8^4}$

Solution   (A) $\dfrac{3^3}{3^5} = 3^{3-5} = 3^{-2}$

(B) $\dfrac{8^{-3}}{8^4} = 8^{-3-4} = 8^{-7}$

(C) $\dfrac{3^3}{3^5} = \dfrac{1}{3^{5-3}} = \dfrac{1}{3^2}$ or, using part (A), $\dfrac{3^3}{3^5} = 3^{-2} = \dfrac{1}{3^2}$

(D) $\dfrac{8^{-3}}{8^4} = \dfrac{1}{8^{4-(-3)}} = \dfrac{1}{8^7}$ or, using part (B), $\dfrac{8^{-3}}{8^4} = 8^{-7} = \dfrac{1}{8^7}$

Problem 9   Rewrite, using positive exponents only:

(A) $\dfrac{5^2}{5^6}$ (B) $\dfrac{x^{-2}}{x^6}$

Rewrite, using negative exponents only:

(C) $\dfrac{5^2}{5^6}$ (D) $\dfrac{x^{-2}}{x^6}$

SUMMARY

Table 1 provides a summary of all our work on exponents to this point.

TABLE 1 INTEGER EXPONENTS AND THEIR LAWS (SUMMARY)

DEFINITON OF a^p p an integer, a a real number	LAWS OF EXPONENTS n and m integers, a and b real numbers
1. If p is a positive integer, then $a^p = a \cdot a \cdot \cdots \cdot a$ p factors of a *Example:* $3^5 = 3 \cdot 3 \cdot 3 \cdot 3 \cdot 3$	**1.** $a^m a^n = a^{m+n}$
	2. $(a^n)^m = a^{mn}$
2. If $p = 0$, then $a^p = 1$ $a \neq 0$ *Example:* $3^0 = 1$	**3.** $(ab)^m = a^m b^m$
	4. $\left(\dfrac{a}{b}\right)^m = \dfrac{a^m}{b^m}$
3. If p is a negative integer, then $a^p = \dfrac{1}{a^{-p}}$ $a \neq 0$ *Example:* $3^{-4} = \dfrac{1}{3^{-(-4)}} = \dfrac{1}{3^4}$	**5.** $\dfrac{a^m}{a^n} = a^{m-n} = \dfrac{1}{a^{n-m}}$

Example 10   Rewrite, using positive exponents only:

(A) $x^{-3}x^8$ **(B)** $(x^{-3}y^2)^{-4}$ **(C)** $\left(\dfrac{x^{-1}}{x^{-2}}\right)^{-3}$

(D) $\dfrac{2x^2 y^{-1}}{4x^{-2} y^{-3}}$ **(E)** $\dfrac{10^{-5} \times 10^2}{10^3 \times 10^{-8}}$ **(F)** $\left(\dfrac{x^{-2}y^2}{z^{-3}}\right)^{-2}$

Solution   **(A)** $x^{-3}x^8 = x^{-3+8} = x^5$

(B) $(x^{-3}y^2)^{-4} = (x^{-3})^{-4}(y^2)^{-4} = x^{(-3)(-4)}y^{2(-4)}$

$= x^{12}y^{-8}$

$= x^{12} \cdot \dfrac{1}{y^8}$

$= \dfrac{x^{12}}{y^8}$

(C) $\left(\dfrac{x^{-1}}{x^{-2}}\right)^{-3}$ $\boxed{= \dfrac{(x^{-1})^{-3}}{(x^{-2})^{-3}} = \dfrac{x^{(-1)(-3)}}{x^{(-2)(-3)}}}$ $= \dfrac{x^3}{x^6} = \dfrac{1}{x^3}$

or $\left(\dfrac{x^{-1}}{x^{-2}}\right)^{-3}$ $\boxed{= (x^{-1-(-2)})^{-3} = (x^{-1+2})^{-3}}$

$$= (x^1)^{-3} \quad = \dfrac{1}{x^3}$$

(D) $\dfrac{2x^2y^{-1}}{4x^{-2}y^{-3}}$ $\boxed{= \dfrac{1}{2} \cdot \dfrac{x^2}{x^{-2}} \cdot \dfrac{y^{-1}}{y^{-3}} = \dfrac{1}{2}\, x^{2-(-2)}y^{-1-(-3)}}$

$$= \dfrac{1}{2}x^4y^2$$

or, changing to positive exponents first,

$$\dfrac{2x^2y^{-1}}{4x^{-2}y^{-3}} = \dfrac{1}{2} \cdot \dfrac{x^2x^2y^3}{y} \;\boxed{= \dfrac{1}{2} \cdot x^{2+2}y^{3-1}} = \dfrac{1}{2}x^4y^2$$

(E) $\dfrac{10^{-5} \times 10^2}{10^3 \times 10^{-8}} = \dfrac{10^{-5+2}}{10^{3-8}} = \dfrac{10^{-3}}{10^{-5}} = 10^{-3-(-5)} = 10^2 = 100$

(F) $\left(\dfrac{x^{-2}y^2}{z^{-3}}\right)^{-2}$ $\boxed{= \dfrac{x^{(-2)(-2)}y^{2(-2)}}{z^{(-3)(-2)}}}$ $= \dfrac{x^4y^{-4}}{z^6} = \dfrac{x^4}{y^4z^6}$

Writing expressions using only positive exponents makes it easier to compare two expressions (for example, your answer and the answer in the text), and for this reason answers in this section are requested in such form. There are many instances, however, when it will be preferable to leave negative exponents in an expression. The next section will show such a situation.

Problem 10   Rewrite, using positive exponents only:

(A) $x^{-4}x^{11}$ **(B)** $(x^{-1}y^3)^{-2}$

(C) $\left(\dfrac{x^{-4}}{x^{-3}}\right)^{-2}$ **(D)** $\dfrac{3x^{-4}y^{-2}}{9xy^{-6}}$

(E) $\dfrac{10^8 \times 10^{-4}}{10^{-6} \times 10^2}$ **(F)** $\left(\dfrac{x^{-1}y^2}{xz^{-2}}\right)^{-1}$

It is important to remember that the laws of exponents involve products and quotients, not sums and differences. Consider the following examples:

I. $2^{-1} \cdot 3^{-1} = (2 \cdot 3)^{-1}$

$2^{-1} + 3^{-1} \neq (2 + 3)^{-1}$ $2^{-1} + 3^{-1} = \frac{1}{2} + \frac{1}{3} = \frac{5}{6}$

II. $(2^{-1} \cdot 3^{-1})^2 = 2^{-2}3^{-2}$

$(2^{-1} + 3^{-1})^2 \neq 2^{-2} + 3^{-2}$ $(2^{-1} + 3^{-1})^2 = (\frac{1}{2} + \frac{1}{3})^2$

III. $2^{-2} \cdot 3^{-2} = (2 \cdot 3)^{-2}$

$2^{-2} + 3^{-2} \neq (2 + 3)^{-2}$ $2^{-2} + 3^{-2} = \frac{1}{2^2} + \frac{1}{3^2}$

IV. $2^{-2} \cdot 3^{-2} = \dfrac{1}{2^2 \cdot 3^2}$

$2^{-2} + 3^{-2} \neq \dfrac{1}{2^2 + 3^2}$ $2^{-2} + 3^{-2} = \dfrac{1}{2^2} + \dfrac{1}{3^2}$

Examples II and IV are especially important, since both are commonly misapplied algebraically. In algebraic terms they would be

$(a^{-1}b^{-1})^2 = a^{-2}b^{-2}$ but $(a^{-1} + b^{-1})^2 \neq a^{-2} + b^{-2}$

$a^{-2}b^{-2} = \dfrac{1}{a^2b^2}$ but $a^{-2} + b^{-2} \neq \dfrac{1}{a^2 + b^2}$

Example 11   Rewrite, using positive exponents only:

(A) $(2^{-1} + 3^{-1})^2$

(B) $(a^{-1} + b^{-1})^2$

Solution   **(A)** $(2^{-1} + 3^{-1})^2 = \left(\dfrac{1}{2} + \dfrac{1}{3}\right)^2 = \left(\dfrac{5}{6}\right)^2 = \dfrac{25}{36}$

(B) $(a^{-1} + b^{-1})^2 = \left(\dfrac{1}{a} + \dfrac{1}{b}\right)^2 = \left(\dfrac{b + a}{ab}\right)^2$

$$= \dfrac{b^2 + 2ab + a^2}{a^2b^2}$$

Problem 11   Rewrite, using positive exponents only:

(A) $2^{-2} + 3^{-2}$ **(B)** $a^{-2} + b^{-2}$

ANSWERS TO
MATCHED PROBLEMS

8. **(A)** $\dfrac{1}{x^7}$ **(B)** x^7 **(C)** $0.000\ 000\ 1$ **(D)** $\dfrac{y^4}{x^7}$

9. **(A)** $\dfrac{1}{5^4}$ **(B)** $\dfrac{1}{x^8}$ **(C)** 5^{-4} **(D)** x^{-8}

10. **(A)** x^7 **(B)** $\dfrac{x^2}{y^6}$ **(C)** x^2 **(D)** $\dfrac{y^4}{3x^5}$

      (E) 10^8 **(F)** $\dfrac{x^2}{y^2z^2}$

11. **(A)** $\dfrac{13}{36}$ **(B)** $\dfrac{a^2 + b^2}{a^2b^2}$

EXERCISE 8-2   *Rewrite, using positive exponents only.*

A **1.** 8^0 **2.** 10^0 **3.** 313^0 **4.** $(-201)^0$

   5. 2^{-3} **6.** 3^{-2} **7.** $\dfrac{1}{3^{-3}}$ **8.** $\dfrac{1}{2^{-2}}$

   9. $(-2)^{-2}$ **10.** $(-2)^{-3}$ **11.** $(-3)^{-3}$ **12.** $(-3)^{-2}$

   13. a^{-5} **14.** b^{-6} **15.** $\dfrac{1}{b^{-7}}$ **16.** $\dfrac{1}{a^{-8}}$

   17. $\dfrac{3^{-2}}{3^5}$ **18.** $\dfrac{4^{-1}}{4^3}$ **19.** $\dfrac{4^{-8}}{4^{-5}}$ **20.** $\dfrac{3^{-9}}{3^{-6}}$

   21. $\dfrac{x^7}{x^{-4}}$ **22.** $\dfrac{y^9}{y^{-5}}$ **23.** $\dfrac{y^{-3}}{y^6}$ **24.** $\dfrac{y^{-5}}{y^8}$

   25. $3^5 3^{-7}$ **26.** $2^6 2^{-4}$ **27.** $3^8 3^{-4}$ **28.** $2^4 2^{-7}$

   29. $10^{12} \times 10^{-4}$ **30.** $10^{-5} \div 10^{-1}$ **31.** $10^{-1} \div 10^5$

   32. $10^3 \div 10^{-7}$ **33.** $(10^{-2})^{-2}$ **34.** $(10^{-3})^{-1}$

   35. $(x^{-2})^3$ **36.** $(y^{-3})^3$ **37.** $(y^{-2})^{-4}$

   38. $(x^{-3})^{-2}$ **39.** $(x^{-1}y^2)^2$ **40.** $(x^2y^{-1})^3$

B   **41.** $(x^{-2}y)^{-3}$ **42.** $(x^2y^{-3})^{-1}$ **43.** $\left(\dfrac{a^{-2}}{b}\right)^{-1}$

44. $\left(\dfrac{a^2}{b^{-1}}\right)^{-3}$ **45.** $\dfrac{x^{-1}y^4}{x^{-5}y^{-3}}$ **46.** $\dfrac{x^4y^{-1}}{x^{-1}y^{-4}}$

47. $\dfrac{10^{-1} \times 10^4}{10^6 \times 10^{-5}}$ **48.** $\dfrac{10^8 \times 10^{-2}}{10^7 \times 10^{-11}}$ **49.** $(a^2a^{-5})^{-2}$

50. $(x^{-1}x^4)^{-3}$ **51.** $\left(\dfrac{x^{-2}}{x^{-4}}\right)^{-1}$ **52.** $\left(\dfrac{a^{-3}}{a^{-2}}\right)^{-2}$

53. $(3a^2b^{-1})^{-2}$ **54.** $(2a^{-1}b^3)^{-1}$ **55.** $\dfrac{1}{(3x^{-3}y^2)^{-1}}$

56. $\dfrac{1}{(2xy^{-3})^{-2}}$ **57.** $\left(\dfrac{a^{-1}}{3b}\right)^{-1}$ **58.** $\left(\dfrac{a}{2b^{-1}}\right)^{-2}$

C   **59.** $(3^{-1} + 4^{-1})^{-1}$ **60.** $(2^{-1} + 3^{-1})^{-1}$

61. $(2^{-1} + 3^{-1})^{-2}$ **62.** $(3^{-1} + 4^{-1})^{-2}$

63. $(10^{-2} + 10^{-3})^{-1}$ **64.** $(10^{-1} + 10^{-2})^{-1}$

65. $\left(\dfrac{2xy^{-1}}{3x^{-2}y}\right)^{-1}$ **66.** $\left(\dfrac{4x^{-1}y^2}{3xy^{-1}}\right)^{-1}$

67. $\left(\dfrac{3x^{-2}y^{-1}}{2xy}\right)^{-2}$ **68.** $\left(\dfrac{6a^{-3}b^{-4}}{3a^2b^{-1}}\right)^{-2}$

69. $\left(\dfrac{10a^3b^{-2}}{5a^{-1}b^2}\right)^{-1}$ **70.** $\left(\dfrac{9a^{-1}b^{-1}}{6a^{-2}b^{-2}}\right)^{-3}$

71. $\dfrac{10a^{-1}10^{-3}a^2}{10^{-1}a^4}$ **72.** $\dfrac{10^{-2}a10^{-3}a^{-1}}{10^4a^{-6}}$

73. $(a^{-1} + b^{-1})^{-1}$ **74.** $(a^{-1} + b^{-1})^{-2}$

75. $(x^{-2} - y^{-2})^{-2}$ **76.** $(x^{-1} - y^{-1})^{-1}$

8-3
SCIENTIFIC NOTATION

- Scientific Notation
- Complicated Arithmetic
- Application

Work in science often involves the use of very, very large numbers:

The energy density of a laser beam can go as high as 10,000,000,000,000 watts per square centimeter.

Also involved is the use of very, very small numbers:

The probable mass of a hydrogen atom is
0.000 000 000 000 000 000 000 001 7 gram.

Writing and working with numbers of this type in standard decimal notation is generally awkward. It is often convenient to represent this type of number in a notation, *scientific notation,* which we introduce in this section.

SCIENTIFIC NOTATION

To write a number in **scientific notation** means to write it as the product of a number between 1 and 10 (excluding 10) and an integer power of 10. Any decimal fraction, however large or small, can be so represented. For example:

$$3 = 3 \times 10^0 \qquad\qquad 0.2 = 2 \times 10^{-1}$$
$$43 = 4.3 \times 10^1 \qquad\qquad 0.02 = 2 \times 10^{-2}$$
$$435 = 4.35 \times 10^2 \qquad\quad 0.002 = 2 \times 10^{-3}$$
$$4{,}351 = 4.351 \times 10^3 \qquad 0.000\ 2 = 2 \times 10^{-4}$$

Recall how powers of 10 are related to decimals:

$$\vdots$$
$$100{,}000 = 10^5$$
$$10{,}000 = 10^4$$
$$1{,}000 = 10^3$$
$$100 = 10^2$$
$$10 = 10^1$$
$$1 = 10^0$$
$$0.1 = 10^{-1}$$
$$0.01 = 10^{-2}$$
$$0.001 = 10^{-3}$$
$$0.000\ 1 = 10^{-4}$$
$$0.000\ 01 = 10^{-5}$$
$$\vdots$$

There is a simple rule for shifting the decimal point when converting to scientific notation.

Converting Positive Numbers to Scientific Notation

1. If the number is greater than or equal to 10, the number of places the decimal point is shifted left appears as a positive exponent.
2. If the number is less than 10 but greater than or equal to 1, the decimal place is not shifted at all, and the exponent used is 0.
3. If the number is less than 1, the number of places the decimal point is shifted right appears as a negative exponent.

Thus,

$$3,450,000 = 3.450\ 000 \times 10^6 = 3.45 \times 10^6$$

6 Places
left

Positive
exponent

$$3.45 = 3.45 \times 10^0$$

0 Places
shifted

Zero
exponent

and

$$0.000\ 034\ 5 = 000\ 003.45 \times 10^{-5} = 3.45 \times 10^{-5}$$

5 Places
right

Negative
exponent

Work is easily checked by remembering that multiplying by 10 shifts the decimal point to the right and dividing by 10 (that is, multiplying by 10^{-1}) shifts it left:

$$3.45 \times 10^6 = 3.4\ 5\ 0\ 0\ 0\ 0 = 3,450,000$$

Shift right 6 times

$$3.45 \times 10^{-5} = 0\ 0\ 0\ 0\ 0\ 3.4\ 5 = 0.000\ 034\ 5$$

Shift left 5 times

Example 12   Write in scientific notation:

(A) 380   (B) 10,400   (C) 0.065   (D) 0.000 41

Solution   (A) $380 = 3\ 8\ 0 = 3.8 \times 10^2$
(B) $10,400 = 1\ 0\ 4\ 0\ 0 = 1.04 \times 10^4$
(C) $0.065 = 0\ 0\ 6\ 5 = 6.5 \times 10^{-2}$
(D) $0.000\ 41 = 0\ 0\ 0\ 0\ 4\ 1 = 4.1 \times 10^{-4}$

Problem 12   Write in scientific notation:

(A) 65,000   (B) 880   (C) 0.004 5   (D) 0.000 006

The following chart may help give you some feeling for the magnitude involved with powers of 10 and, therefore, with numbers in scientific notation.

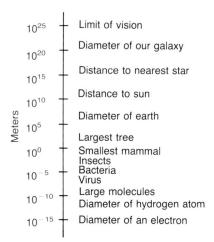

COMPLICATED ARITHMETIC

Scientific notation can be helpful in handling certain types of arithmetic calculations that involve very large or very small numbers.

Example 13   Evaluate, using scientific notation:

$$\frac{(600{,}000)(0.000\ 15)}{(0.02)(2{,}250{,}000{,}000)}$$

Solution

$$\frac{(600{,}000)(0.000\ 15)}{(0.02)(2{,}250{,}000{,}000)} = \frac{6 \times 10^5 \times 1.5 \times 10^{-4}}{2 \times 10^{-2} \times 2.25 \times 10^9}$$

$$= \frac{6 \times 1.5}{2 \times 2.25} \cdot \frac{10^5 \times 10^{-4}}{10^{-2} \times 10^9}$$

$$= \frac{9}{4.5} \cdot \frac{10^1}{10^7} = 2 \cdot \frac{1}{10^6}$$

$$= 2 \times 10^{-6}$$

Problem 13   Evaluate, using scientific notation:

$$\frac{(0.000\ 08)(5{,}000{,}000{,}000)}{(2{,}500{,}000)(0.000\ 002)}$$

APPLICATION

We are able to look back in time by looking out into space. Since light travels at a fast but finite rate, we see heavenly bodies not as they exist now but as they existed some time in the past. If the distance between the sun and the earth is approximately 9.3×10^7 miles and if light travels at the rate of approximately 1.86×10^5 miles per second, we see the sun as it was how many minutes ago?

$$d = rt$$

$$t = \frac{d}{r} = \frac{9.3 \times 10^7}{1.86 \times 10^5} = 5 \times 10^2 = 500 \text{ seconds or } \frac{500}{60} \approx 8.3 \text{ minutes}$$

Hence, we always see the sun as it was 8.3 minutes ago.

ANSWERS TO
MATCHED PROBLEMS

12. (A) 6.5×10^4 (B) 8.8×10^2 (C) 4.5×10^{-3}
(D) 6×10^{-6}

13. 8×10^4 or 80,000

EXERCISE 8-3   A   *Write in scientific notation.*

1. 2000	**2.** 4500	**3.** 108,000
4. 3,000,000	**5.** 412	**6.** 965
7. 48	**8.** 72	**9.** 0.63
10. 0.082	**11.** 0.046	**12.** 0.55
13. 0.000 44	**14.** 0.000 06	**15.** 0.000 095
16. 0.000 8	**17.** 0.000 003	**18.** 0.000 002 5
19. 0.000 001 8	**20.** 0.000 007	**21.** 1
22. 10		

Write as a decimal fraction.

23. 3×10^4	**24.** 2×10^5	**25.** 4×10^{-3}
26. 6×10^{-4}	**27.** 8×10^{-2}	**28.** 7×10^{-5}
29. 3.4×10^6	**30.** 5.1×10^5	**31.** 4.8×10^8
32. 1.5×10^{-6}	**33.** 2.4×10^{-4}	**34.** 1.6×10^{-5}
35. 3.2×10^{-6}	**36.** 7.5×10^{-2}	

B   *Write in scientific notation.*

37. 6,350,000,000	**38.** 1,125,000,000,000
39. 0.000 000 000 845	**40.** 0.000 000 000 65

41. 0.000 000 480 5   **42.**   0.000 000 200 6

43. The distance that light travels in 1 year is called a light-year. It is approximately 5,870,000,000,000 miles.

44. The energy of a laser beam can go as high as 10,000,000,000,000 watts.

45. The mass of one water molecule is 0.000 000 000 000 000 000 000 03 gram.

46. The nucleus of an atom has a diameter of a little more than 1/100,000 that of the whole atom.

Write as a decimal fraction.

47. 5.25×10^4 **48.** 4.68×10^5

49. 4.15×10^{-3} **50.** 8.24×10^{-4}

51. The distance from the earth to the sun is approximately 9.3×10^7 miles.

52. The diameter of the sun is approximately 8.65×10^5 miles.

53. The diameter of a red corpuscle is approximately 7.5×10^{-5} centimeter.

54. The probable mass of a hydrogen atom is 1.7×10^{-24} gram.

Simplify and express answers in scientific notation.

55. $(3 \times 10^4)(5 \times 10^{-3})$ **56.** $(4 \times 10^5)(3 \times 10^{-7})$

57. $(6 \times 10^4)(4 \times 10^{-6})$ **58.** $(2 \times 10^8)(8 \times 10^5)$

59. $\dfrac{32 \times 10^4}{2 \times 10^5}$ **60.** $\dfrac{28 \times 10^6}{2 \times 10^4}$

61. $\dfrac{66 \times 10^8}{6 \times 10^5}$ **62.** $\dfrac{45 \times 10^3}{3 \times 10^6}$

C   *Convert each numeral to scientific notation and simplify. Express answer in scientific notation and as a decimal fraction.*

63. $\dfrac{(21,000,000)(6,000)}{0.0063}$

64. $\dfrac{(0.000\ 48)(2,000,000,000)}{(0.016)(60,000)}$

65. $\dfrac{(3,600)(0.000\ 002)}{(0.001\ 8)(8,000,000)}$

66. $\dfrac{(0.027)(2,000,000)}{0.000\ 9}$

67. In 1929 Vernadsky, a biologist, estimated that all the free oxygen of the earth is 1.5×10^{21} grams and that it is produced by life alone. If 1 gram is approximately 2.2×10^{-3} pound, what is the amount of free oxygen in pounds?

68. If the mass of the earth is 6×10^{27} grams and each gram is 1.1×10^{-6} ton, find the mass of the earth in tons.

69. Some high-speed computers are currently performing single addition in 10^{-7} second (100 nanoseconds). How many additions would such a computer be able to perform in 1 second? In 1 minute?

70. If electricity travels in a computer circuit at the speed of light (1.86×10^{5} miles per second), how far will it travel in the time it takes the computer in the preceding problem to complete a single addition? (Size of circuits is becoming a critical problem in computer design.) Give the answer in miles and in feet.

8-4
SQUARE ROOTS AND RADICALS

- Definition of Square Root
- Irrational Numbers
- Square Root Properties
- Simplest Radical Form

Going from exponents to radicals in the same chapter may seem unnatural; however, exponents and radicals have a lot more in common than one might first expect. We will comment briefly on this relationship before the end of the chapter. In advanced courses the relationship is developed in detail.

DEFINITION OF SQUARE ROOT

In this and the next two sections we will take a careful look at the square root radical

and some of its properties. To start we define a square root of a number:

Definition of Square Root
x is a square root of y if $x^2 = y$.

Example 14   Find two square roots of 4.

Solution   2 is a square root of 4, since $2^2 = 4$. In addition, -2 is a square root of 4, since $(-2)^2 = 4$.

Problem 14   Find two square roots of 9.

How many square roots of a real number are there? The following result, which we state without proof, answers this question:

Number of Square Roots

(A)   Every positive real number has exactly two real square roots, each the opposite or negative of the other.
(B)   Negative real numbers have no real-number square roots (since no real number squared can be negative—think about this).
(C)   The square root of 0 is 0.

The following notation is adopted for square roots:

Square Root Notation

For a a positive number:

$\sqrt{a}$ is the positive square root of a. $(\sqrt{a})^2 = a$
$-\sqrt{a}$ is the negative square root of a. $(-\sqrt{a})^2 = a$

Note: $\sqrt{-a}$ is not a real number.

Example 15   Evaluate if possible:

(A) $\sqrt{4}$ (B) $-\sqrt{4}$ (C) $\sqrt{-4}$ (D) $\sqrt{0}$

Solution   (A) $\sqrt{4} = 2$.   (B) $-\sqrt{4} = -2$.
(C) $\sqrt{-4}$ is not a real number.   (D) $\sqrt{0} = 0$.

Problem 15   Evaluate if possible:

(A) $\sqrt{9}$ (B) $-\sqrt{9}$ (C) $\sqrt{-9}$ (D) $\sqrt{0}$

IRRATIONAL NUMBERS

It can be shown that if a is a positive integer that is not the square of an integer, than

$$-\sqrt{a} \quad \text{and} \quad \sqrt{a}$$

are irrational numbers. Thus,

$$-\sqrt{7} \quad \text{and} \quad \sqrt{7} \quad \text{\small 7 is not the square of an integer.}$$

name irrational numbers that are, respectively, the negative and positive square roots of 7.

SQUARE ROOT PROPERTIES

Note that $\sqrt{6^2} = \sqrt{36} = 6$. Note also that $\sqrt{4}\sqrt{36} = 2 \cdot 6 = 12$ and $\sqrt{4 \cdot 36} = \sqrt{144} = 12$; therefore, $\sqrt{4}\sqrt{36} = \sqrt{4 \cdot 36}$.
   Finally note that

$$\frac{\sqrt{36}}{\sqrt{4}} = \frac{6}{2} = 3 \quad \text{and} \quad \sqrt{\frac{36}{4}} = \sqrt{9} = 3$$

Therefore,

$$\frac{\sqrt{36}}{\sqrt{4}} = \sqrt{\frac{36}{4}}$$

These examples suggest the following general properties:

Properties of Radicals
For a and b nonnegative real numbers:
1. $\sqrt{a^2} = a$ $\qquad\qquad$ $\sqrt{3^2} = 3$
2. $\sqrt{a}\sqrt{b} = \sqrt{ab}$ $\qquad$ $\sqrt{2}\sqrt{3} = \sqrt{2 \cdot 3}$
3. $\dfrac{\sqrt{a}}{\sqrt{b}} = \sqrt{\dfrac{a}{b}}, b \neq 0$ $\quad$ $\dfrac{\sqrt{2}}{\sqrt{3}} = \sqrt{\dfrac{2}{3}}$

Example 16   Simplify, using the properties of radicals:

(A) $\sqrt{5}\sqrt{10}$ $\qquad$ **(B)** $\dfrac{\sqrt{32}}{\sqrt{8}}$ $\qquad$ **(C)** $\sqrt{\dfrac{7}{4}}$

Solution   **(A)** $\sqrt{5}\sqrt{10} = \sqrt{5 \cdot 10} = \sqrt{50} = \sqrt{25 \cdot 2} = \sqrt{25}\sqrt{2} = 5\sqrt{2}$

     (B) $\dfrac{\sqrt{32}}{\sqrt{8}} = \sqrt{\dfrac{32}{8}} = \sqrt{4} = 2$ **(C)** $\sqrt{\dfrac{7}{4}} = \dfrac{\sqrt{7}}{\sqrt{4}} = \dfrac{\sqrt{7}}{2}$ or $\dfrac{1}{2}\sqrt{7}$

Problem 16   Simplify as in Example 16:

     (A) $\sqrt{3}\sqrt{6}$ **(B)** $\dfrac{\sqrt{18}}{\sqrt{2}}$ **(C)** $\sqrt{\dfrac{11}{9}}$

SIMPLEST RADICAL FORM

The foregoing definitions and results allow us to change algebraic expressions containing radicals to a variety of equivalent forms. One form that is often useful is called the simplest radical form.

Definition of the Simplest Radical Form for Square Roots

An algebraic expression that contains square root radicals is in **simplest radical form** if all three of the following conditions are satisfied:

1. No **radicand** (the expression within the radical sign) when expressed in completely factored form contains a factor raised to a power greater than 1. ($\sqrt{x^3}$ violates this condition.)
2. No radical appears in a denominator. ($3/\sqrt{5}$ violates this condition.)
3. No fraction appears within a radical. ($\sqrt{\frac{2}{3}}$ violates this condition.)

It should be understood that forms other than the simplest radical form may be more useful on occasion. The situation dictates the choice.

Example 17   Change to simplest radical form—all variables represent positive real numbers:

     (A) $\sqrt{72}$ **(B)** $\sqrt{8x^3}$

Solution   **(A)** $\sqrt{72} = \sqrt{6^2 \cdot 2}$ Violates Condition 1, since 6 is raised to a power greater than 1.

         $= \sqrt{6^2}\sqrt{2}$ $\sqrt{ab} = \sqrt{a}\sqrt{b}$

         $= 6\sqrt{2}$ $\sqrt{a^2} = a$ $(a \geq 0)$

     (B) $\sqrt{8x^3} = \sqrt{(2^2x^2)(2x)}$ Violates Condition 1. Separate $8x^3$ into a perfect square part (2^2x^2) and what is left over ($2x$); then use multiplication property 2.

         $= \sqrt{2^2x^2}\sqrt{2x}$ $\sqrt{ab} = \sqrt{a}\sqrt{b}$

         $= 2x\sqrt{2x}$ $\sqrt{a^2} = a$ $(a \geq 0)$

Problem 17   Repeat Example 17 for

(A) $\sqrt{32}$ **(B)** $\sqrt{18y^3}$

Example 18   Change to simplest radical form—all variables represent positive real numbers:

(A) $\dfrac{3x}{\sqrt{3}}$ **(B)** $\sqrt{\dfrac{x}{2}}$

Solution   **(A)** $3x/\sqrt{3}$ has a radical in the denominator; hence, it violates Condition 2. To remove the radical from the denominator we multiply top and bottom by $\sqrt{3}$ to obtain $\sqrt{3^2}$ in the denominator:

$$\frac{3x}{\sqrt{3}} = \frac{3x}{\sqrt{3}} \cdot \frac{\sqrt{3}}{\sqrt{3}}$$

$$= \frac{3x\sqrt{3}}{\sqrt{3^2}}$$

$$= \frac{3x\sqrt{3}}{3} = x\sqrt{3}$$

(B) $\sqrt{x/2}$ has a fraction within the radical; hence, it violates Condition 3. To remove the fraction from the radical, we multiply the top and bottom of $x/2$ inside the radical by 2 to make the denominator a perfect square:

$$\sqrt{\frac{x}{2}} = \sqrt{\frac{2 \cdot x}{2 \cdot 2}}$$

$$= \sqrt{\frac{2x}{2^2}}$$

$$= \frac{\sqrt{2x}}{\sqrt{2^2}} = \frac{\sqrt{2x}}{2}$$

Problem 18   Repeat Example 18 for

(A) $\dfrac{2x}{\sqrt{2}}$ **(B)** $\sqrt{\dfrac{y}{3}}$

In the preceding discussion we restricted variables to nonnegative quantities. If we lift this restriction, then

$$\sqrt{a^2} = a$$

is correct for only certain values of a and is not true for others. Which values? If a is positive or 0, then it is true; if a is negative, then it is false. For example, let us test $\sqrt{a^2} = a$ for $a = 2$ and for $a = -2$:

$$
\begin{array}{ll}
a = 2 & a = -2 \\
\hline
\sqrt{2^2} \overset{?}{=} 2 & \sqrt{(-2)^2} \overset{?}{=} -2 \\
\sqrt{4} \overset{?}{=} 2 & \sqrt{4} \overset{?}{=} -2 \\
2 \overset{\checkmark}{=} 2 & 2 \neq -2
\end{array}
$$

Problems 59 and 60 in Exercise 8-4 suggest how $\sqrt{a^2}$ should be interpreted if we allow a to take on any real value. All the other problems in Exercise 8-4 restrict variables to positive real numbers; thus, $\sqrt{a^2} = a$ is correct for this restriction.

ANSWERS TO
MATCHED PROBLEMS

14. $-3, 3$

15. **(A)** 3 **(B)** -3 **(C)** Not a real number   **(D)** 0

16. **(A)** $3\sqrt{2}$ **(B)** 3 **(C)** $\dfrac{\sqrt{11}}{3}$ or $\frac{1}{3}\sqrt{11}$

17. **(A)** $4\sqrt{2}$ **(B)** $3y\sqrt{2y}$

18. **(A)** $x\sqrt{2}$ **(B)** $\dfrac{\sqrt{3y}}{3}$ or $\frac{1}{3}\sqrt{3y}$

EXERCISE 8-4

In Problems 1–46, simplify and express each answer in simplest radical form. All variables represent positive real numbers unless stated to the contrary.

A **1.** $\sqrt{16}$ **2.** $\sqrt{25}$ **3.** $-\sqrt{81}$ **4.** $-\sqrt{49}$

5. $\sqrt{x^2}$ **6.** $\sqrt{y^2}$ **7.** $\sqrt{9m^2}$ **8.** $\sqrt{4u^2}$

9. $\sqrt{8}$ **10.** $\sqrt{18}$ **11.** $\sqrt{x^3}$ **12.** $\sqrt{m^3}$

13. $\sqrt{18y^3}$ **14.** $\sqrt{8x^3}$ **15.** $\sqrt{\frac{1}{4}}$ **16.** $\sqrt{\frac{1}{9}}$

17. $-\sqrt{\frac{4}{9}}$ **18.** $-\sqrt{\frac{9}{16}}$ **19.** $\dfrac{1}{\sqrt{x^2}}$ **20.** $\dfrac{1}{\sqrt{y^2}}$

21. $\dfrac{1}{\sqrt{3}}$ **22.** $\dfrac{1}{\sqrt{5}}$ **23.** $\sqrt{\frac{1}{3}}$ **24.** $\sqrt{\frac{1}{5}}$

25. $\dfrac{1}{\sqrt{x}}$ **26.** $\dfrac{1}{\sqrt{y}}$ **27.** $\sqrt{\dfrac{1}{x}}$ **28.** $\sqrt{\dfrac{1}{y}}$

29. $\sqrt{25x^2y^4}$ **30.** $\sqrt{49x^4y^2}$

B **31.** $\sqrt{4x^5y^3}$ **32.** $\sqrt{9x^3y^5}$ **33.** $\sqrt{8x^7y^6}$

34. $\sqrt{18x^8y^5}$

35. $\dfrac{1}{\sqrt{3y}}$

36. $\dfrac{1}{\sqrt{2x}}$

37. $\dfrac{4xy}{\sqrt{2y}}$

38. $\dfrac{6x^2}{\sqrt{3x}}$

39. $\dfrac{2x^2y}{\sqrt{3xy}}$

40. $\dfrac{3a}{\sqrt{2ab}}$

41. $\sqrt{\frac{2}{3}}$

42. $\sqrt{\frac{3}{5}}$

43. $\sqrt{\dfrac{3m}{2n}}$

44. $\sqrt{\dfrac{6x}{7y}}$

45. $\sqrt{\dfrac{4a^3}{3b}}$

46. $\sqrt{\dfrac{9m^5}{2n}}$

In Problems 47–52, approximate each to two decimal places using a hand calculator. For example:

(A) $\sqrt{35}\sqrt{40} = \sqrt{35 \cdot 40} = \sqrt{(2^2 \cdot 5^2)(2 \cdot 7)} = 10\sqrt{14}$
$\qquad = (10)(3.742) = 37.42$

(B) $\sqrt{\dfrac{7}{5}} = \dfrac{\sqrt{7}}{\sqrt{5}} = \dfrac{\sqrt{7}\sqrt{5}}{\sqrt{5}\sqrt{5}} = \dfrac{\sqrt{35}}{5} = \dfrac{5.916}{5} = 1.18$

47. $\sqrt{6}\sqrt{3}$

48. $\sqrt{2}\sqrt{6}$

49. $\sqrt{\frac{1}{5}}$

50. $\sqrt{\frac{1}{3}}$

51. $\dfrac{\sqrt{33}}{\sqrt{2}}$

52. $\dfrac{\sqrt{23}}{\sqrt{5}}$

C *Express in simplest radical form.*

53. $\dfrac{\sqrt{2x}\sqrt{5}}{\sqrt{20x}}$

54. $\dfrac{\sqrt{6}\sqrt{8x}}{\sqrt{3x}}$

55. $\sqrt{a^2 + b^2}$

56. $\sqrt{m^2 + n^2}$

57. $\sqrt{x^4 - 2x^2}$

58. $\sqrt{m^3 + 4m^2}$

59. Is $\sqrt{x^2} = x$ true for $x = 4$? For $x = -4$?

60. Is $\sqrt{x^2} = |x|$ true for $x = 4$? For $x = -4$?

61. If we define the symbol $5^{1/2}$ in such a way that the laws of exponents continue to hold—in particular, $(5^{1/2})^2 = 5^{2(1/2)} = 5$ or $5^{1/2} \cdot 5^{1/2} = 5^{(1/2)+(1/2)} = 5$—how should it be defined?

62. If $x^2 = y^2$, does it necessarily follow that $x = y$? [*Hint:* Can you find a pair of numbers that make the first equation true but the second equation false?]

63. Find the fallacy in the following "proof" that all real numbers are equal: If m and n are any real numbers, then

$$(m - n)^2 = (n - m)^2$$
$$m - n = n - m$$
$$2m = 2n$$
$$m = n$$

APPLICATIONS

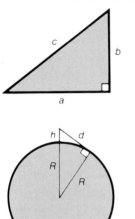

64. *Pythagorean theorem*   In a right triangle, the square of the length of the hypotenuse is equal to the sum of the squares of the lengths of the sides, $c^2 = a^2 + b^2$, or equivalently, $b = \sqrt{c^2 - a^2}$. If a right triangle has hypotenuse 25 centimeters and one side 7 centimeters, how long is the other side?

65. *Sight distance*   The figure in the margin shows how to find the distance d to the horizon from an altitude h above the earth's surface. From the Pythagorean Theorem (see Problem 64), $(h + R)^2 = R^2 + d^2$, or equivalently, $d = \sqrt{(h + R)^2 - R^2}$. Use $R = 3950$ miles as the radius of the earth to find d when h is $\frac{1}{2}$ mile.

66. *Pendulum*   The period T of a pendulum of length L is given by the formula

$$T = 2\pi\sqrt{\frac{L}{g}}$$

where g is the acceleration of gravity. Use $g = 32$ to find the period of a pendulum 3 feet long.

67. *Inventory*   Under certain conditions, the optimum order size S for an inventory item that has annual demand D, order cost C, and annual holding cost H is given by

$$S = \sqrt{\frac{2DC}{H}}$$

Find the optimum order size for an item with annual demand 72,000 cases, order cost $20 per order, and annual holding cost $1.25 per case.

8-5
SUMS AND DIFFERENCES OF RADICALS

Algebraic expressions can often be simplified by combining terms that contain exactly the same radical forms. We proceed in essentially the same way that we do when we combine like terms. You will recall that the distributive law played a central role in this process. Remember, we wrote

$$3x + 5x \quad \boxed{= (3 + 5)x} \quad = 8x$$

and concluded that we could combine like terms by adding their numerical coefficients. We have a similar mechanical rule for radicals:

> **Mechanical Rule for Adding Radicals**
>
> Two terms involving identical radicals can be combined into a single term by adding numerical coefficients.

Example 19 Simplify:

(A) $3\sqrt{2} + 5\sqrt{2}$ (B) $2\sqrt{m} - 7\sqrt{m}$
(C) $3\sqrt{x} - 2\sqrt{5} + 4\sqrt{x} - 7\sqrt{5}$

Solution (A) $3\sqrt{2} + 5\sqrt{2} \;\boxed{= (3 + 5)\sqrt{2}} \;= 8\sqrt{2}$

(B) $2\sqrt{m} - 7\sqrt{m} \;\boxed{= (2 - 7)\sqrt{m}} \;= -5\sqrt{m}$

(C) $3\sqrt{x} - 2\sqrt{5} + 4\sqrt{x} - 7\sqrt{5} \;\boxed{= 3\sqrt{x} + 4\sqrt{x} - 2\sqrt{5} - 7\sqrt{5}}$

$$= 7\sqrt{x} - 9\sqrt{5}$$

Problem 19 Simplify:

(A) $2\sqrt{3} + 4\sqrt{3}$ (B) $3\sqrt{x} - 5\sqrt{x}$
(C) $2\sqrt{y} - 3\sqrt{7} + 4\sqrt{y} - 2\sqrt{7}$

Occasionally terms containing radicals can be combined after they have been expressed in simplest radical form.

Example 20 Express in simplest radical form and simplify:

(A) $4\sqrt{8} - 2\sqrt{18}$ (B) $2\sqrt{12} - \sqrt{\dfrac{1}{3}}$

Solution (A) $4\sqrt{8} - 2\sqrt{18} \;\boxed{\begin{aligned} &= 4 \cdot \sqrt{4} \cdot \sqrt{2} - 2 \cdot \sqrt{9} \cdot \sqrt{2} \\ &= 4 \cdot 2 \cdot \sqrt{2} - 2 \cdot 3 \cdot \sqrt{2} \end{aligned}}$

$$\begin{aligned} &= 8\sqrt{2} - 6\sqrt{2} \\ &= 2\sqrt{2} \end{aligned}$$

(B) $2\sqrt{12} - \sqrt{\dfrac{1}{3}} = 2 \cdot \sqrt{4} \cdot \sqrt{3} - \sqrt{\dfrac{1}{3} \cdot \dfrac{3}{3}}$

$$= 4\sqrt{3} - \dfrac{\sqrt{3}}{3}$$

$$= \left(4 - \dfrac{1}{3}\right)\sqrt{3}$$

$$= \dfrac{11}{3}\sqrt{3} \text{ or } \dfrac{11\sqrt{3}}{3}$$

Problem 20   Express in simplest radical form and simplify:

(A) $5\sqrt{3} - 2\sqrt{12}$ **(B)** $3\sqrt{8} - \sqrt{\tfrac{1}{2}}$

ANSWERS TO
MATCHED PROBLEMS
19. **(A)** $6\sqrt{3}$ **(B)** $-2\sqrt{x}$ **(C)** $6\sqrt{y} - 5\sqrt{7}$

20. **(A)** $\sqrt{3}$ **(B)** $\dfrac{11\sqrt{2}}{2}$ or $\dfrac{11}{2}\sqrt{2}$

EXERCISE 8-5   *Simplify by combining as many terms as possible. All variables represent positive real numbers. Use exact radical forms only.*

A   **1.** $5\sqrt{2} + 3\sqrt{2}$ **2.** $7\sqrt{3} + 2\sqrt{3}$ **3.** $6\sqrt{x} - 3\sqrt{x}$

4. $12\sqrt{m} - 3\sqrt{m}$ **5.** $4\sqrt{7} - 3\sqrt{5}$ **6.** $2\sqrt{3} + 5\sqrt{2}$

7. $\sqrt{y} - 4\sqrt{y}$ **8.** $2\sqrt{a} - 7\sqrt{a}$

9. $3\sqrt{5} - \sqrt{5} + 2\sqrt{5}$ **10.** $4\sqrt{7} - 6\sqrt{7} + \sqrt{7}$

11. $2\sqrt{x} - \sqrt{x} + 3\sqrt{x}$ **12.** $\sqrt{n} - 4\sqrt{n} - 2\sqrt{n}$

13. $3\sqrt{2} - 2\sqrt{3} - \sqrt{2}$ **14.** $\sqrt{5} - 2\sqrt{3} + 3\sqrt{5}$

15. $2\sqrt{x} - \sqrt{y} + 3\sqrt{y}$ **16.** $\sqrt{m} - \sqrt{n} - 2\sqrt{n}$

B   **17.** $\sqrt{8} - \sqrt{2}$ **18.** $\sqrt{18} + \sqrt{2}$

19. $\sqrt{27} - 3\sqrt{12}$ **20.** $\sqrt{8} - 2\sqrt{32}$

21. $\sqrt{8} + 2\sqrt{27}$ **22.** $2\sqrt{12} + 3\sqrt{18}$

23. $\sqrt{4x} - \sqrt{9x}$ **24.** $\sqrt{8mn} + 2\sqrt{18mn}$

25. $\sqrt{24} - \sqrt{12} + 3\sqrt{3}$ **26.** $\sqrt{8} - \sqrt{20} + 4\sqrt{2}$

C   **27.** $\sqrt{\tfrac{2}{3}} - \sqrt{\tfrac{3}{2}}$ **28.** $\sqrt{\tfrac{1}{8}} + \sqrt{8}$

29. $\sqrt{\dfrac{xy}{2}} + \sqrt{8xy}$ **30.** $\sqrt{\dfrac{3uv}{2}} - \sqrt{24uv}$

31. $\sqrt{12} - \sqrt{\frac{1}{2}}$

32. $\sqrt{\frac{3}{5}} + 2\sqrt{20}$

33. $\sqrt{\frac{1}{2}} + \frac{\sqrt{2}}{2} + \sqrt{8}$

34. $\frac{\sqrt{3}}{3} + 2\sqrt{\frac{1}{3}} + \sqrt{12}$

8-6
PRODUCTS AND QUOTIENTS INVOLVING RADICALS

- Products
- Quotients—Rationalizing Denominators

We now consider several types of products and quotients that involve radicals. The distributive law again plays a central role in our approach to these problems. In the examples that follow, all variables represent positive real numbers.

PRODUCTS

The following examples illustrate several types of products.

Example 21 Multiply and simplify:

(A) $\sqrt{2}(\sqrt{2} - \sqrt{3})$ (B) $\sqrt{x}(\sqrt{x} - 3)$ (C) $(\sqrt{2} - 3)(\sqrt{2} + 5)$
(D) $(\sqrt{x} - 3)(\sqrt{x} + 5)$ (E) $(\sqrt{a} + \sqrt{b})^2$

Solution (A) $\sqrt{2}(\sqrt{2} - 3) \;\boxed{= \sqrt{2}\sqrt{2} - 3\sqrt{2}} \;= 2 - 3\sqrt{2}$

(B) $\sqrt{x}(\sqrt{x} - 3) \;\boxed{= \sqrt{x}\sqrt{x} - 3\sqrt{x}} \;= x - 3\sqrt{x}$

(C) $(\sqrt{2} - 3)(\sqrt{2} + 5) \;\boxed{= \sqrt{2}\sqrt{2} - 3\sqrt{2} + 5\sqrt{2} - 15}$

You can use the FOIL method to multiply out this product.

$$= 2 + 2\sqrt{2} - 15$$
$$= 2\sqrt{2} - 13$$

(D) $(\sqrt{x} - 3)(\sqrt{x} + 5) \;\boxed{= \sqrt{x}\sqrt{x} - 3\sqrt{x} + 5\sqrt{x} - 15}$

$$= x + 2\sqrt{x} - 15$$

(E) $(\sqrt{a} + \sqrt{b})^2 = (\sqrt{a})^2 + 2\sqrt{a}\sqrt{b} + (\sqrt{b})^2$ *Note:* $(\sqrt{a} + \sqrt{b})^2 \neq a + b$
$$= a + 2\sqrt{ab} + b$$

Problem 21 Multiply and simplify:

(A) $\sqrt{3}(2 - \sqrt{3})$ (B) $\sqrt{y}(2 + \sqrt{y})$ (C) $(\sqrt{3} - 1)(\sqrt{3} + 4)$
(D) $(\sqrt{y} + 2)(\sqrt{y} - 5)$ (E) $(\sqrt{x} - \sqrt{y})^2$

Example 22 Show that $(2 - \sqrt{3})$ is a solution of the equation $x^2 - 4x + 1 = 0$.

Solution
$$x^2 - 4x + 1 = 0$$
$$(2 - \sqrt{3})^2 - 4(2 - \sqrt{3}) + 1 \overset{?}{=} 0$$
$$4 - 4\sqrt{3} + 3 - 8 + 4\sqrt{3} + 1 \overset{?}{=} 0$$
$$0 \overset{\checkmark}{=} 0$$

Problem 22   Show that $(2 + \sqrt{3})$ is a solution of $x^2 - 4x + 1 = 0$.

Example 23   Reduce to lowest terms: $\dfrac{6 - \sqrt{12}}{10}$.

Solution $\dfrac{6 - \sqrt{12}}{10} = \dfrac{6 - \sqrt{4 \cdot 3}}{10}$ Be careful: $\dfrac{6 - \sqrt{12}}{10} \neq \dfrac{\overset{3}{\cancel{6}} - \sqrt{12}}{\underset{5}{\cancel{10}}}$

$$= \dfrac{6 - 2\sqrt{3}}{10} = \dfrac{\overset{1}{\cancel{2}}(3 - \sqrt{3})}{\underset{5}{\cancel{10}}} = \dfrac{3 - \sqrt{3}}{5}$$

Problem 23   Reduce to lowest terms: $\dfrac{12 - \sqrt{32}}{8}$.

QUOTIENTS—RATIONALIZING DENOMINATORS

Recall that to express $\sqrt{2}/\sqrt{3}$ in simplest radical form, we multiplied the numerator and denominator by $\sqrt{3}$ to clear the denominator of the radical:

$$\frac{\sqrt{2}}{\sqrt{2}} = \frac{\sqrt{2} \cdot \sqrt{3}}{\sqrt{3} \cdot \sqrt{3}} = \frac{\sqrt{6}}{3}$$

The denominator is thus converted to a rational number. The process of converting irrational denominators to rational forms is called **rationalizing the denominator**.

How can we rationalize the binomial denominator in

$$\frac{1}{\sqrt{3} - \sqrt{2}}$$

Multiplying the numerator and denominator by $\sqrt{3}$ or $\sqrt{2}$ does not help. Try it! Recall the product

$$(a - b)(a + b) = a^2 - b^2$$

This suggests that if we multiply the numerator and denominator by the denominator, only with the middle sign changed, we can obtain squares of each term in the denominator. Thus,

$$\frac{1}{\sqrt{3} - \sqrt{2}} = \frac{1(\sqrt{3} + \sqrt{2})}{(\sqrt{3} - \sqrt{2})(\sqrt{3} + \sqrt{2})} = \frac{\sqrt{3} + \sqrt{2}}{(\sqrt{3})^2 - \sqrt{2})^2}$$

$$= \frac{\sqrt{3} + \sqrt{2}}{3 - 2} = \sqrt{3} + \sqrt{2}$$

Example 24 Rationalize denominators and simplify:

(A) $\frac{\sqrt{2}}{\sqrt{6} - 2}$ (B) $\frac{\sqrt{x} - \sqrt{y}}{\sqrt{x} + \sqrt{y}}$

Solution (A) $\frac{\sqrt{2}}{\sqrt{6} - 2} = \frac{\sqrt{2}(\sqrt{6} + 2)}{(\sqrt{6} - 2)(\sqrt{6} + 2)} = \frac{\sqrt{12} + 2\sqrt{2}}{6 - 4}$

$$= \frac{2\sqrt{3} + 2\sqrt{2}}{2} = \frac{2(\sqrt{3} + \sqrt{2})}{2} = \sqrt{3} + \sqrt{2}$$

(B) $\frac{\sqrt{x} - \sqrt{y}}{\sqrt{x} + \sqrt{y}} = \frac{(\sqrt{x} - \sqrt{y})(\sqrt{x} - \sqrt{y})}{(\sqrt{x} + \sqrt{y})(\sqrt{x} - \sqrt{y})} = \frac{x - 2\sqrt{xy} + y}{x - y}$

Problem 24 Rationalize denominators and simplify:

(A) $\frac{\sqrt{2}}{\sqrt{2} + 3}$ (B) $\frac{\sqrt{x} + \sqrt{y}}{\sqrt{x} - \sqrt{y}}$

ANSWERS TO
MATCHED PROBLEMS

21. (A) $2\sqrt{3} - 3$ (B) $2\sqrt{y} + y$ (C) $3\sqrt{3} - 1$
(D) $y - 3\sqrt{y} - 10$ (E) $x - 2\sqrt{xy} + y$
22. $(2 + \sqrt{3})^2 - 4(2 + \sqrt{3}) + 1 = 4 + 4\sqrt{3} + 3 - 8 - 4\sqrt{3} + 1 = 0$
23. $\frac{3 - \sqrt{2}}{2}$
24. (A) $\frac{2 - 3\sqrt{2}}{-7}$ or $\frac{-2 + 3\sqrt{2}}{7}$ (B) $\frac{x + 2\sqrt{xy} + y}{x - y}$

EXERCISE 8-6   *In Problems 1–28, multiply and simplify where possible.*

A   **1.** $4(\sqrt{5} + 2)$ **2.** $3(\sqrt{3} - 4)$ **3.** $2(5 - \sqrt{2})$
4. $5(3 - \sqrt{5})$ **5.** $\sqrt{2}(\sqrt{2} + 3)$ **6.** $\sqrt{3}(\sqrt{3} + 2)$
7. $\sqrt{5}(\sqrt{5} - 4)$ **8.** $\sqrt{7}(\sqrt{7} - 2)$ **9.** $\sqrt{3}(2 - \sqrt{3})$
10. $\sqrt{2}(3 - \sqrt{2})$ **11.** $\sqrt{x}(\sqrt{x} - 3)$ **12.** $\sqrt{y}(\sqrt{y} - 8)$
13. $\sqrt{m}(3 - \sqrt{m})$ **14.** $\sqrt{n}(4 - \sqrt{n})$

B   **15.** $\sqrt{6}(\sqrt{2} - 1)$ **16.** $\sqrt{3}(5 + \sqrt{6})$

17. $\sqrt{5}(\sqrt{10} + \sqrt{5})$ **18.** $\sqrt{20}(\sqrt{5} - 1)$

19. $(\sqrt{2} - 1)(\sqrt{2} + 3)$ **20.** $(2 - \sqrt{3})(3 + \sqrt{3})$

21. $(\sqrt{x} + 2)(\sqrt{x} - 3)$ **22.** $(\sqrt{m} - 3)(\sqrt{m} - 4)$

23. $(\sqrt{5} + 2)^2$ **24.** $(\sqrt{3} - 3)^2$

25. $(2\sqrt{2} - 5)(3\sqrt{2} + 2)$ **26.** $(4\sqrt{3} - 1)(3\sqrt{3} - 2)$

27. $(3\sqrt{x} - 2)(2\sqrt{x} - 3)$ **28.** $(4\sqrt{y} - 2)(3\sqrt{y} + 1)$

29. Show that $3 - \sqrt{2}$ is a solution to $x^2 - 6x + 7 = 0$.

30. Show that $3 + \sqrt{2}$ is a solution to $x^2 - 6x + 7 = 0$.

Reduce by removing common factors from numerator and denominator.

31. $\dfrac{8 + 4\sqrt{2}}{12}$ **32.** $\dfrac{6 - 2\sqrt{3}}{6}$ **33.** $\dfrac{-3 - 6\sqrt{5}}{9}$

34. $\dfrac{-4 + 2\sqrt{7}}{4}$ **35.** $\dfrac{6 - \sqrt{18}}{3}$ **36.** $\dfrac{10 + \sqrt{8}}{2}$

C   *Rationalize denominators and simplify.*

37. $\dfrac{1}{\sqrt{11} + 3}$ **38.** $\dfrac{1}{\sqrt{5} + 2}$ **39.** $\dfrac{2}{\sqrt{5} + 1}$

40. $\dfrac{4}{\sqrt{6} - 2}$ **41.** $\dfrac{\sqrt{y}}{\sqrt{y} + 3}$ **42.** $\dfrac{\sqrt{x}}{\sqrt{x} - 2}$

43. $\dfrac{\sqrt{3} + 2}{\sqrt{3} - 2}$ **44.** $\dfrac{\sqrt{2} - 1}{\sqrt{2} + 2}$ **45.** $\dfrac{\sqrt{x} + 2}{\sqrt{x} - 3}$

46. $\dfrac{\sqrt{a} - 3}{\sqrt{a} + 2}$ **47.** $\dfrac{\sqrt{5} + \sqrt{3}}{\sqrt{5} - \sqrt{3}}$ **48.** $\dfrac{\sqrt{x}}{\sqrt{x} - \sqrt{y}}$

49. $\dfrac{1 + \sqrt{3}}{\sqrt{3} - \sqrt{2}}$ **50.** $\dfrac{\sqrt{7}}{\sqrt{7} + \sqrt{2}}$

8-7
RADICAL EQUATIONS

An equation that involves a variable within a radical sign is called a **radical equation**. Some examples are

$$\sqrt{x - 3} = 5 \qquad 2\sqrt{x} = x - 3 \qquad \sqrt{x + 7} = \sqrt{x^2 + 5}$$

The key to solving radical equations is the following property of real numbers:

If $a = b$, then $a^2 = b^2$.

Restated, this says, if both sides of an equation are squared, then every solution of the original equation is also a solution to the resulting squared equation. To solve a radical equation, we will square to remove the radicals.

Example 25   Solve $\sqrt{x - 3} = 5$.

Solution $\sqrt{x - 3} = 5$ Square both sides.

$(\sqrt{x - 3})^2 = 5^2$ Recall $(\sqrt{a})^2 = a$. This is the definition of $\sqrt{a}$.

$x - 3 = 25$

$x = 28$

Check $\sqrt{28 - 3} = \sqrt{25} = 5$ as desired.

Problem 25   Solve $\sqrt{3x + 1} = 4$.

Example 26   Solve $5\sqrt{x} = x + 6$.

Solution $5\sqrt{x} = x + 6$ Square both sides.

$25x = x^2 + 12x + 36$ Simplify.

$0 = x^2 - 13x + 36$ Factor.

$0 = (x - 9)(x - 4)$ Solve by setting each factor equal 0.

$x = 9$ or $x = 4$

Check $x = 9$: $5\sqrt{x} = 5\sqrt{9} = 5 \cdot 3 = 15$
$x + 6 = 9 + 6 = 15$
so 9 is a solution.

$x = 4$: $5\sqrt{x} = 5\sqrt{4} = 5 \cdot 2 = 10$
$x + 6 = 4 + 6 = 10$
so 4 is also a solution.

Problem 26   Solve $5\sqrt{x} = x + 4$.

The following example shows why it is important to check all solutions.

Example 27   Solve $2\sqrt{x} = x - 3$.

Solution $2\sqrt{x} = x - 3$ Square both sides.

$4x = x^2 - 6x + 9$ Simplify.

$0 = x^2 - 10x + 9$ Solve by factoring.

$0 = (x - 9)(x - 1)$

$x = 9$ or $x = 1$

Check $x = 9$: $2\sqrt{x} = 2\sqrt{9} = 2 \cdot 3 = 6$
$x - 3 = 6$
so 9 is a solution.

$x = 1$: $2\sqrt{x} = 2\sqrt{1} = 2 \cdot 1 = 2$
$x - 3 = -2$
so 1 is not a solution.

In this example, one of the two possible solutions turns out not to be a solution. This is because squaring both sides of an equation may result in extra solutions that do not satisfy the original equation. These are called **extraneous solutions**. Said differently, each solution of the original is included in the solutions of the square, but the converse is not necessarily true; the squared equation may have solutions that are not solutions to the original equation.

Problem 27   Solve $\sqrt{x} = x - 12$.

ANSWERS TO   **25.** $x = 5$ **26.** $x = 1$ and $x = 16$
MATCHED PROBLEMS   **27.** $x = 16$ ($x = 9$ is extraneous)

EXERCISE 8-7   *Solve.*

A   **1.** $\sqrt{2x + 6} = 4$ **2.** $\sqrt{2x - 6} = 4$

3. $\sqrt{2x - 1} = 3$ **4.** $\sqrt{2x + 1} = 3$

5. $\sqrt{2x + 1} = -1$ **6.** $\sqrt{2x - 1} = -3$

7. $3\sqrt{x + 1} = x + 3$ **8.** $4\sqrt{x + 1} = x + 4$

B   **9.** $\sqrt{x} = x$ **10.** $\sqrt{x} = -x$

11. $3\sqrt{x} = x$ **12.** $\sqrt{2x} = \dfrac{1}{2}x$

13. $\sqrt{3x} = \dfrac{1}{3}x$ **14.** $2\sqrt{x} = x$

15. $6\sqrt{x} = x + 5$ **16.** $7\sqrt{x} = x + 10$

C   **17.** $\sqrt{x - 1} = x - 3$ **18.** $\sqrt{x + 5} = x - 1$

19. $2\sqrt{x + 2} = x - 1$ **20.** $3\sqrt{x + 5} = x + 5$

21. $1 + \sqrt{x} = x - 1$ **22.** $3 + \sqrt{2x} = x - 1$

<h2>8-8
CHAPTER REVIEW</h2>

The definition of a^p for p an integer and the **five basic exponent laws** can be summarized as follows *(8-1, 8-2):*

DEFINITION OF a^p p an integer, a a real number	LAWS OF EXPONENTS n and m integers, a and b real numbers
1. If p is a positive integer, then $a^p = a \cdot a \cdots a \qquad p \text{ factors of } a$	**1.** $a^m a^n = a^{m+n}$
	2. $(a^n)^m = a^{mn}$
2. If $p = 0$, then $a^p = 1 \qquad a \neq 0$	**3.** $(ab)^m = a^m b^m$
3. If p is a negative integer, then $a^p = \dfrac{1}{a^{-p}} \qquad a \neq 0$	**4.** $\left(\dfrac{a}{b}\right)^m = \dfrac{a^m}{b^m}$
	5. $\dfrac{a^m}{a^n} = a^{m-n} = \dfrac{1}{a^{n-m}}$

A number is written in **scientific notation** when it is expressed as a product of a number between 1 and 10, excluding 10, and an integer power of 10. *(8-3)*

A number b is a **square root** of the number a if $b^2 = a$. A positive real number a has exactly two square roots: one positive denoted by $\sqrt{a}$ and one negative denoted by $-\sqrt{a}$. Negative real numbers have no real-number square roots; the square root of 0 is 0. The square root **radical** ($\sqrt{}$) satisfies these properties for a and b nonnegative real numbers:

1. $\sqrt{a^2} = a$
2. $\sqrt{a}\sqrt{b} = ab$
3. $\dfrac{\sqrt{a}}{\sqrt{b}} = \sqrt{\dfrac{a}{b}}, b \neq 0$ *(8-4)*

An algebraic expression that contains square root radicals is in **simplest radical form** if all three of the following conditions are satisfied:

1. No **radicand** (the expression within the radical sign) when expressed in completely factored form contains a factor raised to a power greater than 1. ($\sqrt{x^3}$ violates this condition.)
2. No radical appears in a denominator. ($3/\sqrt{5}$ violates this condition.)
3. No fraction appears within a radical. ($\sqrt{\frac{2}{3}}$ violates this condition.)

Two terms involving identical radicals can be combined into a single term by adding numerical coefficients; for example, $3\sqrt{2} + 4\sqrt{2} = 7\sqrt{2}$. *(8-5)*

The process of converting denominators involving radicals to rational forms is called **rationalizing the denominator**. The product rule

$$(a - b)(a + b) = a^2 - b^2$$

is useful in rationalizing binomial denominators involving square root radicals.   *(8-6)*

A **radical equation** involves a variable within a radical. Such equations are solved by removing radicals by squaring both sides of the equation. This operation may introduce **extraneous solutions**.   *(8-7)*

REVIEW EXERCISE 8-8   *Work through all the problems in this chapter review and check answers in the back of the book. (Answers to all problems are there, and following each answer is a number in italics indicating the section in which that type of problem is discussed.) Where weaknesses show up, review appropriate sections in the text.*

All variables represent positive real numbers.

A   **1.**   Evaluate:
   (A) 2^4 **(B)** 3^{-2}

2.   Evaluate:

   (A) $\left(\dfrac{1}{3}\right)^0$ **(B)** $\dfrac{1}{3^{-2}}$

Rewrite, using positive exponents only.

3. $\left(\dfrac{2x^2}{3y^3}\right)^2$ **4.** $(x^2y^{-3})^{-1}$

5.   Multiply $(3 \times 10^4)(2 \times 10^{-6})$ and express your answer:
   (A)   In scientific notation   **(B)**   As a decimal fraction

Simplify and express in simplest radical form.

6. $-\sqrt{25}$ **7.** $\sqrt{4x^2y^4}$ **8.** $\sqrt{\dfrac{25}{y^2}}$

9. $4\sqrt{x} - 7\sqrt{x}$ **10.** $\sqrt{5}(\sqrt{5} + 2)$

Solve:

11. $\sqrt{x - 3} = 3$

B   **12.** $\sqrt{x + 4} = x - 2$

13.   Evaluate:
   (A) $(3^{-2})^{-1}$ **(B)** $10^{-21}10^{19}$

14. Evaluate:

(A) $\dfrac{3^{-2}}{3}$ (B) $(25^{-5})(25^{5})$

Rewrite, using positive exponents only.

15. $\dfrac{1}{(2x^2y^{-3})^{-2}}$

16. $\dfrac{3m^4n^{-7}}{6m^2n^{-2}}$

17. Change $\dfrac{(480{,}000)(0.005)}{1{,}200{,}000}$ to scientific notation and evaluate. Express your answer:

(A) In scientific notation   (B) As a decimal fraction

Simplify and express in simplest radical form.

18. $\sqrt{36x^4y^7}$

19. $\dfrac{1}{\sqrt{2y}}$

20. $\sqrt{\dfrac{3x}{2y}}$

21. $\sqrt{\tfrac{2}{3}} + \sqrt{\tfrac{3}{2}}$

22. $(\sqrt{3} - 1)(\sqrt{3} + 2)$

C *Rewrite, using positive exponents only.*

23. $\left(\dfrac{9m^3n^{-3}}{3m^{-2}n^2}\right)^{-2}$

24. $(x^{-1} + y^{-1})^{-1}$

Simplify and express in simplest radical form.

25. $\dfrac{\sqrt{8m^3n^4}}{\sqrt{12m^2}}$

26. $\dfrac{\sqrt{3}}{\sqrt{3} - \sqrt{2}}$

27. $\dfrac{\sqrt{x} - 2}{\sqrt{x} + 2}$

28. $\sqrt{4x^4 + 16x^2}$

29. The volume of mercury increases linearly with temperature over a fairly wide temperature range. (This is why mercury is often used in thermometers.) If 1 cubic centimeter of mercury at 0°C is heated to a temperature of T°C, its volume is given by the formula

$$V = 1 + (1.8 \times 10^{-4})T$$

Find the volume of the sample at (2×10^2)°C as a decimal fraction.

30. If a is a square root of b, then does $a^2 = b$ or does $b^2 = a$?

31. For which real numbers does $\sqrt{x^2} = |x|$?

32. *Solve:* $\sqrt{x + 5} = x - 1$

9

QUADRATIC EQUATIONS

The equation

$$\tfrac{1}{2}x - \tfrac{1}{3}(x + 3) = 2 - x$$

is a first-degree equation in one variable since it can be transformed into the equivalent equation

$$7x - 18 = 0$$

which is a special case of

$$ax + b = 0 \qquad a \neq 0 \quad \text{First-degree equation}$$

We have solved many equations of this type and found that they always have a single solution.

In this chapter we will consider the next class of polynomial equations called quadratic equations. A **quadratic equation** in one variable is any equation that can be written in the form

$$ax^2 + bx + c = 0 \qquad a \neq 0 \quad \text{Quadratic equation}$$

where x is a variable and a, b, and c are constants. We will refer to this form as the **standard form** for the quadratic equation. The equations

$$2x^2 - 3x + 5 = 0 \qquad \text{and} \qquad 15 = 180t - 16t^2$$

are both quadratic equations, since they are either in the standard form or can be transformed into this form.

Problems that give rise to quadratic equations are many and varied. For example, to find the dimensions of a rectangle with an area of 36 square inches and

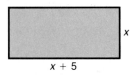

length 5 inches more than its width, we are led to the equation

$$x(x + 5) = 36$$
$$x^2 + 5x = 36$$

or

$$x^2 + 5x - 36 = 0$$

We actually have at hand all the tools we need to solve equations of this type—it is a matter of putting this material together in the right way. Putting this material together in the right way is the subject of this chapter.

9-1
SOLUTION BY FACTORING AND SQUARE ROOT

- Solution by Factoring
- Solution by Square Root

In this section, we will consider two elementary methods of solving quadratic equations. The methods, however, apply only in certain situations. More general methods are introduced in Sections 9-2 and 9-3.

SOLUTION BY FACTORING

If the coefficients a, b, and c in the quadratic equations

$$ax^2 + bx + c = 0$$

are such that $ax^2 + bx + c$ can be written as the product of two first-degree factors with integer coefficients, then the quadratic equation can be quickly and easily solved by the method of factoring as was done in Section 6-7.

Example 1   Solve $x^2 - 9x + 20 = 0$

Solution

$$x^2 - 9x + 20 = 0$$
$$(x - 4)(x - 5) = 0$$
$$x - 4 = 0 \quad \text{or} \quad x - 5 = 0$$
$$x = 4 \quad \text{or} \quad x = 5$$

Problem 1   Solve $x^2 - 7x - 30 = 0$

SOLUTION BY SQUARE ROOT

Some quadratic equations can be solved simply by taking square roots. This method applies when the first-degree term of the quadratic equation is missing. A key step in the process uses this result:

For $a \geq 0$, if $x^2 = a$, then $x = \pm\sqrt{a}$.

The method is very fast, and it leads to a general method for solving all quadratic equations, as will be seen in the next section. A few examples should make the process clear.

Example 2

$$x^2 - 9 = 0 \qquad \text{Notice that the first-degree term is missing.}$$

$$x^2 = 9 \qquad \text{What number squared is 9?}$$

$$\boxed{x = \pm\sqrt{9}} \qquad \text{Short for } \sqrt{9} \text{ or } -\sqrt{9}.$$

$$x = \pm 3$$

Problem 2   Solve $x^2 = 16$ by the square root method.

Example 3 $x^2 - 7 = 0$

$$x^2 = 7 \quad \text{What number squared is 7?}$$

$$x = \pm\sqrt{7}$$

Problem 3   Solve $x^2 - 8 = 0$.

Example 4 $2x^2 - 3 = 0$

$$2x^2 = 3$$

$$x^2 = \frac{3}{2}$$

$$x = \pm\sqrt{\frac{3}{2}} \quad \text{or} \quad \pm\frac{\sqrt{6}}{2}$$

Problem 4   Solve $3x^2 - 2 = 0$.

Example 5 $(x - 2)^2 = 16$ \quad Solve for $(x - 2)$ first; then solve for x.

$$x - 2 = \pm 4$$

$$x = 2 \pm 4$$

$$x = 6, -2$$

Problem 5   Solve $(x + 3)^2 = 25$.

Example 6 $(x + \frac{1}{2})^2 = \frac{5}{4}$ \quad Solve for $(x + \frac{1}{2})$ first; then solve for x.

$$x + \tfrac{1}{2} = \pm\sqrt{\tfrac{5}{4}}$$

$$x + \tfrac{1}{2} = \pm\frac{\sqrt{5}}{2}$$

$$x = -\frac{1}{2} \pm \frac{\sqrt{5}}{2}$$

$$x = \frac{-1 \pm \sqrt{5}}{2}$$

Problem 6   Solve $(x - \frac{1}{3})^2 = \frac{7}{9}$.

Example 7 $x^2 = -9$

Solution   There is no solution in the real numbers, since no real number squared is negative.

Problem 7   Solve $x^2 + 4 = 0$.

The introduction to Chapter 1 posed the following problem:

A rectangular field is twice as long as it is wide and has an area of 6,962 square yards. What are its dimensions?

We can now restate the problem in algebraic terms and quickly obtain the solution. Let x = the width of the field so $2x$ = the length. The area is $x \cdot 2x$, so

$$2x^2 = 6,962$$
$$x^2 = 3,481$$
$$x = \pm\sqrt{3,481} = \pm59$$

Since the problem requires a positive width, the only solution that makes sense physically is $x = 59$. Thus, the field is 59 yards by 118 yards.

ANSWERS TO
MATCHED PROBLEMS

1. $x = -3, 10$ **2.** $x = \pm4$ **3.** $x = \pm\sqrt{8}$ or $\pm2\sqrt{2}$

4. $x = \pm\sqrt{\dfrac{2}{3}}$ or $\pm\dfrac{\sqrt{6}}{3}$ **5.** $x = -8, 2$ **6.** $x = \dfrac{1 \pm \sqrt{7}}{3}$

7. No real solutions

EXERCISE 9-1 **A** *Solve by factoring.*

1. $x^2 - 8x + 15 = 0$ **2.** $x^2 + 2x - 15 = 0$

3. $x^2 + 3x - 28 = 0$ **4.** $x^2 - 3x + 18 = 0$

5. $x^2 - x - 42 = 0$ **6.** $x^2 + 9x + 8 = 0$

7. $x^2 + 4x - 21 = 0$ **8.** $x^2 - 3x - 70 = 0$

9. $x^2 + 11x + 28 = 0$ **10.** $x^2 + 10x + 24 = 0$

Solve for all real solutions by the square root method.

11. $x^2 = 16$ **12.** $x^2 = 49$ **13.** $m^2 - 64 = 0$

14. $n^2 - 25 = 0$ **15.** $x^2 = 3$ **16.** $y^2 = 2$

17. $u^2 - 5 = 0$ **18.** $x^2 - 11 = 0$ **19.** $a^2 = 18$

20. $y^2 = 8$ **21.** $x^2 - 12 = 0$ **22.** $n^2 - 27 = 0$

23. $x^2 = \frac{4}{9}$ **24.** $y^2 = \frac{9}{16}$ **25.** $9x^2 = 4$

26. $16y^2 = 9$ **27.** $9x^2 - 4 = 0$ **28.** $16y^2 - 9 = 0$

B **29.** $25x^2 - 4 = 0$ **30.** $9x^2 - 1 = 0$ **31.** $4t^2 - 3 = 0$

32. $9x^2 - 7 = 0$ **33.** $2x^2 - 5 = 0$ **34.** $3m^2 - 7 = 0$

35. $3m^2 - 1 = 0$ **36.** $5n^2 - 1 = 0$ **37.** $(y - 2)^2 = 9$

38. $(x - 3)^2 = 4$ **39.** $(x + 2)^2 = 25$ **40.** $(y + 3)^2 = 16$

41. $(y - 2)^2 = 3$ **42.** $(y - 3)^2 = 5$ **43.** $(x - \frac{1}{2})^2 = \frac{9}{4}$

44. $(x - \frac{1}{3})^2 = \frac{4}{9}$ **45.** $(x - 3)^2 = -4$ **46.** $(t + 1)^2 = -9$

C   **47.** $(x - \frac{3}{2})^2 = \frac{4}{9}$ **48.** $(y + \frac{5}{2})^2 = \frac{5}{2}$

Solve by factoring.

49. $2x^2 - 5x - 3 = 0$ **50.** $3x^2 + x - 2 = 0$

51. $3x^2 + 5x - 2 = 0$ **52.** $2x^2 + 5x + 3 = 0$

53. $4x^2 + 7x - 2 = 0$ **54.** $3x^2 - x - 4 = 0$

55. Solve for b: $a^2 + b^2 = c^2$.   **56.** Solve for v: $k = \frac{1}{2}mv^2$.

APPLICATIONS   **57.** The pressure p in pounds per square foot from a wind blowing at v miles per hour is given approximately by $p = 0.003v^2$. If a pressure gauge on a bridge registers a wind pressure of 14.7 pounds per square foot, what is the velocity of the wind?

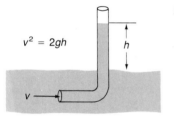

$v^2 = 2gh$

58. One method of measuring the velocity of water in a river is to use an L-shaped tube as indicated in the figure. Torricelli's law in physics tells us that the height (in feet) that the water is pushed up into the tube above the surface is related to the water's velocity (in feet per second) by the formula $v^2 = 2gh$, where g is approximately 32 feet per second per second. [*Note:* The device can also be used as a simple speedometer for a boat.] How fast is a stream flowing if $h = 0.5$ foot? Find the answer to two decimal places.

9-2

SOLUTION BY
COMPLETING THE
SQUARE

- Completing a Square
- Solution of Quadratic Equations by Completing the Square

The factoring and square root methods discussed in the last section are fast and easy to use when they apply. Unfortunately, many quadratic equations will not yield to either method as stated. For example, the simple-looking polynomial in

$$x^2 + 4x - 6 = 0$$

cannot be factored using integer coefficients, and the square root method is not applicable either. The equation requires a new method if it can be solved at all.

In this section we will discuss a method, called **solution by completing the**

square, that will work for all quadratic equations. In the next section we will use this method to develop a general formula that will be used in the future whenever the methods of the preceding section fails.

The method of completing the square is based on the process of transforming the standard quadratic equation.

$$ax^2 + bx + c = 0 \tag{1}$$

into the form

$$(x + A)^2 = B \tag{2}$$

where A and B are constants. This last equation can be solved easily (assuming $B \geq 0$) by the square root method discussed in the last section. That is,

$$(x + A)^2 = B$$
$$x + A = \pm\sqrt{B}$$
$$x = -A \pm \sqrt{B}$$

COMPLETING A SQUARE

In Section 6-4, we learned to recognize a perfect square binomial:

$$(A + B)^2 = A^2 + 2AB + B^2$$
$$(x + B)^2 = x^2 + 2Bx + B^2$$

In the second form, we note that the last term, B^2, is the square of one-half the coefficient of x in the middle term. Thus, to complete the square of $x^2 + bx$, we add a third term, $(b/2)^2$, which is the square of one-half the coefficient of x. This result is summarized in the following box:

Completing the Square

To **complete the square** of a quadratic of the form

$$x^2 + bx$$

add the square of one-half of the coefficient of x, that is, add

$$\left(\frac{b}{2}\right)^2$$

Then

$$x^2 + bx + \left(\frac{b}{2}\right)^2 = \left(x + \frac{b}{2}\right)^2$$

Note: The coefficient of x^2 must be 1 for this rule to apply.

Example 8   Complete the square and factor the resulting expression.

   (A) $x^2 + 8x$

   (B) $x^2 - 7x$

Solution   **(A)** $x^2 + 8x + \left(\dfrac{8}{2}\right)^2 = x^2 + 8x + 16 = (x + 4)^2$

   (B) $x^2 - 7x + \left(\dfrac{-7}{2}\right)^2 = x^2 - 7x + \dfrac{49}{4} = \left(x - \dfrac{7}{2}\right)^2$

Problem 8   Complete the square and factor the resulting expression.

   (A) $x^2 - 3x$

   (B) $x^2 + 6x$

SOLUTION OF QUADRATIC EQUATIONS BY COMPLETING THE SQUARE

Solving quadratic equations by the method of completing the square is best illustrated by examples. In this course we are going to be interested only in real-number solutions.

Example 9   Solve $x^2 + 4x - 6 = 0$.

Solution

$x^2 + 4x - 6 = 0$ Add 6 to both sides of the equation to leave the left side in the form $x^2 + Bx$.

$x^2 + 4x = 6$ Complete the square on the left side. The same amount must be added to the right side to preserve the equality.

$x^2 + 4x + 4 = 6 + 4$ Factor the left side as a perfect square.

$(x + 2)^2 = 10$ Solve by square roots.

$x + 2 = \pm\sqrt{10}$

$x = -2 \pm \sqrt{10}$

Problem 9   Solve $x^2 + 6x + 4 = 0$.

Example 10   Solve $2x^2 + 6x - 3 = 0$.

Solution $2x^2 + 6x - 3 = 0$ Divide both sides by 2 to
                                    change the left side to a
                                    form where the coefficient
                                    of x^2 is 1.

$$x^2 + 3x - \frac{3}{2} = 0$$ Proceed as in Example 9.

$$x^2 + 3x = \frac{3}{2} \qquad \left(\frac{3}{2}\right)^2 = \frac{9}{4}.$$

$$x^2 + 3x + \frac{9}{4} = \frac{3}{2} + \frac{9}{4}$$

$$\left(x + \frac{3}{2}\right)^2 = \frac{15}{4}$$

$$x + \frac{3}{2} = \pm\sqrt{\frac{15}{4}}$$

$$x = -\frac{3}{2} \pm \sqrt{\frac{15}{4}}$$

$$= \frac{-3}{2} \pm \frac{\sqrt{15}}{2}$$

$$= \frac{-3 \pm \sqrt{15}}{2}$$

Problem 10   Solve $3x^2 + 4x - 1 = 0$.

The method of completing the square may be summarized as follows:

1.   Write the quadratic equation in standard form: $ax^2 + bx + c = 0$.
2.   Divide both sides by a to obtain a standard form with the coefficient of x^2 equal to 1, say

$$x^2 + Bx + C = 0$$

3.   Substitute the constant C from each side:

$$x^2 + Bx = -C$$

4.   Complete the square of $x^2 + Bx$ by adding $(B/2)^2$ to each side to obtain

$$x^2 + Bx + \left(\frac{B}{2}\right)^2 = \left(x + \frac{B}{2}\right)^2 = -C + \left(\frac{B}{2}\right)^2$$

5.   Solve by the method of square roots.

ANSWERS TO
MATCHED PROBLEMS

8.   (A) $x^2 - 3x + \dfrac{9}{4} = \left(x - \dfrac{3}{2}\right)^2$ **(B)** $x^2 + 6x + 9 = (x + 3)^2$

9. $x = -3 \pm \sqrt{5}$ **10.** $x = \dfrac{-2 \pm \sqrt{7}}{3}$

EXERCISE 9-2   A   *Complete the square and factor.*

1. $x^2 - 8x$ **2.** $x^2 + 4x$ **3.** $x^2 + 10x$

4. $x^2 - 12x$ **5.** $x^2 - 10x$ **6.** $x^2 - 2x$

Solve by the method of completing the square.

7. $x^2 - 8x + 6 = 0$ **8.** $x^2 + 4x - 3 = 0$

9. $x^2 + 10x - 1 = 0$ **10.** $x^2 - 12x + 10 = 0$

B   *Complete the square and factor.*

11. $x^2 + 7x$ **12.** $x^2 + 5x$

13. $x^2 - 3x$ **14.** $x^2 - x$

Solve by the method of completing the square.

15. $x + 7x - 5 = 0$ **16.** $x + 5x + 3 = 0$

17. $x^2 - 3x + 1 = 0$ **18.** $x^2 - x - 3 = 0$

19. $x^2 - 11x + 28 = 0$ **20.** $x^2 - 10x + 23 = 0$

C   **21.** $2x^2 + 4x - 5 = 0$ **22.** $2x^2 + 6x - 1 = 0$

23. $2x^2 + 5x - 4 = 0$ **24.** $2x^2 + x - 6 = 0$

25. $x^2 + 12x + 30 = 0$ **26.** $x^2 + 5x + 5 = 0$

27. $3x^2 - 6x + 1 = 0$ **28.** $3x^2 + 2x - 1 = 0$

29. $x^2 + 2x = 3$ **30.** $2x^2 - 5x = 3$

31. $2x^2 - 5x = -3$ **32.** $4x^2 + 3x = 1$

9-3

**THE QUADRATIC
FORMULA**

- Deriving the Quadratic Formula
- Use of the Quadratic Formula
- The Discriminant
- Which Method?

We can now apply the method of completing the square developed in the last section to obtain a general formula for solving any quadratic equation.

DERIVING THE QUADRATIC FORMULA

We apply the steps for the method of completing the square to the general quadratic equation in standard form

$$ax^2 + bx + c = 0 \qquad a \neq 0$$

1. Write the equation in standard form: we are given the equation in standard form

$$ax^2 + bx + c = 0$$

2. Divide both sides by a to obtain a standard form with coefficient of x^2 equal to 1:

$$x^2 + \frac{b}{a}x + \frac{c}{a} = 0$$

3. Subtract the constant term from both sides:

$$x^2 + \frac{b}{a}x = -\frac{c}{a}$$

4. Complete the square of $x^2 + \dfrac{b}{a}x$ by adding the square of one-half the coefficient of x, that is, $\dfrac{1}{2}$ of $\dfrac{b}{a}$, to both sides:

$$x^2 + \frac{b}{a}x + \left(\frac{b}{2a}\right)^2 = -\frac{c}{a} + \left(\frac{b}{2a}\right)^2$$

5. Solve by the method of square roots:

$$\left(x + \frac{b}{2a}\right)^2 = -\frac{c}{a} + \frac{b^2}{4a^2}$$

$$= \frac{-4ac + b^2}{4a^2} = \frac{b^2 - 4ac}{4a^2}$$

$$x + \frac{b}{2a} = \pm\sqrt{\frac{b^2 - 4ac}{4a^2}}$$

$$= \pm\frac{\sqrt{b^2 - 4ac}}{\sqrt{4a^2}}$$

$$= \pm\frac{\sqrt{b^2 - 4ac}}{2a}$$

We need to note two things at this stage. If $b^2 - 4ac < 0$, the equation has no solution in the set of real numbers. Assume, therefore, that $b^2 - 4ac \geq 0$. Also, $\sqrt{4a^2}$ is either $2a$ or $-2a$, but we need only use $2a$, since there is already a $\pm$ sign in the expression.† Continuing:

$$x = -\frac{b}{2a} \pm \frac{\sqrt{b^2 - 4ac}}{2a}$$

$$x = \frac{-b \pm \sqrt{b^2 - 4ac}}{2a}$$

This last equation, the solution to $ax^2 + bx + c = 0$, is called the **quadratic formula**.

$$x = \frac{-b \pm \sqrt{b^2 - 4ac}}{2a} \qquad a \neq 0 \qquad \text{QUADRATIC FORMULA}$$

USE OF THE QUADRATIC FORMULA

The quadratic formula yields the solution to any quadratic equation. However, we will limit our interest to real-number solutions in this course. The following examples show us how to use the quadratic formula. The first example was worked in the last section by completing the squares.

Example 11   Solve $2x^2 + 6x - 3 = 0$ using the quadratic formula.

Solution $2x^2 + 6x - 3 = 0$ The equation is in standard form, with $a = 2$, $b = 6$, and $c = -3$.

$$x = \frac{-b \pm \sqrt{b^2 - 4ac}}{2a}$$ Substitute for a, b, and c in the formula.

$$x = \frac{-6 \pm \sqrt{6^2 - 4 \cdot 2(-3)}}{2 \cdot 2}$$

$$= \frac{-6 \pm \sqrt{36 + 24}}{4} = \frac{-6 \pm \sqrt{60}}{4} = \frac{-6 \pm 2\sqrt{15}}{4}$$

$$= \frac{2(-3 \pm \sqrt{15})}{4} = \frac{-3 \pm \sqrt{15}}{2}$$

---

† If a is positive, $\sqrt{4a^2} = 2a$ and

$$\pm\frac{\sqrt{b^2 - 4ac}}{\sqrt{4a^2}} = \pm\frac{\sqrt{b^2 - 4ac}}{2a}$$

If a is negative, $\sqrt{4a^2} = -2a$ and

$$\pm\frac{\sqrt{b^2 - 4ac}}{\sqrt{4a^2}} = \mp\frac{\sqrt{b^2 - 4ac}}{2a} = \pm\frac{\sqrt{b^2 - 4ac}}{2a}$$

Problem 11   Solve $3x^2 + 4x - 1 = 0$ using the quadratic formula.

Example 12   Solve $3x^2 + \dfrac{1}{2}x - 1 = 0$.

Solution $3x^2 + \dfrac{1}{2}x - 1 = 0$ It will be easier to clear the equations of fractions first. Multiply by the LCD.

$6x^2 + x - 2 = 0$ Here $a = 6$, $b = 1$, $c = -2$.

$$x = \frac{-1 \pm \sqrt{1 - 4 \cdot 6(-2)}}{2 \cdot 6}$$

$$= \frac{-1 \pm \sqrt{49}}{12}$$

$$= \frac{-1 \pm 7}{12}$$

$$x = \frac{1}{2}, \frac{-2}{3}$$

Problem 12   Solve $2x^2 + \dfrac{1}{3}x - 1 = 0$.

Example 13   Solve $16x^2 - 24x + 9 = 0$.

Solution   Here $a = 16$, $b = -24$, and $c = 9$.

$$x = \frac{24 \pm \sqrt{(-24)^2 - 4 \cdot 16 \cdot 9}}{2 \cdot 16}$$

$$= \frac{24 \pm \sqrt{576 - 576}}{32}$$

$$= \frac{24}{32} = \frac{3}{4}$$

Problem 13   Solve $25x^2 - 40x + 16 = 0$.

Example 14   Solve $x^2 + x + 1 = 0$.

Solution   Here $a = 1$, $b = 1$, and $c = 1$.

$$x = \frac{-1 \pm \sqrt{1 - 4 \cdot 1 \cdot 1}}{2 \cdot 1} = \frac{-1 \pm \sqrt{-3}}{2}$$

Since the expression under the radical is negative, it does not represent a real number. This equation has no real solution.

Problem 14   Solve $x^2 - 2x + 3 = 0$.

THE DISCRIMINANT

Notice that in Examples 11 and 12, the equation had two real roots and the radical expression $\pm\sqrt{b^2 - 4ac}$ accounted for this. In Example 13, on the other hand, the equation had only one root and the radical expression equaled 0. Finally, in Example 14, the equation had no real root because the quantity in the radical was negative. The quantity $b^2 - 4ac$ thus provides an indicator for the number of real roots of a quadratic equation, discriminating between the three possibilities of 0, 1, or 2 roots. The expression $b^2 - 4ac$ is therefore called the **discriminant**.

Discriminant Test

$ax^2 + bx + c = 0$ a, b, c real numbers, $a \neq 0$

$b^2 - 4ac$	ROOTS
Positive	Two real roots
Zero	One real root
Negative	No real roots

Example 15   Apply the discriminant test to determine the number of real roots of the equation:

(A) $2x^2 - 3x + 1 = 0$
(B) $3x^2 + 5x + 4 = 0$
(C) $25x^2 + 10x + 1 = 0$

Solution   **(A)** The discriminant $b^2 - 4ac$ here is equal to

$$(-3)^2 - 4 \cdot 2 \cdot 1 = 9 - 8 = 1$$

so the equation has two real roots. Check that they are 1 and $\frac{1}{2}$.
(B) The discriminant $b^2 - 4ac$ here is equal to

$$5^2 - 4 \cdot 3 \cdot 4 = -23$$

so the equation has no real roots.
(C) The discriminant $b^2 - 4ac$ here is equal to

$$10^2 - 4 \cdot 25 \cdot 1 = 0$$

so the equation has one real root. Check that it is $-\frac{1}{5}$.

Problem 15 Apply the discriminant test to determine the number of real roots of the equation:

(A) $25x^2 - 30x + 9 = 0$
(B) $9x^2 + 3x + 1 = 0$
(C) $4x^2 + 5x + 1 = 0$

WHICH METHOD?

In normal practice the quadratic formula is used whenever the square root method or the factoring method does not produce results. These latter methods are generally faster when they apply, however, and should be used.

Note that any quadratic equation of the form

$$ax^2 + c = 0 \quad \text{Note that the } bx \text{ term is missing.}$$

can always be solved (if solutions exist in the real numbers) by the square root method, since the equation is equivalent to $x^2 = -c/a$. And any equation of the form

$$ax^2 + bx = 0 \quad \text{Note that the } c \text{ term is missing.}$$

can always be solved by factoring, since $ax^2 + bx = x(ax + b)$.

It is important to realize, however, that the quadratic formula can always be used and will produce the same results as any of the other methods. For example, let us solve

$$2x^2 + 7x - 15 = 0$$

in two ways.

Suppose you observe that the polynomial factors. Thus,

$$(2x - 3)(x + 5) = 0$$
$$2x - 3 = 0 \quad \text{or} \quad x + 5 = 0$$
$$x = \tfrac{3}{2} \quad \text{or} \quad x = -5$$

Suppose you had used the quadratic formula instead.

$$x = \frac{-b \pm \sqrt{b^2 - 4ac}}{2a} \quad a = 2, b = 7, c = -15$$

$$x = \frac{-(7) \pm \sqrt{7^2 - 4(2)(-15)}}{2(2)}$$

$$x = \frac{-7 \pm \sqrt{169}}{4} = \frac{-7 \pm 13}{4}$$

$$x = \tfrac{3}{2}, -5$$

The quadratic formula produces the same result as the factoring method (as it should), but with a little more work.

11. $x = \dfrac{-2 \pm \sqrt{7}}{3}$ **12.** $x = \dfrac{-1 \pm \sqrt{73}}{12}$

13. $x = \dfrac{4}{5}$ **14.** No real roots

15. **(A)** One   **(B)** No real roots   **(C)** Two

EXERCISE 9-3   **A**   *Specify the constants a, b, and c for each quadratic equation when written in the standard form $ax^2 + bx + c = 0$.*

1. $x^2 + 4x + 2 = 0$ **2.** $x^2 + 8x + 3 = 0$

3. $x^2 - 3x - 2 = 0$ **4.** $x^2 - 6x - 8 = 0$

5. $3x^2 - 2x + 1 = 0$ **6.** $2x^2 - 5x + 3 = 0$

7. $2u^2 = 1 - 3u$ **8.** $m = 1 - 3m^2$

9. $2x^2 - 5x = 0$ **10.** $3y^2 - 5 = 0$

Solve by use of the quadratic formula.

11. $x^2 + 4x + 2 = 0$ **12.** $x^2 + 8x + 3 = 0$

13. $y^2 - 6y - 3 = 0$ **14.** $y^2 - 10y - 3 = 0$

B   **15.** $3t + t^2 = 1$ **16.** $x^2 = 1 - x$

17. $2x^2 - 6x + 3 = 0$ **18.** $2x^2 - 4x + 1 = 0$

19. $3m^2 = 1 - m$ **20.** $3u + 2u^2 = 1$

21. $x^2 = 2x - 3$ **22.** $x^2 + 8 = 4x$

23. $2x = 3 + \dfrac{3}{x}$ **24.** $x + \dfrac{2}{x} = 6$

25. $m^2 = \dfrac{8m - 1}{5}$ **26.** $x^2 = 3x + \dfrac{1}{2}$

27. $3u^2 = \sqrt{3}\, u + 2$ **28.** $t^2 - \sqrt{5}t - 11 = 0$

Apply the discriminant test to determine the number of real roots and, if real roots exist, solve by use of the quadratic formula.

29. $x^2 + 8x + 17 = 0$ **30.** $64x^2 - 48x + 9 = 0$

31. $36x^2 + 12x + 1 = 0$ **32.** $5x^2 + 7x + 2 = 0$

33. $3x^2 - 7x + 3 = 0$

34. $6x^2 - 11x + 6 = 0$

35. $9x^2 - 8x + 2 = 0$

36. $100x^2 + 140x + 49 = 0$

37. $16x^2 - 24x + 9 = 0$

38. $2x^2 + 7x + 5 = 0$

C *The following problems are mixed. Use the most efficient method to find all real solutions to each equation.*

39. $x^2 - x - 6 = 0$

40. $x^2 + 2x - 8 = 0$

41. $x^2 + 7x = 0$

42. $x^2 = 3x$

43. $2x^2 = 32$

44. $3x^2 - 27 = 0$

45. $x^2 + 2x - 2 = 0$

46. $m^2 - 3m - 1 = 0$

47. $2x^2 = 4x$

48. $2y^2 + 3y = 0$

49. $x^2 - 2x = 1$

50. $x^2 - 2 = 2x$

51. $u^2 = 3u - \frac{3}{2}$ 52. $t^2 = \frac{3}{2}(t + 1)$ 53. $M = M^2$

54. $t(t - 3) = 0$ 55. $6y = \dfrac{1 - y}{y}$ 56. $2x + 1 = \dfrac{6}{x}$

57. $l^2 - 50 = 0$

58. $72 = u^2$

59. $(B - 2)^2 = 3$

60. $(u + 3)^2 = 5$

61. $x^2 + 4 = 0$

62. $(x - 2)^2 = -9$

63. $\dfrac{24}{n} = 12n - 28$

64. $3x = \dfrac{84 - 9x}{x}$

65. $\dfrac{24}{10 + x} + 1 = \dfrac{24}{10 - x}$

66. $\dfrac{1.2}{x - 1} + \dfrac{1.2}{x} = 1$

9-4
GRAPHING QUADRATIC EQUATIONS

- Graphing Equations of the Form $y = ax^2$
- Graphing Equations of the Form $y = x^2 + k$ and $y = (x - h)^2$
- Graphing Equations of the Form $y = ax^2 + bx + c$
- Graphs and Solutions to Quadratic Equations

In Chapter 4, we defined the solution set of the linear equation

$$y = mx + b$$

to be the set of all pairs of real numbers (x, y) that make the equation true. The graph of the equation was the graph of all these ordered pairs and turned out always to be a straight line. In this section, we extend these ideas to quadratic equations

$$y = ax^2 + bx + c$$

A **solution** to such an equation is again a pair of real numbers (x, y) that make the equation true. The **solution set** for the equation is the set of all such pairs, and the **graph of the equation** is the graph consisting of all solution pairs. The graph is a curve called a **parabola**.

GRAPHING EQUATIONS OF THE FORM $y = ax^2$

To graph $y = x^2$ we make a table of some of its values and plot them:

x	y
-3	9
-2	4
-1	1
0	0
1	1
2	4
3	9

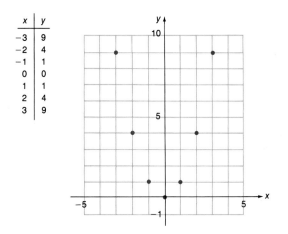

The graph is not a straight line. If we plot more values, the graph would fill in to look like this:

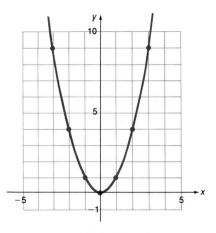

This is the graph of $y = x^2$.

If we want to graph $y = -x^2$, we make a table of values as we did above, and plot the points:

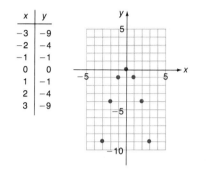

x	y
-3	-9
-2	-4
-1	-1
0	0
1	-1
2	-4
3	-9

Notice that all the y values are simply the negatives of those obtained before for $y = x^2$ and the effect is just to turn our previous plot of points upside down. The same is true of the complete graph:

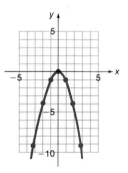

To graph an equation like $y = 2x^2$, we again calculate and plot some values:

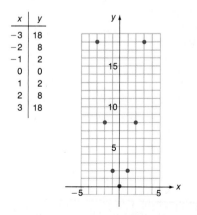

x	y
-3	18
-2	8
-1	2
0	0
1	2
2	8
3	18

The complete graph is shown in Figure 1A. Figure 1B shows $y = x^2$ and $y = 2x^2$ on the same coordinate system for comparison purposes. This comparison is also the reason we are still using the same scale on both axes. Using a smaller scale on the y axis, as discussed in Section 4-2, would make plotting easier but would disguise the changes in the graphs we are considering.

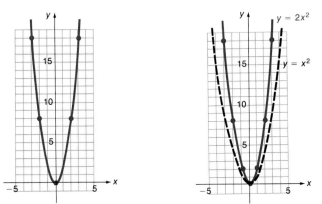

FIGURE 1(A)   **FIGURE 1(B)**

The effect of multiplying x^2 by 2 is to "stretch" the graph geometrically. Multiplying by a factor between 0 and 1 would "flatten" it. Multiplying by a negative number has a comparable effect but also turns the graph upside down. Figure 2 shows several graphs of equations of the form $y = ax^2$.

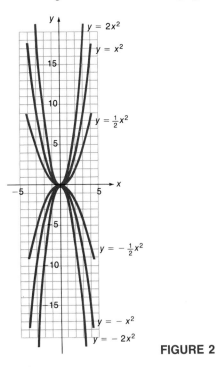

FIGURE 2

Example 16   Graph: **(A)** $y = 3x^2$ **(B)** $y = -3x^2$

Solution   **(A)** Make a table of some values, plot these points, and fill in the graph. We need only plot enough points to see the expected shape of the graph.

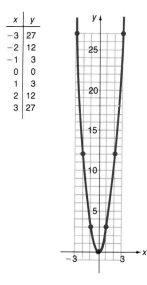

x	y
-3	27
-2	12
-1	3
0	0
1	3
2	12
3	27

(B) The graph of $y = -3x^2$ is simply the graph obtained in part (A) turned upside down:

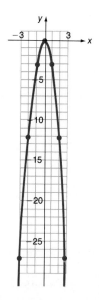

Problem 16   Graph: **(A)** $y = 4x^2$ **(B)** $y = -4x^2$

Example 17   Graph $y = x^2$, $y = 3x^2$, and $y = \frac{1}{3}x^2$ on the same coordinate system.

Solution   The graphs of $y = x^2$ and $y = 3x^2$ are already known. To plot $y = \frac{1}{3}x^2$, we proceed as always by calculating and plotting enough values to see the shape of the graph.

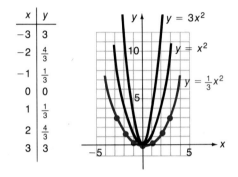

x	y
-3	3
-2	$\frac{4}{3}$
-1	$\frac{1}{3}$
0	0
1	$\frac{1}{3}$
2	$\frac{4}{3}$
3	3

Problem 17   Graph $y = -x^2$, $y = -4x^2$, and $y = -\frac{1}{4}x^2$ on the same coordinate system.

GRAPHING EQUATIONS OF THE FORM
$y = x^2 + k$ and $y = (x - h)^2$

To graph $y = x^2 + 1$, once again make a table and plot:

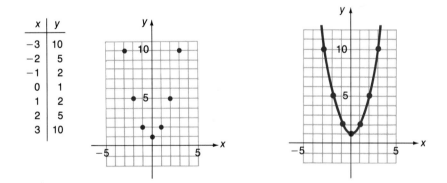

x	y
-3	10
-2	5
-1	2
0	1
1	2
2	5
3	10

Notice that each y value is 1 more than in our original table for $y = x^2$ and the plot of points is the same as for $y = x^2$, except that it is raised 1 unit. The same is true for the complete graph, shown above.

In general, the graph of $y = x^2 + k$ is the graph of $y = x^2$ raised k units if k is positive and lowered $|k|$ units if k is negative.

Example 18 Graph: **(A)** $y = x^2 - 2$ **(B)** $y = -x^2 + 3$

Solution **(A)** The graph is the graph of $y = x^2$ lowered 2 units.
(B) The graph is the graph of $y = -x^2$ raised 3 units.

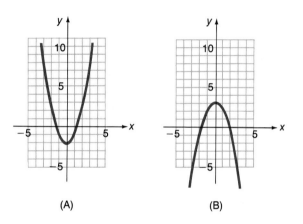

(A)   (B)

Problem 18 Graph: **(A)** $y = x^2 + 3$ **(B)** $y = -x^2 - 2$

To graph $y = (x - 1)^2$, as usual we calculate and plot a few points:

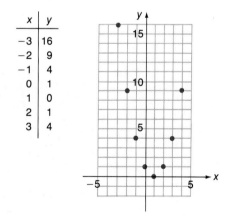

x	y
-3	16
-2	9
-1	4
0	1
1	0
2	1
3	4

We notice that the y values are the same as in the table for $y = x^2$, but they occur for values of x one unit greater. That is, the y value 9 occurs at $x = -2$

and 4 instead of at -3 and 3. Also the plot of points is the same as for $y = x^2$, except it is shifted 1 unit to the right. The same is true for the complete graph:

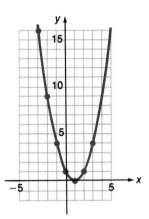

In general, the graph of $y = (x - h)^2$ is the graph of $y = x^2$ moved h units to the right if h is positive or $|h|$ units to the left if h is negative.

Example 19   Graph: **(A)** $y = (x - 2)^2$ **(B)** $y = (x + 2)^2$

Solution   **(A)** The graph is the same as $y = x^2$ but moved 2 units to the right.
(B) Since $x + 2 = x - (-2)$, here $h = -2$. The graph is the same as $y = x^2$ but moved 2 units to the left.

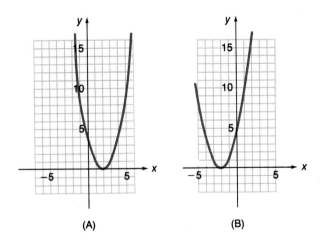

Problem 19   Graph: **(A)** $y = (x + 3)^2$ **(B)** $y = (x - 3)^2$

GRAPHING EQUATIONS OF THE FORM $y = ax^2 + bx + c$

The graphing techniques learned above, along with completing the square, can be put together to obtain the graph of the general quadratic equation

$$y = ax^2 + bx + c$$

We rewrite the quadratic as

$$y = a\left(x^2 + \frac{b}{a}x\right) + c$$

and complete the square inside the parentheses:

$$y = a\left(x^2 + \frac{b}{a}x + \frac{b^2}{4a^2}\right) + c - \frac{b^2}{4a}$$

The last term $\dfrac{b^2}{4a}$ is subtracted, since we added $a \cdot \dfrac{b^2}{4a^2} = \dfrac{b^2}{4a}$, and we do not want to change the value of the right-hand side of the equation. Recognizing the perfect square, we get

$$y = a\left(x + \frac{b}{2a}\right)^2 + \left(c - \frac{b^2}{4a}\right)$$

$$= a\left[x - \left(-\frac{b}{2a}\right)\right]^2 + \left(c - \frac{b^2}{4a}\right)$$

Using what we learned above about shifting the graph of $y = x^2$, we observe the following:

1. The effect of subtracting $-\dfrac{b}{2a}$ from x is to move the graph of $y = x^2$ to the right by $-\dfrac{b}{2a}$ units if $\dfrac{-b}{2a}$ is positive and to the left by $\left|\dfrac{-b}{2a}\right|$ units if $\dfrac{-b}{2a}$ is negative.

2. The effect of multiplying the square term by a is to stretch or flatten the graph, and possibly (if a is negative) to turn it upside down.

3. The effect of adding the term $\left(c - \dfrac{b^2}{4a}\right)$ is to move the graph up by $c - \dfrac{b^2}{4a}$ units if $c - \dfrac{b^2}{4a}$ is positive and down by $\left|c - \dfrac{b^2}{4a}\right|$ units if $c - \dfrac{b^2}{4a}$ is negative.

From all this we can conclude the following about graphing quadratics:

Graphing $y = ax^2 + bx + c$

1. The basic shape of the graph is the same as $y = ax^2$—the graph looks like

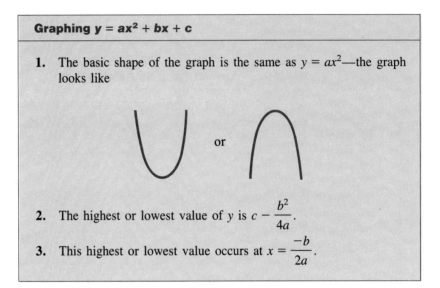

or

2. The highest or lowest value of y is $c - \dfrac{b^2}{4a}$.

3. This highest or lowest value occurs at $x = \dfrac{-b}{2a}$.

Graph: **(A)** $y = x^2 + x - 2$ **(B)** $y = -4x^2 - 9x + 9$

(A) 1. The shape of the graph is the same as $y = x^2$; that is, the graph looks like

2. The lowest point has y value

$$c - \frac{b^2}{4a} = -2 - \frac{1}{4} = -\frac{9}{4}$$

3. The lowest point occurs at

$$x = \frac{-b}{2a} = \frac{-1}{2} = -\frac{1}{2}$$

We will plot a couple of points near $x = -\frac{1}{2}$ to locate the graph completely:

x	y
1	0
0	−2
−1	−2
−2	0

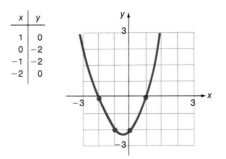

(B) 1. The shape of the graph is the same as $y = -4x^2$, that is the graph looks like

2. The highest point has value

$$y = c - \frac{b^2}{4a} = 9 - \frac{81}{-16} = \frac{225}{16} = 14\frac{1}{16}$$

3. This highest value occurs at

$$x = \frac{-b}{2a} = \frac{9}{-8} = -\frac{9}{8}$$

We plot a couple of points near $x = -\frac{9}{8}$ to completely locate the graph:

x	y
0	9
−1	14
−2	12
−3	0

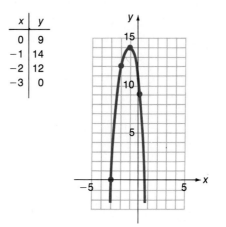

Graph: **(A)** $y = x^2 - x - 6$ **(B)** $y = -x^2 + x + 2$

GRAPHS AND SOLUTIONS TO QUADRATIC EQUATIONS

If the graph of $y = ax^2 + bx + c$ crosses the x axis, then at that value of x, the value of y is 0. That is, such a value of x is a solution to

$$ax^2 + bx + c = 0$$

In Example 20(A) above, the graph of $y = x^2 + x - 2$ crossed the x axis at $x = -2$ and $x = 1$, the roots of the quadratic equation $x^2 + x - 2 = 0$. In Example 20(B), the graph of $y = -4x^2 - 9x + 9$ shows one root, $x = -3$, both in the table and on the graph. The graph also shows there is a second root, apparently between 0 and 1. The root can be found to be $x = \frac{3}{4}$ by factoring or using the quadratic formula.

In general, a quadratic equation has 0, 1, or 2 real roots. These cases correspond to the following situations geometrically:

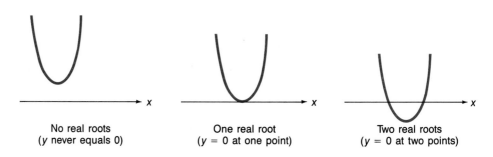

No real roots	One real root	Two real roots
(y never equals 0)	($y = 0$ at one point)	($y = 0$ at two points)

or to similar pictures with the graphs upside down. The graph of a quadratic equation is a curve called a **parabola**. The curve has interesting geometric properties and is studied more thoroughly in later courses.

ANSWERS TO
MATCHED PROBLEMS

16.   (A)   **(B)**

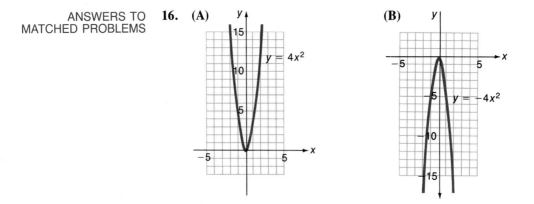

17.

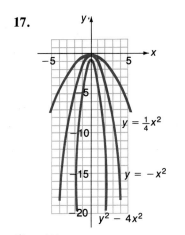

$y = \frac{1}{4}x^2$

$y = -x^2$

$y^2 - 4x^2$

18. (A)

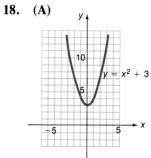

$y = x^2 + 3$

(B)

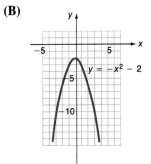

$y = -x^2 - 2$

19. (A)

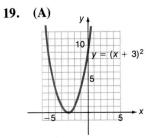

$y = (x + 3)^2$

(B)

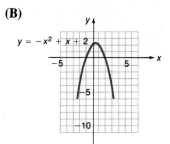

$y = (x - 3)^2$

20. (A)

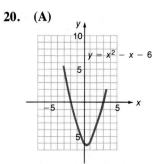

$y = x^2 - x - 6$

(B)

$y = -x^2 + x + 2$

Graph.

A   **1.** $y = 5x^2$ **2.** $y = 6x^2$ **3.** $y = -5x^2$

     4. $y = -6x^2$ **5.** $y = \dfrac{1}{5}x^2$ **6.** $y = \dfrac{1}{6}x^2$

     7. $y = -\dfrac{1}{5}x^2$ **8.** $y = -\dfrac{1}{6}x^2$ **9.** $y = \dfrac{3}{2}x^2$

     10. $y = -\dfrac{3}{2}x^2$ **11.** $y = -\dfrac{2}{3}x^2$ **12.** $y = \dfrac{2}{3}x^2$

B   **13.** $y = x^2 - 1$ **14.** $y = x^2 - 3$ **15.** $y = x^2 + 2$

     16. $y = x^2 + 4$ **17.** $y = -x^2 + 1$ **18.** $y = -x^2 - 1$

     19. $y = -x^2 - 3$ **20.** $y = -x^2 + 2$ **21.** $y = (x - 4)^2$

     22. $y = (x - 5)^2$ **23.** $y = (x + 4)^2$ **24.** $y = (x + 5)^2$

     25. $y = -(x - 1)^2$ **26.** $y = -(x - 2)^2$

     27. $y = -(x + 1)^2$ **28.** $y = (x + 2)^2$

C   **29.** $y = x^2 - 6x + 5$ **30.** $y = x^2 - 5x + 6$

     31. $y = x^2 - 4x + 3$ **32.** $y = x^2 - 8x + 15$

     33. $y = x^2 - 6x + 10$ **34.** $y = x^2 + 4x - 5$

     35. $y = x^2 - 3x$ **36.** $y = x^2 + 5x$

     37. $y = 4x^2 - 8x$ **38.** $y = 3x^2 + 12x$

     39. $y = x^2 - 25$ **40.** $y = x^2 - 36$

9-5

APPLICATIONS

- Literal Equations
- Applications

We conclude this chapter by solving literal equations for a squared variable and by considering other applications.

LITERAL EQUATIONS

We have previously solved literal equations for one variable in terms of the others. The formulas involved only the first power of the variable to be isolated. If the formula involves the square of that variable, the methods for solving quadratic equations may be applied.

Example 21 Solve for the indicated variable in terms of the other variables:

(A) $V = \pi r^2 h$ for r (volume of a cylinder, r positive)

(B) $S = \dfrac{n}{2}(n + 1)$ for n (sum of first n positive integers)

Solution (A) $V = \pi r^2 h$ Divide by πh, the coefficient of r^2.

$$\frac{V}{\pi h} = r^2$$ Solve by the square root method.

$$r = \sqrt{\frac{V}{\pi h}}$$ Since r is positive, only the positive square root is used.

(B) $S = \dfrac{n}{2}(n + 1)$ Clear fractions.

$$2S = n(n + 1)$$ Multiply out.

$$2S = n^2 + n$$

$$0 = n^2 + n - 2S$$ Apply the quadratic formula with $a = 1$, $b = 1$, $c = -2S$.

$$n = \frac{-1 \pm \sqrt{1 + 8S}}{2}$$ Since n must be positive to make sense in our example, use only the positive solution.

$$n = \frac{-1 + \sqrt{1 + 8S}}{2}$$

Problem 21 Solve for the indicated variable in terms of the other variables:

(A) $A = \pi(R + r)(R - r)$ for R (area of a disk of radius R with a hole of radius r, all variables positive)
(B) $c^2 = a^2 + b^2$ for a (Pythagorean theorem, all variables positive)

APPLICATIONS

Many real-world problems lead directly to quadratic equations for their solutions. Since quadratic equations often have two solutions, it is important to check both of the solutions in the original problem to see if one or both must be rejected. It is often the case that only one of the solutions will make sense in the context of the original application.

To get started, our first example is a relatively easy word problem involving numbers. The second example is a geometric problem that is slightly more involved. Remember to draw figures, make diagrams, write down related formulas, and so on. Use scratch paper to try out ideas.

Example 22   If the reciprocal of a number is subtracted from the original number, the difference is $\frac{8}{3}$. Find the number.

Solution   Let x = The number. Then

$$x - \frac{1}{x} = \frac{8}{3}$$ Write an equation.

$$3x \cdot x - 3x \cdot \frac{1}{x} = 3x \cdot \frac{8}{3}$$ Clear fractions.

$$3x^2 - 3 = 8x$$ Convert to standard form.

$$3x^2 - 8x - 3 = 0$$ Solve by one of the methods discussed in earlier sections.

$$(3x + 1)(x - 3) = 0$$ Factoring works.

$$3x + 1 = 0 \quad \text{or} \quad x - 3 = 0$$

$$3x = -1 \qquad\qquad x = 3$$ Both answers satisfy the original conditions, as you can easily check.

$$x = -\tfrac{1}{2}$$

Problem 22   The sum of a number and its reciprocal is $\frac{5}{2}$. Find the number.

Example 23   A painting measuring 6 by 8 inches has a frame of uniform width with a total area equal to the area of the painting. How wide is the frame? Give the answer in simplest radical form and as a decimal fraction to two decimal places.

Solution   Let x be the width of the frame.

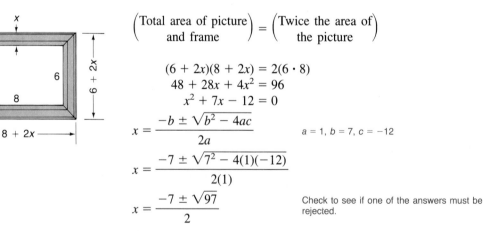

$$\left(\begin{matrix}\text{Total area of picture}\\ \text{and frame}\end{matrix}\right) = \left(\begin{matrix}\text{Twice the area of}\\ \text{the picture}\end{matrix}\right)$$

$$(6 + 2x)(8 + 2x) = 2(6 \cdot 8)$$
$$48 + 28x + 4x^2 = 96$$
$$x^2 + 7x - 12 = 0$$

$$x = \frac{-b \pm \sqrt{b^2 - 4ac}}{2a}$$ $a = 1, b = 7, c = -12$

$$x = \frac{-7 \pm \sqrt{7^2 - 4(1)(-12)}}{2(1)}$$

$$x = \frac{-7 \pm \sqrt{97}}{2}$$ Check to see if one of the answers must be rejected.

The negative answer must be rejected, since it has no meaning relative to the original problem; hence,

$$x = \frac{-7 + \sqrt{97}}{2} \approx 1.42 \text{ inches}$$

Problem 23 If the length and width of a rectangle 4 by 2 inches are each increased by the same amount, the area of the new rectangle will be twice the old. What are the dimensions to two decimal places of the new rectangle?

Example 24 A fishing boat takes 3 hours longer to go 24 kilometers up a river than to return. If the boat cruises at 6 kilometers per hour in still water, what is the rate of the current?

Solution Let c = Rate of current.

$$\text{Time up} = \text{Time down} + 3$$

$$\frac{\text{Distance up}}{\text{Rate up}} = \frac{\text{Distance down}}{\text{Rate down}} + 3 \quad d = rt, \text{ so } t = d/r.$$

$$\frac{24}{6 - c} = \frac{24}{6 + c} + 3 \qquad \text{Multiply both sides by } (6 - c)(6 + c).$$

$$24(6 + c) = 24(6 - c) + 3(36 - c^2)$$
$$144 + 24c = 144 - 24c + 108 - 3c^2$$
$$3c^2 + 48c - 108 = 0$$
$$c^2 + 16c - 36 = 0$$
$$(c - 2)(c + 18) = 0$$
$$c - 2 = 0 \qquad \text{or} \qquad c + 18 = 0$$
$$c = 2 \qquad\qquad \cancel{c = -18}$$
$$\text{Reject}$$

Rate of current = 2 kilometers per hour

Check
Rate up = 6 − 2 = 4 kilometers per hour
Rate down = 6 + 2 = 8 kilometers per hour
Time up = $\frac{24}{4}$ = 6 hours
Time down = $\frac{24}{8}$ = 3 hours

Thus, it took 3 hours longer to go up than to go down.

Problem 24 If in Example 24 it takes the boat 2 hours longer to go the 24 kilometers up the river than to return, and the boat travels at 5 kilometers per hour in still water, what is the rate of the current?

21. **(A)** $R = \sqrt{\dfrac{A + \pi r^2}{\pi}}$ **(B)** $a = \sqrt{c^2 - b^2}$

22. $\frac{1}{2}$ or 2   **23.**   5.12 by 3.12 inches   **24.**   1 kilometer per hour

EXERCISE 9-5

These problems are not grouped from easy (A) to difficult or theoretical (C). They are grouped somewhat according to type. The most difficult problems are marked with two stars (★★) and the moderately difficult problems with one star (★). The easier problems are not marked.

LITERAL EQUATIONS   *Solve for the indicated letter in terms of the other letters.*

    1. $d = \frac{1}{2}gt^2$ for t (positive)

    2. $A = \pi r(r + l)$ for r (positive)

    3. $A = P(1 + r)^2$ for r (positive)

    4. $P = EI - RI^2$ for I

For each problem set up an appropriate equation and solve.

NUMBER PROBLEMS   **5.**   Find a positive number that is 56 less than its square.

    6.   Find two consecutive positive even integers whose product is 168.

    7.   Find all numbers with the property that when the number is added to itself, the sum is the same as when the number is multiplied by itself.

    8.   Find two numbers such that their sum is 21 and their product is 104.

    9.   The sum of a number and its reciprocal is $\frac{17}{4}$. Find the number or numbers.

    10.   Find all numbers such that 6 times the reciprocal of the number is 1 less than the original number.

BUSINESS AND ECONOMICS   **11.**   If P dollars is invested at r percent compounded annually, at the end of 2 years it will grow to $A = P(1 + r)^2$. At what interest rate will \$100 grow to \$144 in 2 years? [*Note:* $A = 144$ and $P = 100$.]

    12.   Repeat Problem 11 for \$1,000 growing to \$1,210 in 2 years.

    ★**13.**   Cost equations for manufacturing companies are often quadratic in nature. (At very high or very low outputs the costs are more per unit because of inefficiency of plant operation at these extremes.) If the cost equation for manufacturing a certain pharmaceutical drug is $C = x^2 - 10x + 31$, where C is the cost of manufacturing x units per week (both x and C are in thousands), find the output x for a \$15,000 weekly cost.

    ★**14.**   Repeat Problem 13 for a weekly cost of \$6,000.

    ★**15.**   The manufacturing company in Problem 13 sells its pharmaceuticals for \$3 per unit. Thus, its revenue equation is $R = 3x$, where R is revenue and x is the number of units sold per week (both in thousands). Find the break-even points for the company—that is, the output x at which revenue equals cost.

★16. Repeat Problem 15 for the company selling each unit for $6 each.

COMMUNICATIONS ★17. The number of telephone connections c possible through a switchboard to which n telephones are connected is given by the formula $c = n(n - 1)/2$. How many telephones n could be handled by a switchboard that had the capacity of 190 connections? [*Hint:* Find n when $c = 190$.]

★18. Repeat Problem 17 for a switchboard with a capacity of 435 connections.

GEOMETRY *The following theorem may be used where needed:*

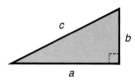

Pythagorean theorem: *A triangle is a right triangle if and only if the square of the longest side is equal to the sum of the squares of the two shorter sides.*

$$c^2 = a^2 + b^2$$

19. Find the length of each side of a right triangle if the second longest side is 1 meter longer than the shortest side and the longest side is 2 meters longer than the shortest side.

20. Find the length of each side of a right triangle if the two shorter sides are 2 and 4 centimeters shorter than the longest side.

★21. Find r in the figure in the margin. Express the answer in simplest radical form. (The radius of the smaller circle is 1 inch.)

★22. Approximately how far would a person be able to see from the top of a mountain 2 miles high (see the figure)? Use a calculator to estimate the answer to the nearest mile.

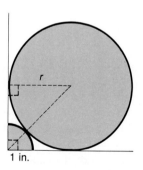

1 in.

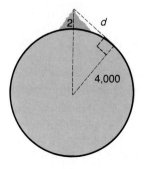

POLICE SCIENCE   **23.** Skid marks are often used to estimate the speed of a car in an accident. It is common practice for an officer to drive the car in question (if it is still running) at a speed of 20 to 30 miles per hour and skid it to a stop near the original skid marks. It is known (from physics) that the speed of the car and the length of the skid marks are related by the formula

$$\frac{d_a}{v_a^2} = \frac{d_t}{v_t^2}$$

where

d_a = length of accident car's skid marks
d_t = length of test car's skid marks
v_a = speed of accident car (to be found)
v_t = speed of test car

Estimate the speed of an accident vehicle if its skid marks are 100 feet and the test car driven at 30 miles per hour produces skid marks of 36 feet.

24. Repeat Problem 23 for an accident vehicle that left skid marks 196 feet long.

RATE–TIME PROBLEMS   **25.** Two boats travel at right angles to each other after leaving the same dock at the same time; 1 hour later they are 25 miles apart. If one travels 17 miles per hour faster than the other, what is the rate of each? [*Hint:* See the theorem preceding Problem 19.]

**26. Repeat Problem 25 with one boat traveling 1 mile per hour faster than the other; after 1 hour they are 5 miles apart.

**27. A motorboat takes 1 hour longer to go 24 miles up a river than to return. If the boat cruises at 10 miles per hour in still water, what is the rate of the current?

**28. A speedboat takes 1 hour longer to go 60 miles up a river than to return. If the boat can cruise at 25 miles per hour on still water, what is the rate of the current?

9-6

CHAPTER REVIEW

The **standard form** of a **quadratic equation** in the variable x is $ax^2 + bx + c = 0$, where a, b, and c are constants with $a \neq 0$. Some quadratic equations can be solved by factoring. A quadratic equation with no first-degree term can be solved by the **square root method**: if $x^2 = N$ with $N > 0$, then $x = \pm\sqrt{N}$. *(9-1)*

To **complete the square** of $x^2 + bx$, add $(b/2)^2$ to obtain the perfect square $x^2 + bx + (b/2)^2 = (x + b/2)^2$. Quadratic equations can be solved by **completing the square**:

1. Write the equation in standard form.
2. If $a \neq 1$, divide both sides by a.
3. Shift the constant term to the other side of the equation.
4. Complete the square.
5. Solve by the method of square roots. *(9-2)*

The solution of the standard-form quadratic equation is given by the **quadratic formula**:

$$x = \frac{-b \pm \sqrt{b^2 - 4ac}}{2a}$$

The expression $b^2 - 4ac$ is called the **discriminant**. The equation has two real roots if the discriminant is positive, one real root if it is zero, and no real roots if it is negative. *(9-3)*

The graph of $y = ax^2$ is related to the graph of $y = x^2$: if $a > 1$, the graph is stretched; if $0 < a < 1$, the graph is flattened; if $a < 0$, the graph is stretched or flattened and also turned upside down. The graph of $y = ax^2 + bx + c$ is related to the graph of $y = ax^2$: it has the same shape but is moved to the right $\dfrac{-b}{2a}$ units if $\dfrac{-b}{2a}$ is positive, to the left $\left|\dfrac{-b}{2a}\right|$ if $\dfrac{-b}{2a}$ is negative, up $c - \dfrac{b^2}{4a}$ units if $c - \dfrac{b^2}{4a}$ is positive, and down $\left|c - \dfrac{b^2}{4a}\right|$ units if $c - \dfrac{b^2}{4a}$ is negative.

(9-4)

REVIEW EXERCISE 9-6   *Work through all the problems in this chapter review and check answers in the back of the book. (Answers to all problems are there, and following each answer is a number in italics indicating the section in which that type of problem is discussed.) Where weaknesses show up, review appropriate sections in the text.*

A   *Find all real solutions by factoring or square root methods.*

1. $x^2 = 25$
2. $x^2 - 3x = 0$
3. $(2x - 1)(x + 3) = 0$
4. $x^2 - 5x + 6 = 0$
5. $x^2 - 2x - 15 = 0$
6. Write $4x = 2 - 3x^2$ in standard form $ax^2 + bx + c = 0$ and identify a, b, and c.
7. Write down the quadratic formula associated with $ax^2 + bx + c = 0$.

8. Use the quadratic formula to solve $x^2 + 3x + 1 = 0$.

9. Solve $x^2 + 3x - 10 = 0$ by any method.

10. Find two positive numbers whose product is 27 if one is 6 more than the other.

11. *Graph:* $y = -2x^2$

B *Find all real solutions by factoring or square root methods.*

12. $3x^2 = 36$ **13.** $10x^2 = 20x$ **14.** $(x - 2)^2 = 16$

15. $3t^2 - 8t - 3 = 0$ **16.** $2x = \dfrac{3}{x} = -5$

17. Solve $x^2 - 6x - 3 = 0$ by completing the square.

18. Solve $3x^2 = 2(x + 1)$ by using the quadratic formula.

19. Solve $2x^2 - 2x = 40$ by any method.

20. Divide 18 into two parts so that their product is 72.

21. The perimeter of a rectangle is 22 inches. If its area is 30 square inches, find the length of each side.

Graph:

22. $y = -x^2 + 4$ **23.** $y = (x + 4)^2$

C *Find all real solutions by factoring or square root methods.*

24. $2x^2 + 27 = 0$ **25.** $(t - \tfrac{3}{2})^2 = \tfrac{3}{2}$ **26.** $\dfrac{8m^2 + 15}{2m} = 13$

27. Solve $2x^2 - 2x - 3 = 0$ by completing the square.

28. Solve $3x - 1 = \dfrac{2(x + 1)}{x + 2}$ by using the quadratic formula.

29. If $b^2 - 4ac > 0$, then the quadratic equation has two real solutions. True (T) or false (F)?

Graph:

30. $y = x^2 - 3x - 4$ **31.** $y = 4x^2 + 4x + 1$

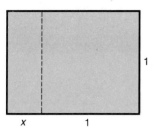

32. A **golden rectangle** is one that has the property that when a square with side equal to the short side of the rectangle is removed from one end, the ratio of the sides of the remaining rectangle is the same as the ratio of the sides of the original rectangle. If the shorter side of the original rectangle is 1, find the shorter side of the remaining rectangle (see the figure). This number is called the golden ratio, and it turns up frequently in the history of mathematics.

APPENDIX A

SETS

- Set Membership and Equality
- Subsets
- Specifying Sets
- Union and Intersection
- Venn Diagrams
- Complements

This appendix introduces basic set terminology, relationships, and operations. The mathematical use of the word *set* does not differ appreciably from the way it is used in everyday language. Words such as ''set,'' ''collection,'' ''bunch,'' and ''flock'' all convey the same idea. Thus, we think of a **set** as any collection of objects with the important property that given any object, it is either a member of the set or it is not. For example, the letter p belongs to our alphabet but the Greek letter π does not.

SET MEMBERSHIP AND EQUALITY

If an object a is in set A, we say that a **is an element of** or **is a member of** set A and write

$a \in A$

If an object is **not an element of** set A, we write

$a \notin A$

Sets are often specified by **listing** their elements between braces { }. For example,

{2, 3, 5, 7}

represents the set with elements 2, 3, 5, and 7. For this set, $3 \in \{2, 3, 5, 7\}$ and $4 \notin \{2, 3, 5, 7\}$. Two sets A and B are said to be **equal**, and we write

$A = B$

if the two sets have exactly the same elements. We write

$A \neq B$

if sets A and B are **not equal**.

The order of listing the elements in a set does not matter; thus,

$\{3, 4, 5\} = \{4, 3, 5\} = \{5, 4, 3\}$

Also, elements in a set are not listed more than once. For example, the set of letters in the word ''letter'' is

$\{e, l, t, r\}$

Example 1   If $A = \{2, 4, 6\}$, $B = \{3, 5, 7\}$, and $C = \{4, 6, 2\}$, replace each question mark with $\in$, $\notin$, $=$, or $\neq$, as appropriate:

(A) $4 \ ? \ A$	**(B)** $3 \ ? \ A$	**(C)** $7 \ ? \ B$
(D) $2 \ ? \ B$	**(E)** $A \ ? \ C$	**(F)** $A \ ? \ B$

Solution

(A) $4 \in A$	**(B)** $3 \notin A$	**(C)** $7 \in B$
(D) $2 \notin B$	**(E)** $A = C$	**(F)** $A \neq B$

Problem 1   If $P = \{1, 3, 5\}$, $Q = \{2, 3, 4\}$, and $R = \{3, 4, 2\}$, replace each question mark with $\in$, $\notin$, $=$, or $\neq$, as appropriate:

(A) $1 \ ? \ P$	**(B)** $3 \ ? \ Q$	**(C)** $5 \ ? \ R$
(D) $4 \ ? \ P$	**(E)** $P \ ? \ Q$	**(F)** $Q \ ? \ R$

SUBSETS

From time to time we will be interested in sets within sets, called subsets. We say that a set A is a **subset** of set B if every element in set A is in set B. For example, the set of all women in a mathematics class would form a subset of all students in the class. The notation

$A \subset B$

is used to indicate that A is a subset of B.

A set with no elements is called the **empty** or **null** set. It is symbolized by

$$\varnothing$$

For example, the set of all months of the year beginning with B is an empty or null set and would be designated by $\varnothing$. For any set A, $\varnothing \subset A$ and $A \subset A$.

Example 2   Which of the following are subsets of the set $\{2, 3, 5, 7\}$?

$$A = \{2, 3, 5\} \quad B = \{2\} \quad C = \{2, 3, 5, 7\}$$
$$D = \varnothing \quad E = \{1, 2, 3\} \quad F = 3$$

Solution   The sets A, B, C, and D are all subsets of $\{2, 3, 5, 7\}$. In each case every element in the subset is in $\{2, 3, 5, 7\}$. The set $\{1, 2, 3\}$ is not a subset of $\{2, 3, 5, 7\}$, since $1 \notin \{2, 3, 5, 7\}$. The object 3 is different from the set $\{3\}$. We have $3 \in \{2, 3, 5, 7\}$ and $\{3\} \subset \{2, 3, 5, 7\}$ but 3, and therefore F, is not a subset of $\{2, 3, 5, 7\}$.

Problem 2   Which of the following are subsets of the set $\{2, 4, 6, 8\}$?

$$A = \{2, 4\} \quad B = \{2, 4, 6, 8\} \quad C = \{4\}$$
$$D = 4 \quad E = \varnothing \quad F = \{2, 4, 6, 8, 10\}$$

SPECIFYING SETS

The method of specifying sets by **listing** the elements, as in Example 1, is clear and convenient for small sets. However, if we are interested in specifying a set with a large number of elements, say, the set of all whole numbers from 10 to 10,000, then listing these elements would be tedious and wasteful of space. The **rule method** for specifying sets takes care of situations of this type, as well as others. Using the rule method we would write

$$\{x \mid x \text{ is a whole number from 10 to 10,000}\}$$

which is read "the set of all elements x such that x is a whole number from 10 to 10,000." The vertical bar represents "such that."

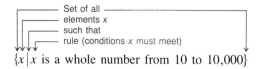

Example 3   If $M = \{3, 4, 5, 6\}$ and $N = \{4, 5, 6, 7, 8\}$, then the set of all elements in M

that are also in N can be written using either the rule method or the listing method as follows:

Rule method: $\{x \mid x \in M \text{ and } x \in N\}$
Listing method: $\{4, 5, 6\}$

Problem 3   Using the sets M and N in Example 3, write the set

$$\{x \mid x \in M \text{ or } x \in N\}$$

using the listing method.

UNION AND INTERSECTION

Sets determined by ''and'' such as in Example 3 occur frequently in practice; the same is true for those determined by ''or'' as in Problem 3. For this reason, we make the following definitions:

$A \cap B$ = the **intersection** of the sets A and B
           = the set of all elements belonging to both sets A and B
           = $\{x \mid x \in A \text{ and } x \in B\}$

$A \cup B$ = the **union** of the sets A and B
           = the set of elements belonging to set A or to set B
           = $\{x \mid x \in A \text{ or } x \in B\}$

The word ''or'' here is used in an inclusive sense meaning one or the other or both.

Example 4   Let $A = \{2, 3, 5, 7\}$ and $B = \{1, 2, 3, 4\}$. Find $A \cap B$ and $A \cup B$.

Solution $A \cap B = \{2, 3\}$ the set of all elements belonging to set A and to set B

$A \cup B = \{1, 2, 3, 4, 5, 7\}$ the set of all elements belonging to set A or to set B or to both.

Problem 4   Let $A = \{2, 4, 6, 8\}$ and $B = \{1, 2, 3, 4\}$. Find $A \cap B$ and $A \cup B$.

VENN DIAGRAMS

Set relations and operations may be visualized in diagrams called **Venn diagrams**.

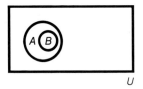

Here the rectangle represents all objects under consideration; this set is called the **universal set** and usually is denoted by U. It depends on the context in which one is working. If, for instance, you were interested in sets of students at a particular college, the universal set could be all students at that school. In the diagram, A represents a subset of U. To represent $B \subset A$, draw

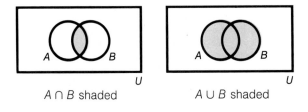

The intersection and union of two sets A and B are represented by the shaded regions in the following diagrams:

$A \cap B$ shaded $A \cup B$ shaded

COMPLEMENTS

In the Venn diagram

the region outside the circle represents all those elements in the universal set that are not in A, that is, the set

$$\{x \mid x \in U \text{ but } x \notin A\}$$

This set is called the **complement** of A and is usually denoted by A'.

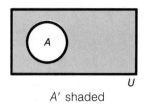

A′ shaded

Example 5 Let $U = \{1, 2, 3, 4, 5, 6, 7, 8, 9, 10\}$ and $A = \{2, 3, 5, 7\}$. Give the complement of A by the listing method.

Solution $A' = \{1, 4, 6, 8, 9, 10\}$

Problem 5 Let U be as in Example 5 and $B = \{2, 4, 6, 8, 10\}$. Give B' by the listing method.

ANSWERS TO
MATCHED PROBLEMS

1. **(A)** $1 \in P$ **(B)** $3 \in Q$ **(C)** $5 \notin R$ **(D)** $4 \notin P$
   (E) $P \neq Q$ **(F)** $Q = R$
2. A, B, C, E 3. $\{3, 4, 5, 6, 7, 8\}$
4. $A \cap B = \{2, 4\}, A \cup B = \{1, 2, 3, 4, 6, 8\}$
5. $B' = \{1, 3, 5, 7, 9\}$

EXERCISE A   **A**   *In Problems 1 to 10, indicate which statements are true (T) or false (F).*

1. $4 \in \{2, 3, 4\}$ 2. $7 \notin \{2, 3, 4\}$

3. $6 \notin \{2, 3, 4\}$ 4. $7 \in \{2, 3, 4\}$

5. $\{3, 4, 5\} = \{5, 3, 4\}$ 6. $\{1, 2, 3, 4\} = \{4, 2, 3, 1\}$

7. $\{3, 5, 7\} \neq \{4, 7, 5, 3\}$ 8. $\{4, 6, 3\} \neq \{6, 3, 4\}$

9. $\{2, 3\} \subset \{2, 3, 4\}$ 10. $\{4, 5\} \subset \{2, 3, 4\}$

Given sets

  $P = \{1, 3, 5, 7\}$ $Q = \{2, 4, 6, 8\}$ $R = \{5, 1, 7, 3\}$

replace each question mark with $\in$, $\notin$, $=$, *or* $\neq$, *as appropriate.*

11. $5 \, ? \, P$ 12. $6 \, ? \, Q$ 13. $6 \, ? \, R$ 14. $4 \, ? \, P$

15. $P \, ? \, R$ 16. $Q \, ? \, R$ 17. $P \, ? \, Q$ 18. $R \, ? \, P$

B   *Indicate the following sets by using the listing method. If the set is empty, write* $\varnothing$.

19. $\{x \,|\, x$ is a counting number between 5 and 10$\}$

20. $\{x \mid x$ is a counting number between 10 and 15$\}$

21. $\{x \mid x$ is a counting number between 7 and 8$\}$

22. $\{x \mid x$ is a counting number between 10 and 11$\}$

23. $\{x \mid x$ is a day of the week$\}$

24. $\{x \mid x$ is a month of the year$\}$

25. $\{x \mid x$ is a letter in "alababa"$\}$

26. $\{x \mid x$ is a letter in "millimeter"$\}$

27. $\{u \mid u$ is a state in the United States smaller than Rhode Island$\}$

28. $\{u \mid u$ is a day of the week starting with the letter $k\}$

If $U = \{1, 2, 3, 4, 5, 6, 7, 8\}$ and

$$A = \{1, 2, 3, 4\} \qquad B = \{2, 4, 6, 8\} \qquad C = \{1, 3, 5, 7\}$$

indicate each set by using the listing method.

29. $A \cap B$	**30.** $A \cap C$	**31.** $B \cap C$
32. $A \cup B$	**33.** $B \cup C$	**34.** $A \cup C$
35. A'	**36.** B'	**37.** C'
C **38.** $\varnothing'$	**39.** $(A \cup B)'$	**40.** $(A \cap B)'$
41. $A' \cap B'$	**42.** $A' \cup B'$	

43. List all the subsets of $\{1, 2\}$. (There are a total of four.)

44. List all the subsets of $\{1, 2, 3\}$. (There are a total of eight.)

A general Venn diagram for three sets A, B, and C is

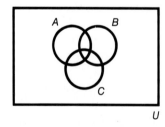

Use such a Venn diagram and shade the indicated set.

45. $(A \cup B) \cap C$	**46.** $(A \cap B) \cup C$
47. $(A \cap B) \cap C$	**48.** $(A \cap B) \cap C'$
49. $(A \cup B)' \cap C'$	**50.** $A \cap (B \cup C)'$

APPENDIX B

A WORD PROBLEM TECHNIQUE

A strategy for solving word problems is given in Section 2-8.

Strategy for Solving Word Problems

1. Read the problem very carefully—several times if necessary.
2. Write down important facts and relationships on a piece of scratch paper. Draw figures if it is helpful. Write down any formulas that might be relevant.
3. Identify unknown quantities in terms of a single variable if possible.
4. Look for key words and relationships in a problem that will lead to an equation involving the variables introduced in step 3.
5. Solve the equation. Write down all the solutions asked for in the original problem.
6. Check the solutions in the original problem.

As noted there, the key step and often the most difficult one is step 4, finding the equation. There is no general technique for doing this but there is a procedure that works well for many students and can be used in a wide variety of word problems.

If you have difficulty finding the relationships that lead to an appropriate equation to solve, guess a numerical answer and try it to see if it works. This then becomes an arithmetic problem, exactly the same as checking your answer after solving the problem. Most likely the guess will be incorrect, but in checking you will better see the structure of the problem. You can then replace your guess by a variable and follow your same logic to get the appropriate equation. Some examples will illustrate the process.

Example 1   Find three consecutive integers whose sum is 66.

Solution   Suppose we guess 18, 19, 20. The sum $18 + 19 + 20$ is 57, not 66, so our guess is wrong. If we replace our guess of 18 by x, then 19 is replaced by $x + 1$, and 20 by $x + 2$. The sum is $x + (x + 1) + (x + 2)$ and must equal 66, so we get the equation:

$$x + (x + 1) + (x + 2) = 66$$

The solution is completed in Example 33, Section 2-8.

Example 2   In a pile of coins that is composed of only dimes and nickels, there are 7 more dimes than nickels. If the total value of all the coins in the pile is $1, how many of each type of coin is in the pile?

Solution   Let us guess 4 nickels. Since there are 7 more dimes than nickels, this would require that there be 11 dimes. Is the total value of 4 nickels and 11 dimes equal to $1 (that is, 100 cents) as required? Check:

Value of nickels in cents	$4 \cdot 5 =$	20
Value of dimes in cents	$11 \cdot 10 =$	110
Total value in cents		130

Our guess is wrong, since $130 \neq 100$, that is, $1.30 \neq 1. To find the equation, replace the guess of 4 by x and follow the same argument. The number of dimes is now $x + 7$ and

Value of nickels in cents	$x \cdot 5 =$	$5x$
Value of dimes in cents	$(x + 7) \cdot 10 =$	$10(x + 7)$
Total value in cents		$5x + 10(x + 7)$

Since the total value should be 100 cents, our equation is

$$5x + 10(x + 7) = 100$$

The solution is completed in Example 36, Section 2-8.

Example 3   A car leaves town A and travels at 55 miles per hour toward town B at the same time a car leaves town B and travels 45 miles per hour toward town A. If the towns are 600 miles apart, how long will it take the two cars to meet? Set up an equation and solve.

Solution   We guess the cars will meet in 5 hours. Then

Car from A to B travels	$55 \cdot 5 = 275$ miles
Car from B to A travels	$45 \cdot 5 = 225$ miles

The cars have thus traveled 500 miles, so they have not yet met. (This also tells us that the guess of 5 is too small.)

Now replace the guess of 5 by x.

Car from A to B travels $\quad 55 \cdot x = 55x$ miles
Car from B to A travels $\quad 45 \cdot x = 45x$ miles

The total miles must be 600, so we get the equation

$$55x + 45x = 600$$

The solution is completed in Example 37, Section 2-8.

The remaining examples in this appendix involve fractions.

Example 4 An airplane flew out to an island from the mainland and back in 5 hours. How far is the island from the mainland if the pilot averaged 600 miles per hour going to the island and 400 returning?

Solution We will guess the distance to be 1,000 miles. Then to go to the island at a rate of 600 miles per hour would take $\dfrac{1,000}{600} = 1\frac{2}{3}$ hours. $\left(\text{If } d = rt, \text{ then } t = \dfrac{d}{r}.\right)$

The return trip would take $\dfrac{1,000}{400} = 2\frac{1}{2}$ hours. The total time for the round trip is then $1\frac{2}{3} + 2\frac{1}{2} = 4\frac{1}{6}$ hours, which is too little, since it is supposed to be 5 hours. (This also tells us that 1,000 is too small a guess: the island must be farther away.)

Now replace our guess of 1,000 by the variable x.

$$\text{Time to the island} = \frac{x}{600}$$

$$\text{Time from the island} = \frac{x}{400}$$

$$\text{Total time} = \frac{x}{600} + \frac{x}{400}$$

Since the total time should be 5, the equation is

$$\frac{x}{600} + \frac{x}{400} = 5$$

The solution is completed in Example 19, Section 4-7.

Example 5   A chemical storeroom has a 40% acid solution and an 80% acid solution. How many deciliters must be taken from each to obtain 12 deciliters of a 50% solution?

Solution   Let us guess 8 deciliters of the weaker solution and 4 deciliters of the stronger. Will the mixture have the right amount of acid?

	VOLUME	% ACID	AMOUNT ACID
WEAK SOLUTION	8 dl	40%	$8 \times 0.4 = 3.2$ dl
STRONG SOLUTION	4 dl	80%	$4 \times 0.8 = 3.2$ dl
MIXTURE	12 dl	50%	6.4 dl

Since 6.4 is more than 50% of 12, that is, more than 6, our guess is incorrect (and we have used too much of the strong solution).

Now replace our guess of 4 deciliters by x. The remaining 8 deciliters guessed is replaced by $12 - x$ to get an equation in one variable or by y to get two equations in two variables.

One-variable approach:

	VOLUME	% ACID	AMOUNT ACID
WEAK SOLUTION	x dl	40%	$0.4x$
STRONG SOLUTION	$(12 - x)$ dl	80%	$0.8(12 - x)$
MIXTURE	12 dl	50%	$0.5(12) = 6$

The equation must be

$$0.4x + 0.8(12 - x) = 6$$

which we solve as follows:

$$0.4x + 9.6 - 0.8x = 6$$
$$-0.4x = -3.6$$
$$x = \frac{-3.6}{-0.4} = 9$$

Thus we should use 9 deciliters of the weak solution and 3 deciliters of the strong.

Two-variable approach:

	VOLUME	% ACID	AMOUNT ACID
WEAK SOLUTION	x dl	40%	$0.4x$
STRONG SOLUTION	y dl	80%	$0.8y$
MIXTURE	12 dl	50%	6

The two equations are

$$x + y = 12$$
$$0.4x + 0.8y = 6$$

This solution is completed in Example 24, Section 4-8.

Example 6   A fishing boat takes 3 hours longer to go 24 kilometers up a river than to return. If the boat cruises at 6 kilometers per hour in still water, what is the rate of the current?

Solution   We will guess 4 kilometers per hour. Then the boat would go upstream at a rate of $6 - 4 = 2$ kilometers per hour and downstream at a rate of $6 + 4 = 10$ kilometers per hour. Going upstream will take 24 km/2 km/h = 12 hours (remember if $d = rt$, $t = d/r$). Going downstream would take $\frac{24}{10} = 2.4$ hours. The difference in time is $12 - 2.4$, which is not 3 hours, so our guess is wrong.

Now replace our guess of 4 by x. The rates are the $6 - x$ going upstream (replacing $6 - 4 = 2$ by $6 - x$) and $6 + x$ going downstream. The times become

Going upstream $\dfrac{24}{6 - x}$

Going downstream $\dfrac{24}{6 + x}$

The equation is then

$$\frac{24}{6 - x} - \frac{24}{6 + x} = 3$$

The solution is completed in Example 19, Section 9-6.

There is no exercise set for this appendix. There are an ample number of word problems in the text—especially in Sections 2-8, 3-6, 3-7, 3-8, 3-9, 4-7, 4-8, 4-9, and 9-6—upon which to practice this technique.

Appendix C

FUNCTIONS

The relationships

$$y = mx + b \qquad \text{(see Chapter 4)}$$
$$y = ax^2 + bx + c \qquad \text{(see Chapter 9)}$$

share the important characteristic that for each value of x there is just one value of y determined. These are examples of a correspondence between variables called a **function**. The concept is introduced briefly in this appendix.

C-1
FUNCTIONS

- Functions
- Common Ways of Specifying Functions

The function concept is among the most important concepts in mathematics. Your efforts to understand and use this concept will be rewarded many times.

You have already encountered functions in everyday life. For example:

To each item on the shelf in a grocery store there corresponds a price.

To each square there corresponds an area.

To each number there corresponds its cube.

To each student there corresponds a grade point average.

One of the most important aspects of science is establishing relationships *between various phenomena*. Once a relation is known, predictions can be made. An engineer can use a formula to predict pressures on a bridge for various wind speeds; an economist would like to predict unemployment rates given various levels of government spending; a chemist can use a formula to predict the pressure of an enclosed gas given its temperature; and so on. Establishing and working with such relationships is so fundamental to both pure and applied science that people have found it desirable to describe them in the precise language of mathematics.

FUNCTIONS

What do all the above examples of functions have in common? Each deals with the matching of elements from a first set, called the **domain** of the function, with elements in a second set, called the **range** of the function. Let us consider an example in more detail. Suppose from a student record office we select five names with their corresponding grade point averages (GPAs). Suppose we also list the students' telephone numbers. The information is summarized in Tables 1 and 2.

TABLE 1

DOMAIN (NAME)	RANGE (GPA)
Jones, Robert	→ 2.4
Jones, Ruth	→ 2.9
Jones, Sally	→ 3.8
Jones, Samuel	→ 3.4
Jones, Sandra	

TABLE 2

DOMAIN (NAME)	RANGE (TELEPHONE NUMBER)
Jones, Robert	→ 841-2315
	→ 841-2403
Jones, Ruth	→ 838-5106
Jones, Sally	
Jones, Samuel	→ 715-0176
Jones, Sandra	→ 732-1934

Only first correspondence is an example of a function. This important term, **function**, is now defined.

Definition of a Function

A **function** is a rule (process or method) that produces a correspondence between a first set called the **domain** and a second set called the **range** such that to each element in the domain there corresponds *one and only one* range element.

The student-to-GPA correspondence is a function, since to each domain element (name) there corresponds one and only one range element (GPA). On the other hand, the student–to–phone number correspondence is not a function, since in one case two range elements (telephone numbers) correspond to one domain element (name)—Robert Jones has two telephone numbers.

In most of the material that follows, the domains and ranges of functions will be sets of numbers. In such cases we will refer to the domain and range elements as *values*.

Example 1   Indicate which correspondence rules are functions:

(A) Domain	Range	**(B)** Domain	Range	**(C)** Domain	Range
1 $\longrightarrow$ 5		$-2 \longrightarrow -1$		3 $\longrightarrow$ 1	
2 $\longrightarrow$ 7		$0 \longrightarrow 0$		$\qquad$ 3	
3 $\longrightarrow$ 9		2		7 $\longrightarrow$ 8	
		4 $\longrightarrow$ 1		9 $\longrightarrow$ 9	

Solution   **(A)** *Function.* Exactly one range value corresponds to each domain value.
(B) *Function.* Exactly one range value corresponds to each domain value.
(C) *Not a function.* Two range values correspond to the domain value 3.

Problem 1   Indicate which correspondence rules are functions:

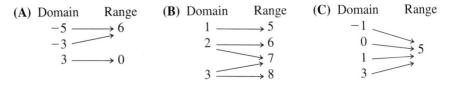

COMMON WAYS OF SPECIFYING FUNCTIONS

The arrow method of specifying functions illustrated above is convenient for an introduction to the subject—using it we can easily identify which rules are functions. However, in actual practice, functions are more generally specified

TABLE 3 COMMON WAYS OF SPECIFYING FUNCTIONS

METHOD	ILLUSTRATION	EXAMPLE
Equations	$y = x^2$	$x = 3$ corresponds to $y = 9$
Tables	$\begin{array}{c\|c} u & v \\ \hline 3 & 2 \\ 1 & 1 \\ 5 & 2 \end{array}$	$v = 2$ corresponds to $u = 3$
Sets of ordered pairs of elements	$\{(3, 2), (1, 1), (5, 2)\}$ $\{(x, y)\|y = 2x - 1, x \in R\}$	3 corresponds to 2 $x = 5$ corresponds to $y = 9$
Graphs		$x = 2$ corresponds to $y = 4$

by a rule (such as an equation), by a table, by a set of ordered pairs of elements, or by a graph. (See Table 3.) Often we will use equations to specify functions.

If a correspondence rule is specified by a set of ordered pairs of elements, then the set of first components forms the domain and the set of second components forms the range.

Example 2 Given the set

$$F = \{(0, 0), (1, -1), (1, 1), (4, -2), (4, 2)\}$$

(A) Write this rule, using arrows as in Example 1. Indicate domain and range.

(B) Graph the set in a rectangular coordinate system.

(C) Is the rule a function? Explain.

Solution **(A)** Domain Range **(B)**

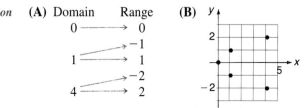

(C) The rule is not a function, since more than one range value corresponds to a given domain value. (For F to be a function, no two ordered pairs in F can have the same first coordinate.)

It is very easy to determine whether a rule is a function if you have its graph:

Vertical-Line Test for a Function

A rule is a function if each vertical line in the coordinate system passes through *at most* one point on the graph of the rule.

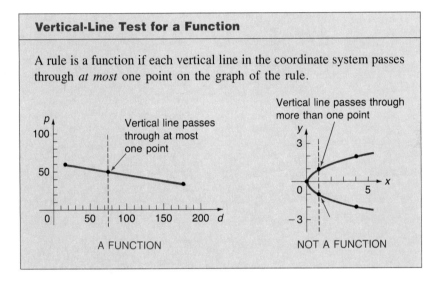

A FUNCTION   NOT A FUNCTION

If a vertical line passes through more than one point on the graph, then all points of intersection will have the same first coordinate (same domain value) and different second coordinates (different range values). Thus, since more than one range value is associated with a given domain value, the rule is not a function.

Problem 2   Given the set $F = \{(-2, 4), (-1, 1), (0, 0), (1, 1), (2, 4)\}$:

(A) Write the correspondence rule, using arrows as in Example 1. Indicate domain and range.
(B) Graph the set of points F.
(C) Is the rule a function? Explain.

We now turn to **rules specified by equations in two variables**. Consider the equation

$$y = 2x - 3$$

For each *input* x we obtain one *output* y. For example:

If $x = 2$, then $y = 2(2) - 3 = 1$.
If $x = -1$, then $y = 2(-1) - 3 = -5$.

The **input** values are **domain** values and the **output** values are **range** values. The equation (a rule) assigns each domain value x a range value y. The variable x is called an independent variable (since values are independently assigned to x from the domain) and y is called a dependent variable (since y's value depends on the value assigned to x). In general:

Definition of Independent and Dependent Variables

Any variable representing domain values is called an **independent variable**; any variable representing range values is called a **dependent variable**.

Unless stated to the contrary, we will adhere to the following convention regarding domains and ranges for functions specified by equations.

Agreement on Domains and Ranges

If a function is specified by an equation and the domain is not indicated, then we will assume that the domain is the set of all real-number replacements of the independent variable (inputs) that produce real values for the dependent variable (outputs). The range is the set of all outputs corresponding to input values.

Most equations in two variables specify correspondence rules, but when does an equation specify a function?

Equations and Functions

If in an equation in two variables there corresponds exactly one value of the dependent variable (output) for each value of the independent variable (input), then the equation specifies a function. If there is more than one output for at least one input, then the equation does not specify a function.

Example 3   Given the rules with independent variables x and dependent variables y:

(1) $x^2 + y^2 = 4$
(2) $x^2 + y = 4$

Which is a function? Explain.

Solution   *Test (1)* Is there a value of x (input) that will produce more than one value of y (output)? Yes. For example, if $x = 0$, then

$$0^2 + y^2 = 4$$
$$y^2 = 4$$
$$y = \pm 2$$

Thus, two outputs result from one input. Therefore, this rule is not a function.

Test (2) Is there a value of x (input) that will produce more than one value of y (output)? Write (2) in the form

$$y = 4 - x^2$$

We see that for each value of x (input), we square it and subtract the result from 4 to obtain a single y (output). For example, if $x = 3$, then

$$y = 4 - 3^2$$
$$= 4 - 9 = -5 \quad \text{And no other number}$$

Therefore, this rule is a function.

Problem 3   Repeat Example 3 for

(1) $y = x^2 - 3$
(2) $y^2 = x - 3$

ANSWERS TO   **1.** **(A)** Function   **(B)** Not a function   **(C)** Function
MATCHED PROBLEMS   **2.** **(A)** Domain   Range   **(B)**

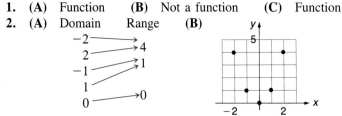

(C) The relation is a function, since each domain value corresponds to exactly one range value.

3. (1) Specifies a function: each replacement of x (input) produces exactly one y (output). (2) Does not specify a function: if $x = 4$, for example, then $y = \pm 1$ (two outputs for one input).

EXERCISE C-1 A *Indicate whether each correspondence rule is or is not a function.*

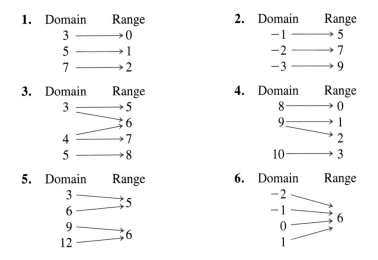

1. Domain   Range
    3 ⟶ 0
    5 ⟶ 1
    7 ⟶ 2

2. Domain   Range
    −1 ⟶ 5
    −2 ⟶ 7
    −3 ⟶ 9

3. Domain   Range
    3 ⟶ 5
       ⟶ 6
    4 ⟶ 7
    5 ⟶ 8

4. Domain   Range
    8 ⟶ 0
    9 ⟶ 1
         ⟶ 2
    10 ⟶ 3

5. Domain   Range
    3
    6 ⟶ 5
    9
    12 ⟶ 6

6. Domain   Range
    −2
    −1 ⟶ 6
    0
    1

Each rule is specified by a graph. Indicate whether it is a function with x as the independent variable.

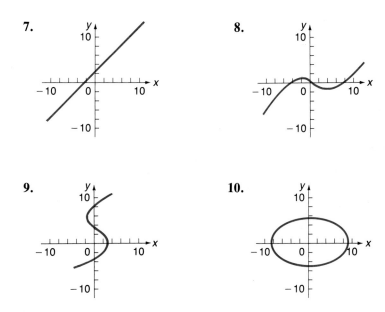

7.

8.

9.

10.

11. 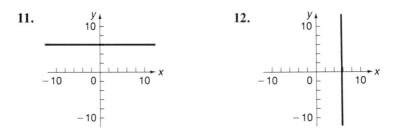   **12.**

B *Each equation specifies a relationship between x and y. Which specify functions given that x is an independent variable?*

13. $y = 3x - 1$ **14.** $y = \dfrac{x}{2} - 1$

15. $y = x^2 - 3x + 1$ **16.** $y = x^3$

17. $y^2 = x$ **18.** $x^2 + y^2 = 25$

19. $x = y^2 - y$ **20.** $x = (y - 1)(y + 2)$

21. $y = x^4 - 3x^2$ **22.** $2x - 3y = 5$

23. $y = \dfrac{x + 1}{x - 1}$ **24.** $y = \dfrac{x^2}{1 - x}$

Graph each correspondence rule. State its domain and range, and indicate which are functions. The variable x is independent.

25. $F = \{(1, 1), (2, 1), (3, 2), (3, 3)\}$

26. $f = \{(2, 4), (4, 2), (2, 0), (4, -2)\}$

27. $G = \{(-1, -2), (0, -1), (1, 0), (2, 1), (3, 2), (4, 1)\}$

28. $g = \{(-2, 0), (0, 2), (2, 0)\}$

C **29.** $y = 5 - 2x, \ x \in \{0, 1, 2, 3, 4\}$ **30.** $y = \dfrac{x}{2} - 4, \ x \in \{0, 2, 4\}$

31. $y^2 = x, \ x \in \{0, 1, 4\}$ **32.** $y = x^2, \ x \in \{-2, 0, 2\}$

33. $x^2 + y^2 = 4, \ x \in \{-2, 0, 2\}$ **34.** $x^2 + y^2 = 9, \ x \in \{-3, 0, 3\}$

C-2
FUNCTION NOTATION

■ The Function Symbol $f(x)$
■ Use of the Function Symbol $f(x)$

We have seen (Section C-1) that a function involves two sets of elements—a domain and a range—and a rule of correspondence that enables us to assign each element in the domain to exactly one element in the range. We use different letters to denote names for numbers; in essentially the same way, we will now use different letters to denote names for functions. For example, f and g may be used to name the two functions

$$f: \quad y = 2x + 1$$
$$g: \quad y = x^2 + 2x - 3$$

THE FUNCTION SYMBOL $f(x)$

If x represents an element in the domain of a function f, then we will often use the symbol

$$f(x)$$

in place of y to designate the number (the output) in the range of the function f to which x is paired (see Figure 1). Do not think of this new function symbol as the product of f and x. It is not. The symbol $f(x)$ is read "f of x" or "the value of f at x." The variable x is an independent variable; y and $f(x)$ are dependent variables.

Domain Range

FIGURE 1

USE OF THE FUNCTION SYMBOL $f(x)$

This new function notation is extremely important, and its correct use should be mastered as early as possible. For example, in place of the more formal representation of the functions f and g above, we can now write

$$f(x) = 2x + 1 \qquad \text{and} \qquad g(x) = x^2 + 2x - 3$$

The function symbols $f(x)$ and $g(x)$ have certain advantages over the variable y in certain situations. For example, if we write $f(3)$ and $g(5)$, then each symbol indicates in a concise way that these are range values of particular functions associated with particular domain values. Let us find $f(3)$ and $g(5)$.

To find $f(3)$, we replace x by 3 wherever x occurs in

$$f(x) = 2x + 1$$

and evaluate the right side:

$$f(\mathbf{3}) = 2 \cdot \mathbf{3} + 1$$
$$= 6 + 1$$
$$= 7$$

Thus,

$$f(3) = 7 \qquad \text{The function } f \text{ assigns the range value 7 to the domain value 3; the ordered pair (3, 7) belongs to } f.$$

To find $g(5)$, we replace x by 5 wherever x occurs in

$$g(x) = x^2 + 2x - 3$$

and evaluate the right side:

$$g(5) = 5^2 + 2 \cdot 5 - 3$$
$$= 25 + 10 - 3$$
$$= 32$$

Thus,

$$g(5) = 32$$ The function g assigns the range value 32 to the domain value 5; the ordered pair (5, 32) belongs to g.

It is very important to understand and remember the definition of $f(x)$:

The Function Symbol $f(x)$

For any element x in the domain of the function f, the function symbol

$$f(x)$$

represents the element in the range of f corresponding to x in the domain of f. [If x is an input value, then $f(x)$ is an output value; or, symbolically, $f: x \rightarrow f(x)$.] The ordered pair $(x, f(x))$ belongs to the function f.

Figure 2, illustrating a "function machine," may give you additional insight into the nature of function and the function symbol $f(x)$. We can think of a function machine as a device that produces exactly one output (range) value for each input (domain) value. (If more than one output value is produced for an input value, then the machine would not be a function machine.)

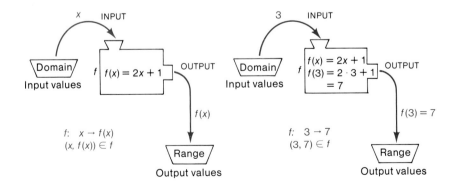

FIGURE 2 "Function machine"—exactly one output for each input

For the function $f(x) = 2x + 1$, the machine takes each domain value (input), multiplies it by 2, then adds 1 to the result to produce the range value (output). Different rules inside the machine result in different functions.

Example 4   Let $f(x) = \dfrac{x}{2} + 1$ and $g(x) = 1 - x^2$. Find:

      (A) $f(6)$ **(B)** $g(-2)$ **(C)** $f(4) + g(0)$

Solution   **(A)** $f(6) = \frac{6}{2} + 1 = 3 + 1 = 4$

      (B) $g(-2) = 1 - (-2)^2 = 1 - 4 = -3$

      (C) $f(4) + g(0) = \overset{f(4)}{(\frac{4}{2} + 1)} + \overset{g(0)}{(1 - 0^2)} = 3 + 1 = 4$

Problem 4   Let $f(x) = \dfrac{x}{3} - 2$ and $g(x) = 4 - x^2$. Find:

      (A) $f(9)$ **(B)** $g(-2)$ **(C)** $f(0) + g(2)$

Example 5   Let $f(x) = \dfrac{x}{2} + 1$ and $g(x) = 1 - x^2$. Find:

      (A) $f(g(3))$ **(B)** $g(f(-4))$

Solution   **(A)** $f(g(3)) = f(1 - 3^2)$ Evaluate $g(3)$ first; then evaluate f for this value.

$$= f(-8) = \dfrac{-8}{2} + 1 = -3$$

      (B) $g(f(-4)) = g\left(\dfrac{-4}{2} + 1\right)$

$$= g(-1) = 1 - (-1)^2 = 0$$

Problem 5   Let $f(x) = \dfrac{x}{3} - 2$ and $g(x) = 3 - x^2$. Find:

      (A) $f(g(3))$ **(B)** $g(f(-3))$

ANSWERS TO   **4.** **(A)** 1   **(B)** 0   **(C)** -2
MATCHED PROBLEMS   **5.** **(A)** -4 **(B)** -6

EXERCISE C-2   **A**   *If $f(x) = 3x - 2$, find the following:*

      1. $f(2)$ **2.** $f(1)$ **3.** $f(-2)$

      4. $f(-1)$ **5.** $f(0)$ **6.** $f(4)$

If $g(x) = x - x^2$, find the following:

7. $g(2)$ **8.** $g(1)$ **9.** $g(4)$

10. $g(5)$ **11.** $g(-2)$ **12.** $g(-1)$

B   *Problems 13 to 30 refer to the functions*

$$f(x) = 10x - 7 \qquad g(t) = 6 - 2t \qquad F(u) = 3u^2 \qquad G(v) = v - v^2$$

Evaluate as indicated.

13. $f(-2)$ **14.** $F(-1)$ **15.** $g(2)$

16. $G(-3)$ **17.** $g(0)$ **18.** $G(0)$

19. $f(3) + g(2)$ **20.** $F(2) + G(3)$

21. $2g(-1) - 3G(-1)$ **22.** $4G(-2) - g(-3)$

23. $\dfrac{f(2) \cdot g(-4)}{G(-1)}$ **24.** $\dfrac{F(-1) \cdot G(2)}{g(-1)}$

25. $F(g(1))$ **26.** $G(F(1))$

27. $g(f(1))$ **28.** $g(G(0))$

29. $f(G(1))$ **30.** $G(g(2))$

31. If $A(w) = \dfrac{w - 3}{w + 5}$, find $A(5)$, $A(0)$, and $A(-5)$.

32. If $h(s) = \dfrac{s}{s - 2}$, find $h(3)$, $h(0)$, and $h(2)$.

APPLICATIONS   *Each of the statements in Problems 33 to 36 can be described by a function. Write an equation that specifies the function.*

33. **Cost function**   The cost $C(x)$ of x records at \$5 per record. (The cost depends on the number of records purchased.)

34. **Cost function**   The total daily cost $C(x)$ of manufacturing x pairs of skis if fixed costs are \$800 per day and the variable costs are \$60 per pair of skis. (The total daily cost depends on the number of skis manufactured per day.)

35. **Temperature conversion**   The temperature in degrees Celsius can be found from the temperature in degrees Fahrenheit by subtracting 32 from the Fahrenheit temperature and multiplying the difference by $\frac{5}{9}$.

36. **Earth science**   The pressure $P(d)$ in the ocean in pounds per square inch depends on the depth d. To find the pressure, divide the depth by 33, add 1 to the quotient, and then multiply the result by 15.

ANSWERS

TO SELECTED
PROBLEMS

CHAPTER 1   EXERCISE 1-1

1. 6, 13   **3.** 67, 402   **5.** Even: 14, 28; odd: 9, 33   **7.** Even: 426; odd: 23, 105, 77
9. Composite: 6, 9; prime: 2, 11   **11.** Composite: 12, 27; prime: 17, 23   **13.** 20, 22, 24, 26, 28, 30
15. 21, 23, 25, 27, 29   **17.** 20, 21, 22, 24, 25, 26, 27, 28, 30   **19.** 23, 29   **21.** $2 \cdot 5$
23. $2 \cdot 3 \cdot 5$ **25.** $2 \cdot 2 \cdot 3 \cdot 7$ **27.** $2 \cdot 2 \cdot 3 \cdot 5$ **29.** $2 \cdot 2 \cdot 3 \cdot 3 \cdot 3$ **31.** $2 \cdot 3 \cdot 5 \cdot 7$ **33.** 36
35. 48   **37.** 24   **39.** 60   **41.** 90   **43.** 5,390   **45.** 630   **47.** 1,400
49. $2 \cdot 2 \cdot 2 \cdot 2 \cdot 5 \cdot 7$ **51.** $2 \cdot 2 \cdot 2 \cdot 5 \cdot 5 \cdot 11$ **53.** $2 \cdot 3 \cdot 3 \cdot 7 \cdot 11$ **55.** No, no, no, yes
57. Finite   **59.** Infinite   **61.** Finite

EXERCISE 1-2

1. 13   **3.** 2   **5.** 17   **7.** 2   **9.** 24   **11.** 80   **13.** 1   **15.** 21   **17.** 8   **19.** 10
21. 5   **23.** 2   **25.** 18   **27.** 12   **29.** 4   **31.** $5x$ **33.** $x + 5$ **35.** $x - 5$ **37.** $5 - x$
39. Constants: $\frac{1}{2}$; variables: A, b, h **41.** Constants: none, variables: d, r, t
43. Constants: none; variables: I, p, r, t **45.** Constants: 2, 3; variables: x, y
47. Constants: 2, 3; variables: u, v **49.** $A = 18$ cm^2, $P = 18$ cm   **51.** $A = 80$ km^2, $P = 36$ km   **53.** 20
55. 33   **57.** 14   **59.** 8   **61.** 5   **63.** 3   **65.** 22   **67.** 684 km   **69.** 600 words
71. $2x + 3$ **73.** $12x - 3$ **75.** $3(x - 8)$ **77.** 105   **79.** 16   **81.** 3   **83.** 4   **85.** 16
87. $3(t + 2)$ **89.** $t + (t + 1) + (t + 2)$ **91.** $t + (t + 2) + (t + 4)$

EXERCISE 1-3

1. T   **3.** F   **5.** T   **7.** T   **9.** T   **11.** T   **13.** F   **15.** $5 = x + 3$ **17.** $8 = x - 3$
19. $18 = 3x$ **21.** $49 = 2x + 7$ **23.** $52 = 5x - 8$ **25.** $4x = 3x + 3$ **27.** $x + 5 = 3(x - 4)$
29. $x + (x + 1) + (x + 2) = 90$ **31.** $x + (x + 2) = 54$ **33.** $x + 2x = 54$ **35.** $50 = x(x + 10)$

437

EXERCISE 1-4

1. $x + 10$ **3.** $28ab$ **5.** $16 + a + b$ **7.** xxx **9.** $2xxxyy$ **11.** $3wwxyyy$ **13.** x^3
15. $2x^3y^2$ **17.** $3xy^2z^3$ **19.** u^{14} **21.** a^6 **23.** w^{19} **25.** y^{16} **27.** 3^{30} (not 9^{30})
29. 9^{11} (not 81^{11}) **31.** $30abc$ **33.** $60uvw$ **35.** $x + y + z + 14$ **37.** $u + v + w + 19$
39. x^7 **41.** y^{10} **43.** $24x^9$ **45.** a^3b^3 **47.** $12x^2y^2$ **49.** $6x^4y^2$ **51.** $5{,}832$ **53.** 24
55. $32{,}768$ **57.** 128 **59.** **(C)** is false, since $9 - 7 \neq 7 - 9$. **(D)** is false, since $14 \div 7 \neq 7 \div 14$.
61. Commutative $+$ **63.** Associative $\times$ **65.** Commutative $\times$ **67.** Commutative $+$
69. Commutative $+$ **71.** Commutative $+$
73. **(A)** $s = 16t^2$ **(B)** Constants: 16, 2; variables: s, t **(C)** 1,024 ft

EXERCISE 1-5

1. Both 12 **3.** Both 45 **5.** $4x + 4y$ **7.** $7m + 7n$ **9.** $6x + 12$ **11.** $10 + 5m$
13. $3(x + y)$ **15.** $5(m + n)$ **17.** $a(x + y)$ **19.** $2(x + 2)$ **21.** $2x + 2y + 2z$ **23.** $3x + 3y + 3z$
25. $7(x + y + z)$ **27.** $2(m + n + 3)$ **29.** $x + x^2$ **31.** $y + y^3$ **33.** $6x^2 + 15x$ **35.** $2m^4 + 6m^3$
37. $6x^3 + 9x^2 + 3x$ **39.** $10x^3 + 15x^2 + 5x + 10$ **41.** $6x^5 + 9x^4 + 3x^3 + 6x^2$ **43.** $10x$ **45.** $11u$
47. $5xy$ **49.** $10x^2y$ **51.** $(7 + 2 + 5)x = 14x$ **53.** $x(x + 2)$ **55.** $u(u + 1)$ **57.** $2x(x^2 + 2)$
59. $x(x + y + z)$ **61.** $3m(m^2 + 2m + 3)$ **63.** $uv(u + v)$ **65.** $8m^5n^4 + 4m^3n^5$
67. $6x^3y^4 + 12x^3y + 3x^2y^3$ **69.** $12x^4yz^4 + 4x^2y^2z^4$ **71.** $uc + vc + ud + vd$ **73.** $x^2 + 5x + 6$
75. $abc(a + b + c)$ **77.** $4xyz(4x^2z + xy + 3yz^2)$

EXERCISE 1-6

1. 4 **3.** 8 **5.** 1 **7.** 1 **9.** 3 **11.** 2 **13.** 1 **15.** $3x, 4x; 2y, 5y$
17. $6x^2, 3x^2, x^2; x^3, 4x^3$ **19.** $2u^2v, u^2v; 3uv^2, 5uv^2$ **21.** $9x$ **23.** $4u$ **25.** $9x^2$ **27.** $10x$
29. $7x + 4y$ **31.** $3x + 5y + 6$ **33.** $m^2n, 5m^2n; 4mn^2, mn^2; 2mn, 3mn$ **35.** $6t^2$ **37.** $4x + 7y + 7z$
39. $11x^3 + 4x^2 + 4x$ **41.** $4x^2 + 3xy + 2y^2$ **43.** $6x + 9$ **45.** $4t^2 + 8t + 10$
47. $3x^3 + 3x^2y + 4xy^2 + 2y^3$ **49.** $8x + 31$ **51.** $3x^2 + 4x$ **53.** $11t^2 + 13t + 17$
55. $3y^3 + 3y^2 + 4y$ **57.** $6x^2 + 5xy + 6y^2$ **59.** $4x^4 + 3x^2y^2 + 3y^4$ **61.** $4m^6 + 9m^5 + 4m^4$
63. $x + (x + 1) + (x + 2) + (x + 3); 4x + 6$ **65.** $9x^2y^2 + 5x^3y^3$ **67.** $8u^3v^3 + 7u^4v^2$
69. $6x^2 + 13x + 6$ **71.** $2x^2 + 5xy + 2y^2$ **73.** $x^3 + 5x^2 + 11x + 15$ **75.** $y(y + 2); y^2 + 2y$
77. $x + x(x + 2) = 180; x^2 + 3x = 180$

REVIEW EXERCISE 1-7

The italicized number(s) in parentheses following each answer indicates the section(s) in which that type of problem is discussed.

1. **(A)** $\{11, 13, 15\}$ **(B)** $\{11, 13\}$ *(1-1)* **2.** 2 *(1-2)* **3.** 11 *(1-2)* **4.** 1 *(1-2)*
5. 20 *(1-2)* **6.** x^{25} *(1-4)* **7.** $6x^8$ *(1-4)* **8.** 2^{25} (not 4^{25}) *(1-4)* **9.** $x^2 + x$ *(1-5)*
10. $10x + 15y + 5z$ *(1-5)* **11.** $6u^3 + 3u^2$ *(1-5)* **12.** $9y$ *(1-6)* **13.** $5m + 5n$ *(1-6)*
14. $7x^2 + 3x$ *(1-6)* **15.** $8x^2y + 2xy^2$ *(1-6)* **16.** $3(m + n)$ *(1-5)* **17.** $8(u + v + w)$ *(1-5)*
18. $x(y + w)$ *(1-5)* **19.** $4(x + 2w)$ *(1-5)* **20.** $12x$ *(1-2)* **21.** $3x + 3$ *(1-2)*
22. $2x - 5$ *(1-2)* **23.** **(A)** 23, 29, 31 **(B)** Finite *(1-1)* **24.** **(A)** 3 **(B)** 1 **(C)** 1 *(1-4, 1-6)*

25. $2 \cdot 2 \cdot 2 \cdot 3 \cdot 5$ *(1-1)* **26.** 36 *(1-1)* **27.** 90 *(1-1)* **28.** 90 *(1-1)* **29.** 180 *(1-1)*

30. 6 *(1-2)* **31.** 6 *(1-2)* **32.** 12 *(1-2)* **33.** 20 *(1-2)* **34.** 24 *(1-2)* **35.** 36 *(1-2)*

36. $18x^8$ *(1-4)* **37.** $12x^3y^5z^4$ *(1-4)* **38.** $6y^5 + 3y^4 + 15y^3$ *(1-5)* **39.** $19u^2 + 7u + 17$ *(1-5, 1-6)*

40. $8x^2 + 22x$ *(1-5, 1-6)* **41.** $3x^2 + 7xy + 2y^2$ *(1-5, 1-6)* **42.** $u(u^2 + u + 1)$ *(1-5)*

43. $3xy(2x + y)$ *(1-5)* **44.** $3m^2(m^3 + 2m^2 + 5)$ *(1-5)* **45.** $24 = 2x - 6$ *(1-3)*

46. $3x = x + 12$ *(1-3)* **47.** $x + (x + 1) + (x + 2) + (x + 3) = 138$ *(1-3)*

48. $x + (x + 2) + (x + 4) = 78$ *(1-3)* **49.** $\{27, 51, 61\}$ *(1-1)* **50.** $\{61\}$ *(1-1)* **51.** 48 *(1-2)*

52. 39 *(1-2)* **53.** $10u^5v^4 + 5u^4v^3 + 10u^3v^2$ *(1-4, 1-5)* **54.** $7x^5 + 11x^3 + 6x^2$ *(1-5, 1-6)*

55. $8x^2 + 10x + 3$ *(1-5, 1-6)* **56.** $3x^2yz(4xz + 3)$ *(1-5)* **57.** $5x^2y^2(4x + y + 3)$ *(1-5)*

58. Commutative $\times$ *(1-4)* **59.** Associative $+$ *(1-4)* **60.** Commutative $+$ *(1-4)*

61. Associative $+$ *(1-4)* **62.** $4x = (x + 2) + (x + 4)$ *(1-3)*

CHAPTER 2 EXERCISE 2-1

1. $-8, -2, +3, +9$ **3.** **5.** **7.** $+4$

9. -10 **11.** -3 **13.** $1, 4, 17, 6{,}035$ **15.** $-21, -2$ **17.** $-21, -2, 0, 1, 4, 17, 6{,}035$

19. $-\frac{3}{5}, 3.14, \sqrt{13}, \frac{2}{9}$ **21.** $+20{,}270$ **23.** -280 **25.** -5 **27.** $+27$ **29.** -3 **31.** $+25$

33. -10 **35.** -9 **39.** $+1$ **41.** $+17$ **43.** -3

EXERCISE 2-2

1. -9 **3.** $+2$ **5.** $+4$ **7.** $+6$ **9.** 0 **11.** Sometimes **13.** Never **15.** -11

17. -5 **19.** $+13$ **21.** $+2$ or -2 **23.** No solution **25.** $+6$ **27.** $+5$ **29.** -5

31. $+5$ **33.** -8 **35.** -7 **37.** $+5$ **39.** -7 **41.** -5 **43.** $+5$ **45.** $+2$

47. $\{+5\}$ **49.** $\{+3\}$ **51.** $\{-6, +6\}$ **53.** $\varnothing$ **55.** $\{0\}$

57. Set of all integers less than or equal to 0 **59.** Set of all integers J

61. Set of all integers greater than or equal to 0 **63.** $\{0\}$

EXERCISE 2-3

1. $+11$ **3.** -3 **5.** -2 **7.** -8 **9.** $+3$ **11.** $+9$ **13.** -6 **15.** -9 **17.** -9

19. -2 **21.** -4 **23.** -5 **25.** -4 **27.** -12 **29.** -622 **31.** -38 **33.** -668

35. -36 **37.** -4 **39.** -4 **41.** -5 **43.** $+5$ **45.** -77 **47.** $-10{,}143$ **49.** $+14$

51. -6 **53.** -2 **55.** $+3$ **57.** \$23 **59.** $-1{,}493$ ft **61.** 0 **63.** $-m$

65. Commutative property, Associative property, Addition of opposites, Definition of addition

EXERCISE 2-4

1. $+5$ **3.** $+13$ **5.** -5 **7.** -5 **9.** $+5$ **11.** $7 > 5$ **13.** $5 < 7$ **15.** $-7 < -5$

17. $-5 > -7$ **19.** $0 < 8$ **21.** $0 > -8$ **23.** $-7 < 5$ **25.** $-842 < 0$ **27.** $900 > -1{,}000$

29. $+14$ **31.** -4 **33.** -6 **35.** -5 **37.** $+15$ **39.** $+87$ **41.** -315 **43.** -245

45. $+17{,}873$ **47.** $-5{,}230$ **49.** $+819$ **51.** $-1{,}705$ **53.** $+1$ **55.** -3 **57.** 0 **59.** 0

61. +8   **63.** +1   **65.** +7   **67.** +4   **69.** +2   **71.** +3   **73.** 0   **75.** +3
77. $(+29,141) - (-35,800) = 64,941$ ft   **79.** $(-245) - (-280) = +35$ ft   **81.** True
83. False; $(+7) - (-3) = +10$, $(-3) - (+7) = -10$ **85.** True
87. False; $|(+9) + (-3)| = +6$, $|+9| + |-3| = +12$

EXERCISE 2-5

1. +32   **3.** −32   **5.** 0   **7.** +2   **9.** −3   **11.** Not defined   **13.** −14   **15.** −14
17. 0   **19.** +3   **21.** −3   **23.** 0   **25.** −5   **27.** −7   **29.** +2   **31.** +4   **33.** −4
35. +30   **37.** −10   **39.** −8   **41.** −51   **43.** +17   **45.** −6   **47.** +8   **49.** 0   **51.** 0
53. Not defined   **55.** +4   **57.** +6   **59.** −20   **61.** 0
63. (A) +12 (B) +12 (C) +12   **65.** (A) +3 (B) +3   **67.** (A) −35 (B) −35   **69.** +8
71. +8   **73.** $x = 0$ **75.** No solution   **77.** +53,116   **79.** −9,728   **81.** −27   **83.** +12
85. +1,469

EXERCISE 2-6

1. 5   **3.** −13   **5.** −3   **7.** −2   **9.** −3   **11.** 1   **13.** −2   **15.** $4x$ **17.** $-4x$
19. $-12y$ **21.** $-3x - 3y$ **23.** $-5x + 3y$ **25.** $6m - 2n$ **27.** $-x + 4y$ **29.** $3x - 2y$
31. $-x + y$ **33.** $-x + 8y$ **35.** $4x - 8y$ **37.** $6xy$ **39.** $-3x^2y$ **41.** $2x^2 + 2x - 3$
43. $2x^2y + 5xy^2 - 6xy$ **45.** $-2x - y$ **47.** $2t - 20$ **49.** $-3y + 4$ **51.** $-10x$ **53.** $x - 14$
55. $6t^2 - 16t$ **57.** −9,683   **59.** $34x - 258y$ **61.** $-48u - 59v$ **63.** $3x - y$ **65.** $-3x + y$
67. $y + 2z$ **69.** $x - y + z$ **71.** $P = 2x + 2(x - 5) = 4x - 10$ **73.** 1   **75.** $-8x^2 - 16x$
77. $13x^2 - 26x + 10$ **79.** Value in cents $= 25x + 10(x + 4) = 35x + 40$

EXERCISE 2-7

1. 3   **3.** −3   **5.** −12   **7.** 5   **9.** −3   **11.** −13   **13.** 8   **15.** −4   **17.** −4
19. 3   **21.** 0   **23.** 3   **25.** 2   **27.** −3   **29.** 7   **31.** 4   **33.** 2   **35.** −4   **37.** 8
39. 7   **41.** 5   **43.** No solution   **45.** 16   **47.** 16   **49.** −15   **51.** 4   **53.** 6
55. No solution   **57.** All numbers   **59.** No solution   **61.** No solution   **63.** All numbers
65. $b = \dfrac{A}{h}$ **67.** $r = \dfrac{d}{t}$ **69.** $r = \dfrac{I}{pt}$ **71.** $P = \dfrac{A}{1 + rt}$ **73.** $x = -7$ **75.** $x = -5$ **77.** 2
79. 1   **81.** −6   **83.** $3x = 12$, $x = 4$

EXERCISE 2-8

1. 25, 26, 27   **3.** 16, 18, 20   **5.** 8 hr   **7.** 13 ft above and 104 ft below   **9.** 239,000 miles
11. 7, 9, 11   **13.** 10 ft by 23 ft   **15.** 7 quarters and 10 dimes   **17.** 5 sec   **19.** 22,000 ft
21. 8 miles   **23.** 70 hr (or 2 days and 22 hr); 1,750 miles   **25.** 130 min (or 2 hr, 10 min)

REVIEW EXERCISE 2-9

1. -4 *(2-2)* **2.** $+3$ *(2-2)* **3.** -5 *(2-3)* **4.** -13 *(2-3)* **5.** $+6$ *(2-4)* **6.** -3 *(2-4)*
7. $+28$ *(2-5)* **8.** -18 *(2-5)* **9.** -4 *(2-5)* **10.** $+6$ *(2-5)* **11.** 0 *(2-5)*
12. Not defined *(2-5)* **13.** -2 *(2-3)* **14.** -16 *(2-5)* **15.** -8 *(2-5)* **16.** $+8$ *(2-5)*
17. 0 *(2-5)* **18.** -6 *(2-5)* **19.** $2x - 8$ *(2-6)* **20.** $5x - 2$ *(2-6)* **21.** $2m + 9n$ *(2-6)*
22. $-6x - 18y$ *(2-6)* **23.** $x = -2$ *(2-7)* **24.** $x = -7$ *(2-7)*
25. **(A)** -245 **(B)** $+14{,}495$ *(2-1)* **26.** 52, 53, 54 *(2-8)* **27.** $+12$ *(2-2)* **28.** $+3$ *(2-2)*
29. -2 *(2-2)* **30.** -10 *(2-4)* **31.** $+9$ *(2-3)* **32.** $+17$ *(2-4)* **33.** -6 *(2-5)*
34. $+12$ *(2-5)* **35.** 0 *(2-5)* **36.** $+34$ *(2-5)* **37.** 0 *(2-5)* **38.** $-2x^2y^2 - 5xy$ *(2-6)*
39. $4y^3 - 7y^2 + 18y$ *(2-6)* **40.** $10x - 24y$ *(2-6)* **41.** $-6x^3y^2 - 10x^2y + 3xy^2$ *(2-6)*
42. $2y - 3$ *(2-6)* **43.** $x - 2y$ *(2-6)* **44.** $m = 9$ *(2-7)* **45.** $x = 2$ *(2-7)*
46. 44, 46, 48, 50 *(2-8)* **47.** 4 nickels and 5 quarters *(2-8)* **48.** -45 *(2-1)*
49. **(A)** $+15$ **(B)** $+5$ *(2-4)* **50.** **(A)** $+1$ **(B)** $+4$ *(2-5)* **51.** $-11x - 8$ *(2-6)*
52. $\{-9\}$ *(2-7)* **53.** 17 hr *(2-8)*

CHAPTER 3   EXERCISE 3-1

1. $\frac{8}{15}$ **3.** $\frac{3}{4}$ **5.** $\frac{1}{9}$ **7.** $\frac{5}{2}$ **9.** $\frac{2}{3}$ **11.** $\frac{2}{3}$ **13.** $\frac{11}{12}$ **15.** $\frac{1}{12}$ **17.** $\frac{19}{24}$ **19.** $\frac{13}{36}$
21. $\frac{2}{3}$ **23.** $\frac{2}{27}$ **25.** 5.8 **27.** 31.662 **29.** 17.73 **31.** 79.64 **33.** 32.5 **35.** 0.00852
37. 0.83 **39.** 0.74 **41.** 38.2 **43.** 7.9

EXERCISE 3-2

1. a: $-\frac{9}{4}$, b: $-\frac{3}{4}$, c: $\frac{7}{4}$ **3.** a: $-\frac{3}{2}$, b: $-\frac{1}{4}$, c: $\frac{1}{2}$, d: $\frac{11}{4}$ **5.** [number line]
7. [number line] **9.** 2 **11.** 15 **13.** 3 **15.** $9x^2$
17. $3x^2$ **19.** $3b$ **21.** $2ab$ **23.** $\frac{3}{2}$ **25.** $\frac{-1}{4}$ **27.** $\dfrac{1}{4y}$ **29.** $\dfrac{4a}{b}$ **31.** $\dfrac{-y^2}{4x}$ **33.** $\dfrac{12y}{5x}$
35. $\frac{2}{3}$ **37.** $\dfrac{x^2 + y}{3(x + y^2)}$

EXERCISE 3-3

1. $\frac{6}{35}$ **3.** $\dfrac{28x}{15y}$ **5.** $\dfrac{3x^2}{2y^3}$ **7.** $\frac{-6}{77}$ or $-\frac{6}{77}$ **9.** $\frac{10}{21}$ **11.** $\frac{21}{25}$ **13.** $\dfrac{14xy}{15}$ **15.** $\frac{-9}{14}$ **17.** $\frac{2}{3}$
19. $\frac{4}{375}$ **21.** 5 **23.** $\frac{3}{2}$ **25.** $\frac{-3}{4}$ **27.** $\dfrac{1}{z}$ **29.** 4 **31.** $2y^2$ **33.** $\dfrac{3x}{2y}$ **35.** y
37. $\dfrac{3ad}{2c}$ **39.** $\dfrac{3v}{2u}$ **41.** $\dfrac{-2x^2}{3y}$ **43.** $\frac{81}{100}$ **45.** 1 **47.** -2 **49.** $\dfrac{adf}{bce}$

EXERCISE 3-4

1. 2   **3.** $\frac{4}{5}$ **5.** $\frac{7}{8}$ **7.** $\frac{19}{15}$ **9.** $\frac{4}{11}$ **11.** $\frac{10}{11}$ **13.** $\frac{1}{8}$ **15.** $-\frac{1}{15}$ **17.** $\dfrac{-3}{5xy}$ **19.** $\dfrac{5y}{x}$

21. $\dfrac{6}{7y}$ **23.** $\dfrac{7}{6x}$ **25.** $\dfrac{13x}{6}$ **27.** $\dfrac{9-10x}{15x}$ **29.** $\frac{65}{84}$ **31.** $\frac{130}{63}$ **33.** $\frac{1}{20}$ **35.** $\dfrac{x^2-y^2}{xy}$

37. $\dfrac{x-2y}{y}$ **39.** $\dfrac{5x+3}{x}$ **41.** $\dfrac{1-3x}{xy}$ **43.** $\dfrac{9+8x}{6x^2}$ **45.** $\dfrac{15-2m^2}{24m^3}$ **47.** $\frac{5}{3}$

49. $\dfrac{3x^2-4x-6}{12}$ **51.** $\dfrac{18y-16x+3}{24xy}$ **53.** $\dfrac{18+4y+3y^2-18y^3}{6y^3}$ **55.** $\dfrac{22y+9}{252}$

57. $\dfrac{15x^2+10x-6}{180}$ **59.** $\dfrac{x-2x^2}{12}$ **61.** $\dfrac{3x+x^2}{6}$ **63.** $\frac{2}{7}$ **65.** $\frac{8}{15}$

EXERCISE 3-5

1. -35 **3.** 6   **5.** $\frac{15}{4}$ **7.** 8   **9.** 12   **11.** 6   **13.** -6 **15.** 36   **17.** $-\frac{4}{3}$ **19.** 20
21. 30   **23.** 15   **25.** $-\frac{5}{6}$ **27.** $\frac{27}{5}$ **29.** 9   **31.** 150   **33.** 11   **35.** $\frac{11}{5}$ **37.** 7.2368
39. -22.1393

EXERCISE 3-6

1. $\frac{1}{2}x$ or $\dfrac{x}{2}$ **3.** $\frac{2}{3}x$ or $\dfrac{2x}{3}$ **5.** $\dfrac{x}{3}+2$ **7.** $\dfrac{2x}{3}-8$ **9.** $\frac{1}{2}(2x-3)$ or $\dfrac{2x-3}{2}$

11. **(A)** $\dfrac{x}{4}+2=\frac{1}{2}$ **(B)** -6 **13.** **(A)** $\dfrac{x}{2}-2=\dfrac{x}{3}$ **(B)** 12   **15.** **(A)** $\dfrac{x}{2}-5=\dfrac{x}{3}+3$ **(B)** 48

17. **(A)** $\dfrac{2x}{3}+5=\dfrac{x}{4}-10$ **(B)** -36 **19.** 7.2 meters   **21.** 75 meters   **23.** 9 cm by 27 cm

25. 84 meters by 24 meters   **27.** 45 cm by 11 cm

EXERCISE 3-7

1. 0.67   **3.** 0.09   **5.** 2.16   **7.** 0.006   **9.** 0.074   **11.** 0.231   **13.** 12%   **15.** 8%
17. 325%   **19.** 0.7%   **21.** 7.2%   **23.** 40.5%   **25.** 48.36   **27.** 240   **29.** 250   **31.** 1.56
33. 0.08   **35.** $210   **37.** $1.98   **39.** 7,840,000   **41.** 39¢ (approximately)   **43.** $400
45. $989.31   **47.** $52

EXERCISE 3-8

1. $\frac{1}{4}$ **3.** $\frac{5}{1}$ **5.** $\frac{1}{3}$ **7.** 8   **9.** 18   **11.** 4   **13.** 600 men   **15.** 36 cm   **17.** 210
19. 125 km   **21.** 2.4 grams   **23.** 4 in.   **25.** $90 per share   **27.** 40 kg   **29.** 5.45 kg
31. 24.84 miles   **33.** 35 oz   **35.** 54.35 yd   **37.** Approx. 2,390   **39.** 24,000 miles

EXERCISE 3-9

1. 45 min   **3.** 400 mi   **5.** 1.5 kg   **7.** 62 in.   **9.** 180 m

11. $T = 80 - 5.5\left(\dfrac{h}{1,000}\right)$ or $T = 80 - 0.0055h$; 10,000 ft   **13.** 225 kg   **15.** 170 cm

REVIEW EXERCISE 3-10

1.  *(3-2)*   **2.** $\dfrac{15x}{8y}$ *(3-2)*   **3.** $\dfrac{6}{5xy}$ *(3-2)*   **4.** $\dfrac{5y}{6}$ *(3-4)*

5. $\dfrac{6 - 5xy}{4y}$ *(3-4)*   **6.** $\frac{5}{6}$ *(3-5)*   **7.** $\frac{3}{2}$ *(3-5)*   **8.** 6 *(3-5)*   **9.** 6 *(3-5)*   **10.** 1 *(3-5)*

11. **(A)** $\frac{3}{10}x = \frac{2}{5}$ **(B)** $x = \frac{4}{3}$ *(3-6)*   **12.** 15 cm by 25 cm *(3-6)*   **13.** 1,380 *(3-7)*

14. $\dfrac{2}{5x^2}$ *(3-2)*   **15.** $\dfrac{9y}{10z}$ *(3-2)*   **16.** $\dfrac{9x - 4y}{12x^2y^2}$ *(3-4)*   **17.** $\dfrac{3 - 2x + x^2}{x^2}$ *(3-4)*

18. $\dfrac{3xz + 18xy - 4yz - 24xyz}{12xyz}$ *(3-4)*   **19.** $\frac{17}{18}$ *(3-4)*   **20.** $2xy - 3$ *(3-5)*   **21.** -12 *(3-5)*

22. 41 *(3-5)*   **23.** $\dfrac{x}{450} = \dfrac{20}{3}$, $x = 3,000$ *(3-8)*   **24.** $\dfrac{x}{40} = \dfrac{1}{2.54}$; $x = 15.75$ in. *(3-8)*

25. 44 *(3-6)*   **26.** $4,128 *(3-7)*   **27.** 0.6 *(3-5)*   **28.** $\frac{-4}{9}$ *(3-3)*

29. $\dfrac{27y^2 - 12xy + 25x^2}{90x^2y^2}$ *(3-4)*   **30.** $\frac{-14}{3}$ *(3-5)*   **31.** 490 *(3-8)*   **32.** 6% *(3-7)*

CHAPTER 4   EXERCISE 4-1

1. T   **3.** T   **5.** T   **7.** T   **9.** T   **11.** T
13. $A(5, 2)$, $B(-2, 3)$, $C(-4, -3)$, $D(3, -2)$, $E(2, 0)$, $F(0, -4)$
15. $A(5, 5)$, $B(8, 2)$, $C(-5, 5)$, $D(-3, 8)$, $E(-5, -6)$, $F(-7, -8)$, $G(5, -5)$, $H(2, -2)$, $I(7, 0)$, $J(-2, 0)$, $K(0, -9)$, $L(0, 4)$

17.

19.

21. $A(2\frac{1}{2}, 1)$, $B(-2\frac{1}{2}, 3\frac{1}{2})$, $C(-2, -4\frac{1}{2})$, $D(3\frac{1}{4}, -3)$, $E(1\frac{1}{4}, 2\frac{1}{4})$, $F(-3\frac{1}{4}, 0)$, $G(1\frac{1}{2}, -4\frac{1}{2})$ **23.**

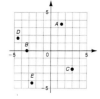

25. (A) III (B) II (C) I (D) IV **27.** $0.250\overline{0}$ **29.** $2.5\overline{5}$ **31.** $0.32\overline{32}$

33. $0.571428\overline{571428}$ **35.** I and III

EXERCISE 4-2

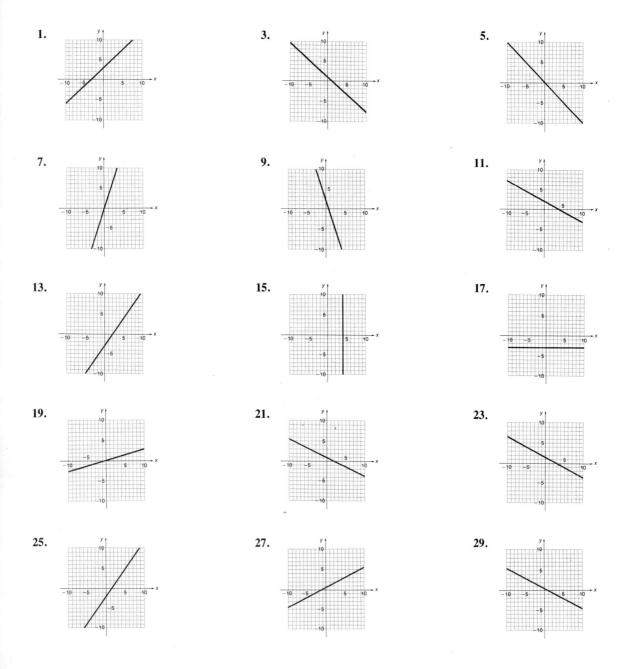

1.

3.

5.

7.

9.

11.

13.

15.

17.

19.

21.

23.

25.

27.

29.

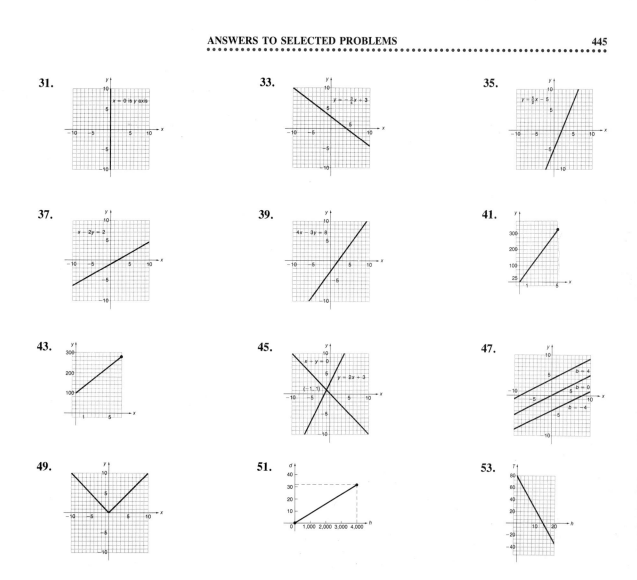

31.

33.

35.

37.

39.

41.

43.

45.

47.

49.

51.

53.

EXERCISE 4-3

1. 1   **3.** 2   **5.** slope 3, y intercept 5   **7.** slope -2, y intercept 4   **9.** $y = 3x - 1$

11. $y = -4x + 1$ **13.** $y = 2x$ **15.** $y = -2x + 4$ **17.** $y = x + 1$ **19.** $y = 2x + 3$ **21.** $-\frac{3}{4}$

23. -1 **25.** slope $\frac{2}{3}$, y intercept $-\frac{4}{3}$ **27.** slope $-\frac{3}{5}$, y intercept $\frac{4}{5}$ **29.** $y = \frac{1}{5}x + \frac{14}{5}$

31. $y = -\frac{1}{2}x + \frac{7}{6}$ **33.** $y = -\frac{3}{4}x + \frac{11}{4}$ **35.** $y = -x$

37.

39.

41.

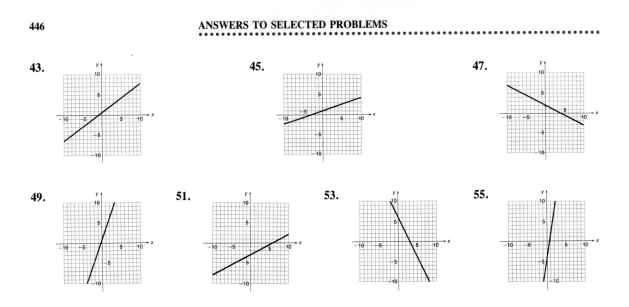

43. **45.** **47.**

49. **51.** **53.** **55.**

57. Slope $\frac{15}{33}$ represents increase of pressure in pounds per square inch per foot of depth.

59. **(A)** $R = \frac{7}{5}C + 5$ **(B)** slope $\frac{7}{5}$, y intercept 5
(C) The retail price is $5 plus 140 percent of cost (the markup is 40% of cost); slope $\frac{7}{5}$ is 140%, y intercept is $5.

61. $F = \frac{9}{5}C + 32$ or $C = \frac{5}{9}(F - 32)$

EXERCISE 4-4

1. $x = 3$, $y = 2$ **3.** $x = 3$, $y = 2$ **5.** $x = 9$, $y = 2$ **7.** $x = 2$, $y = 4$ **9.** $x = 6$, $y = 8$
11. $x = -4$, $y = -3$ **13.** No solution
15. An infinite number of solutions. Any solution of one is a solution of the other.
17. $x + 2y = 4$ becomes $y = -\frac{1}{2}x + 2$ and $2x + 4y = -8$ becomes $y = -\frac{1}{2}x - 2$. Since the slopes (that is, the coefficients of x) are the same and the y intercepts are different, the lines are parallel.
19. Both have the same equation, $y = \frac{1}{2}x + 3$.

EXERCISE 4-5

1. $x = 2$, $y = 3$ **3.** $x = -2$, $y = 3$ **5.** $x = 3$, $y = -1$ **7.** $x = 1$, $y = 4$ **9.** $x = 2$, $y = 4$
11. $m = 8$, $n = 6$ **13.** $u = -2$, $v = -3$ **15.** $x = 250$, $y = 100$ **17.** $x = 4,000$, $y = 280$

EXERCISE 4-6

1. $x = 3$, $y = 2$ **3.** $x = 1$, $y = 4$ **5.** $x = 2$, $y = -4$ **7.** $x = 2$, $y = -1$ **9.** $x = 3$, $y = 2$
11. $x = -1$, $y = 2$ **13.** $x = -2$, $y = 2$ **15.** $x = -1$, $y = 2$ **17.** $x = 1$, $y = -5$
19. $p = -\frac{4}{3}$, $q = 1$ **21.** $m = \frac{3}{2}$, $n = -\frac{2}{3}$ **23.** No solution   **25.** Infinitely many solutions
27. $x = \frac{1}{3}$, $y = -2$ **29.** $m = -2$, $n = 2$ **31.** Limes: 11 cents each; lemons: 4 cents each
33. $x = 1$, $y = 0.2$ **35.** $x = 6$, $y = 4$ **37.** $x = -6$, $y = 12$

EXERCISE 4-7

1. $48t = 156$, $t = 3.25$ hr   **3.** $12t = 30$, $t = 2.5$ min   **5.** $r \cdot 40 = 220$, $r = \$5.50$ per hr
7. $r(5.5) = 550$, $r = 100$ km/hr   **9.** $55t + 50t = 630$, $t = 6$ hr
11. $20t + 30t = 30{,}000$, $t = 600$ min (10 hr)   **13.** If t = time to catch up, then $50t = 45(t + 1)$ and $t = 9$ hr.
15. If t = time to complete the job, then $20t + 30(t - 60) = 30{,}000$; $t = 636$ min (10.6 hr).
17. If t = time that assistant worked, then $21t + 35(t - 5) = 1{,}505$, $t = 30$ hr (assistant), $t - 5 = 25$ hr (chemist).
19. $\dfrac{d}{3} - \dfrac{d}{5} = 12$, $d = 90$ miles

EXERCISE 4-8

1. 30 nickels, 20 dimes   **3.** 3,000 \$10 tickets and 5,000 \$6 tickets   **5.** 2 dl   **7.** 100 ml
9. 75 ml of 30% solution and 25 ml of 70% solution
11. 60 lb of \$3.50-per-pound coffee and 40 lb of \$4.75-per-pound coffee
13. \$7,500 at 8% and \$2,500 at 12%   **15.** 5 liters   **17.** 70 $\frac{1}{2}$-lb packages and 30 $\frac{1}{3}$-lb packages

EXERCISE 4-9

1. 11 ft and 7 ft   **3.** 20 cm by 16 cm   **5.** 3,800 \$7 tickets and 4,400 \$11 tickets
7. \$6,000 at 6% and \$2,000 at 8%   **9.** 40 lb of \$3.70-per-pound coffee and 60 lb of \$5.20-per-pound coffee
11. 70 cl water, 50 cl alcohol   **13.** 25 ml of 30% solution and 75 ml of 70% solution
15. 500 grams and 300 grams   **17.** 80 grams of mix 1 and 60 grams of mix 2
19. 3 ft from the 42-lb end (9 ft from the 14-lb end)
21. Primary wave: 25 sec; secondary wave: 40 sec; distance: 200 km   **23.** 16 in. and 20 in.
25. 36 nickels, 14 dimes   **27.** 84 $\frac{1}{4}$-lb packages and 60 $\frac{1}{2}$-lb packages
29. 10 test tubes for 1 flask; 3 test tubes for 1 mixing dish

REVIEW EXERCISE 4-10

1. *(4-2)*   **2.** *(4-2)*   **3.** *(4-2)*   **4.** *(4-2)*

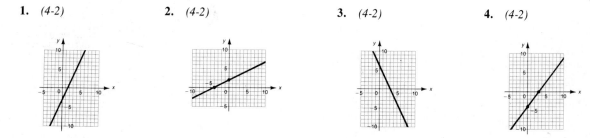

5. $-\frac{3}{5}$ *(4-3)*   **6.** $y = -2x + 5$ *(4-3)*   **7.** $y = 3x - 1$ *(4-3)*   **8.** $y = 3x - 9$ *(4-3)*
9. $x = 6$, $y = 1$ *(4-4)*   **10.** $x = 2$, $y = 1$ *(4-6)*   **11.** $x = -1$, $y = 2$ *(4-4 or 4-6)*
12. $x + y = 30$, $5x + 10y = 230$; 16 dimes, 14 nickels *(4-9)*   **13.** All are true *(4-1)*
14. All are true *(4-1)*

15. *(4-2)*   **16.** *(4-2)*   **17.** $y = \frac{5}{3}x - \frac{7}{3}$ *(4-3)*   **18.** $y = 4x - 7$ *(4-3)*

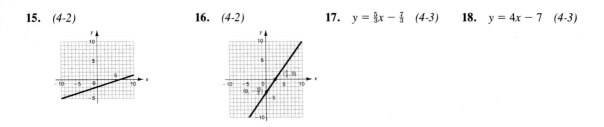

19. $x = 3, y = 3$ *(4-4)*   **20.** $u = 1, v = -2$ *(4-6)*   **21.** $m = -1, n = -3$ *(4-6)*
22. $22t + 13t = 2,800; t = 80$ hr *(4-7)*   **23.** $54t = 48(t + 1); t = 8$ hr *(4-7)*
24. $x + y = 6,000, 0.1x + 0.06y = 440; \$2,000$ at 10% and $\$4,000$ at 6% *(4-9)*
25. $x + y = 100, 0.5x + 0.7y = 66;$ 20 ml of 50% solution and 80 ml of 70% solution *(4-9)*
26. Infinitely many solutions—same line *(4-4)*   **27.** No solution *(4-6)*
28. $90t + 110(t - 20) = 6,000; t = 41$ min *(4-7)*   **29.** $0.4(12 - x) + x = 0.5(12); x = 2$ liters *(4-8)*
30. **(A)** 1.25 hr, 0.75 hr   **(B)** 112.5 miles *(4-9)*

CHAPTER 5   EXERCISE 5-1

1. -8 **3.** -6 **5.** $\frac{4}{9}$ **7.** $\frac{2}{3}$ **9.** $\frac{2}{13}$ **11.** $\frac{22}{7}$ **13.** 2π **15.** $\sqrt{9.9}$ **17.** $\sqrt{\frac{23}{9}}$
19. $a < d$ **21.** $b > a$ **23.** $e < f$ **25.** Right   **27.** $-\frac{8}{15}$ **29.** -3.14 **31.** $-\sqrt{2}$

33. ⊢(⊶⊶)⊶⊶→ x   **35.** ←⊶⊶⊶⊶⊢ x   **37.** ⊢(⊶)⊶⊶⊢ x

39. ⊢(⊶)⊶⊶⊶ x   **41.** ⊢⊶[⊶⊶]⊶ x

EXERCISE 5-2

1. ←⊶⊶⊶)⊶⊶→ x

3. ⊢⊶⊶(⊶⊶→ x

5. ←⊶⊶⊶⊢⊶→ x

7. ⊢⊶[⊶)⊶⊶→ x

9. $-4 \le x < 7$ **11.** $-1 \le x \le 8$ **13.** $-3 < x \le 9$ **15.** $-3 < x < 6$

17. $x > 7$ ⊢(⊶→ x   **19.** $x < -7$ ←⊶)⊶ x   **21.** $x > 4$ ⊢(⊶→ x

23. $x \le -4$ ←⊶]⊶→ x   **25.** $x < -21$ ←⊶)⊶→ x   **27.** $x \ge 21$ ⊢[⊶→ x

29. $x < 2$ ←⊶)⊶→ x   **31.** $x > 2$ ⊢(⊶→ x   **33.** $x \le 5$ ←⊶]⊶→ x

35. $y \le -2$ ⊢]⊶→ y   **37.** $x < 10$ ←⊶)⊶→ x   **39.** $x \ge 3$ ⊢[⊶→ x

41. $u \le -11$ ←⊶]⊶→ u   **43.** $m < -\frac{7}{5}$ ←⊶)⊶→ m   **45.** $x > -4$ ⊢(⊶→ x

47. $-1 < x < 2$ 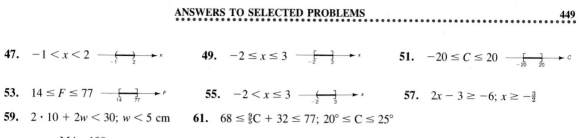 **49.** $-2 \le x \le 3$ **51.** $-20 \le C \le 20$

53. $14 \le F \le 77$ **55.** $-2 < x \le 3$ **57.** $2x - 3 \ge -6; \ x \ge -\frac{3}{2}$

59. $2 \cdot 10 + 2w < 30; \ w < 5$ cm **61.** $68 \le \frac{9}{5}C + 32 \le 77; \ 20° \le C \le 25°$

63. $70 \le \dfrac{MA \cdot 100}{12} \le 120; \ 8.4 \le MA \le 14.4$

EXERCISE 5-3

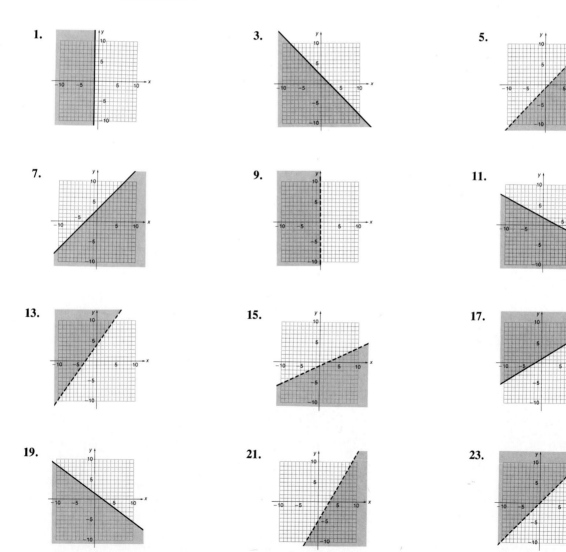

1.   **3.**   **5.**

7.   **9.**   **11.**

13.   **15.**   **17.**

19.   **21.**   **23.**

25. **27.**

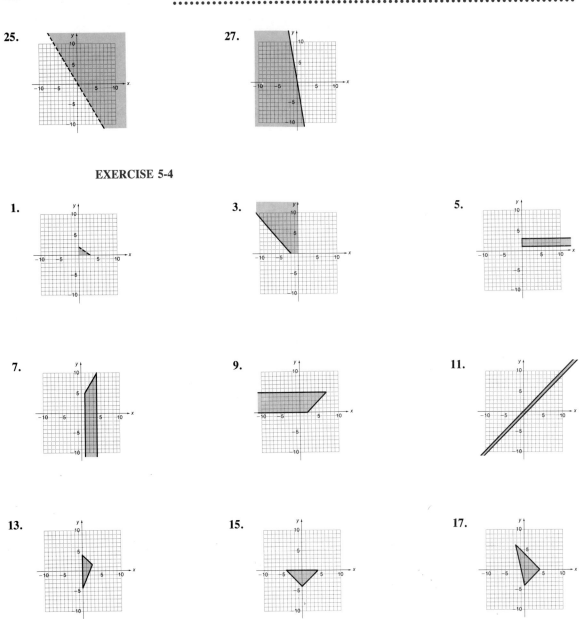

EXERCISE 5-4

1. **3.** **5.**

7. **9.** **11.**

13. **15.** **17.**

REVIEW EXERCISE 5-5

1. **(A)** $\frac{5}{18}$ **(B)** $\frac{19}{24}$ **(C)** $\sqrt{7}$ *(5-1)*

2. **(A)** $\overset{\longleftarrow}{\underset{-5 \quad 0 \quad 5}{\longmapsto}} x$ **(B)** $\overset{}{\underset{-5 \quad 0 \quad 5}{\longmapsto}} x$ *(5-1)* **3.** $x < 6$ *(5-2)*

4. $x \geq -3$ *(5-2)* **5.** $x \leq -3$ *(5-2)* **6.** $-4 \leq x \leq 3$ *(5-2)* **7.** $5x - 5 \leq 10; x \leq 3$ *(5-2)*

8. $x > -1$ 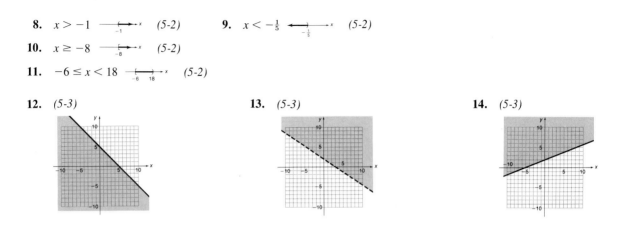 (5-2)   **9.** $x < -\frac{1}{5}$ (5-2)

10. $x \geq -8$ (5-2)

11. $-6 \leq x < 18$ (5-2)

12. (5-3)   **13.** (5-3)   **14.** (5-3)

15. $59 \leq \frac{9}{5}C + 32 \leq 86; \ 15 \leq C \leq 30$ (5-2)

16. (5-4)   **17.** (5-4)   **18.** (5-4)

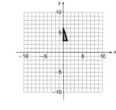

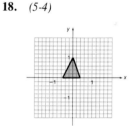

19. (5-4)   **20.** $20 \leq \frac{5}{9}(F - 32) \leq 25; \ 68 \leq F \leq 77$ (5-2)

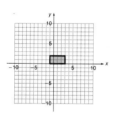

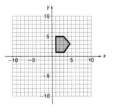

CHAPTER 6   EXERCISE 6-1

1. $7x - 2$ **3.** $8x$ **5.** $x^2 + 7x + 1$ **7.** $3x + 4$ **9.** $x + 6$ **11.** $2x^2 + 3x + 1$
13. $2x^2 + x - 6$ **15.** $2x^3 - 7x^2 + 13x - 5$ **17.** $x^3 - 6x^2y + 10xy^2 - 3y^3$ **19.** 1 **21.** 3
23. 2 **25.** 6 **27.** $4x^3 + 2x^2 + 3x$ **29.** $4x - y$ **31.** $2x - y - z$ **33.** $-x^3 + 4x^2 + 2x - 3$
35. $-a + 2b$ **37.** $-2a + b$ **39.** $-2x^2 + 8x - 4$ **41.** $a^3 + b^3$ **43.** $x^3 + 6x^2y + 12xy^2 + 8y^3$
45. $2x^4 - 5x^3 + 5x^2 + 11x - 10$ **47.** $2x^4 + x^3y - 7x^2y^2 + 5xy^3 - y^4$ **49.** $-x^2 + 17x - 11$
51. $2x^3 - 13x^2 + 25x - 18$

EXERCISE 6-2

1. $x^2 + 3x + 2$ **3.** $y^2 + 7y + 12$ **5.** $x^2 - 9x + 20$ **7.** $n^2 - 7n + 12$ **9.** $s^2 + 5s - 14$
11. $m^2 - 7m - 60$ **13.** $u^2 - 9$ **15.** $x^2 - 64$ **17.** $y^2 + 16y + 63$ **19.** $c^2 - 15c + 54$
21. $x^2 - 8x - 48$ **23.** $a^2 - b^2$ **25.** $x^2 + 4xy + 3y^2$ **27.** $3x^2 + 7x + 2$ **29.** $4t^2 - 11t + 6$
31. $3y^2 - 2y - 21$ **33.** $2x^2 + xy - 6y^2$ **35.** $6x^2 + x - 2$ **37.** $9y^2 - 4$ **39.** $5s^2 + 34s - 7$
41. $6m^2 - mn - 35n^2$ **43.** $12n^2 - 13n - 14$ **45.** $6x^2 - 13xy + 6y^2$ **47.** $x^2 + 6x + 9$
49. $4x^2 - 12x + 9$ **51.** $4x^2 - 20xy + 25y^2$ **53.** $16a^2 + 24ab + 9b^2$ **55.** $x^3 + x^2 - 3x + 1$
57. $6x^3 - 13x^2 + 14x - 12$ **59.** $x^4 - 2x^3 - 4x^2 + 11x - 6$

EXERCISE 6-3

1. $A(2x + 3)$ **3.** $5x(2x + 3)$ **5.** $2u(7u - 3)$ **7.** $2u(3u - 5v)$ **9.** $5mn(2m - 3n)$
11. $2x^2y(x - 3y)$ **13.** $(x + 2)(3x + 5)$ **15.** $(m - 4)(3m - 2)$ **17.** $(x + y)(x - y)$
19. $3x^2(2x^2 - 3x + 1)$ **21.** $2xy(4x^2 - 3xy + 2y^2)$ **23.** $4x^2(2x^2 - 3xy + y^2)$ **25.** $(2x + 3)(3x - 5)$
27. $(x + 1)(x - 1)$ **29.** $(2x - 3)(4x - 1)$ **31.** $2x - 2$ **33.** $2x - 8$ **35.** $2u + 1$
37. $3x(x - 1) + 2(x - 1) = (x - 1)(3x + 2)$ **39.** $3x(x - 4) - 2(x - 4) = (x - 4)(3x - 2)$
41. $4u(2u + 1) - (2u + 1) = (2u + 1)(4u - 1)$ **43.** $(x - 1)(3x + 2)$ **45.** $(x - 4)(3x - 2)$
47. $(2u + 1)(4u - 1)$ **49.** $2m(m - 4) + 5(m - 4) = (m - 4)(2m + 5)$
51. $3x(2x - 3) - 2(2x - 3) = (2x - 3)(3x - 2)$ **53.** $3u(u - 4) - (u - 4) = (u - 4)(3u - 1)$
55. $3u(2u + v) - 2v(2u + v) = (2u + v)(3u - 2v)$ **57.** $3x(2x + y) - 5y(2x + y) = (2x + y)(3x - 5y)$
59. $3u^2 - 12u - u + 4 = 3u(u - 4) - (u - 4) = (u - 4)(3u - 1)$
61. $6u^2 + 3uv - 4uv - 2v^2 = 3u(2u + v) - 2v(2u + v) = (2u + v)(3u - 2v)$
63. $6x^2 + 3xy - 10xy - 5y^2 = 3x(2x + y) - 5y(2x + y) = (2x + y)(3x - 5y)$
65. $3a^2 + 9ab + ab + 3b^2 = 3a(a + 3b) + b(a + 3b) = (a + 3b)(3a + b)$
67. $uw - ux - vw + vx = u(w - x) - v(w - x) = (w - x)(u - v)$

EXERCISE 6-4

1. $(x + 1)(x + 4)$ **3.** $(x + 2)(x + 3)$ **5.** $(x - 1)(x - 3)$ **7.** $(x - 2)(x - 5)$ **9.** Not factorable
11. Not factorable **13.** $(x + 3y)(x + 5y)$ **15.** $(x - 4)^2$ **17.** Not factorable **19.** $(x - 3y)(x - 7y)$
21. Not factorable **23.** $(3x + 1)(x + 2)$ **25.** $(3x - 4)(x - 1)$ **27.** Not factorable **29.** $(x + 1)^2$
31. $(x - 4)(3x - 2)$ **33.** $(3x - 2y)(x - 3y)$ **35.** $(n - 4)(n + 2)$ **37.** Not factorable
39. $(x - 1)(3x + 2)$ **41.** $(x + 6y)(x - 2y)$ **43.** $(u - 4)(3u + 1)$ **45.** $(3x + 5)(2x - 1)$
47. $(3s + 1)(s - 2)$ **49.** Not factorable **51.** $(x - 2)(5x + 2)$ **53.** $(2u + v)(3u - 2v)$
55. $(4x - 3)(2x + 3)$ **57.** $(3u - 2v)(u + 3v)$ **59.** $(u - 4v)(4u - 3v)$ **61.** $(6x + y)(2x - 7y)$
63. $(12x - 5y)(x + 2y)$

EXERCISE 6-5

1. $(3x - 4)(x - 1)$ **3.** Not factorable **5.** $(2x - 1)(x + 3)$ **7.** Not factorable **9.** $(x - 4)(3x - 2)$
11. $(3x + 5)(2x - 1)$ **13.** Not factorable **15.** $(m - 4)(2m + 5)$ **17.** $(u - 4)(3u + 1)$
19. $(2u + v)(3u - 2v)$ **21.** Not factorable **23.** $(4x - 3)(2x + 3)$ **25.** $(4m - 2n)(m + 3n)$
27. Not factorable **29.** $(u - 4v)(4u - 3v)$ **31.** $(6x + y)(2x - 7y)$ **33.** $(6x + 5y)(3x - 4y)$
35. $-13, 13, -8, 8, -7, 7$

EXERCISE 6-6

1. $3x^2(2x + 3)$ **3.** $u^2(u + 2)(u + 4)$ **5.** $x(x - 2)(x - 3)$ **7.** $(x - 2)(x + 2)$ **9.** $(2x - 1)(2x + 1)$
11. Not factorable **13.** $2(x - 2)(x + 2)$ **15.** $(3x - 4y)(3x + 4y)$ **17.** $3uv^2(2u - v)$
19. $xy(2x - y)(2x + y)$ **21.** $3x^2(x^2 + 9)$ **23.** $6(x + 2)(x + 4)$ **25.** $3x(x^2 - 2x + 5)$
27. Not factorable **29.** $4x(3x - 2y)(x + 2y)$ **31.** $(x + 3)(x + y)$ **33.** $(x - 3)(x - y)$
35. $(2a + b)(c - 3d)$ **37.** $(m + n)(2u - v)$ **39.** $2xy(2x + y)(x + 3y)$ **41.** $5y^2(6x + y)(2x - 7y)$
43. $(x - 2)(x^2 + 2x + 4)$ **45.** $(x + 3)(x^2 - 3x + 9)$ **47.** $3m^2(m^2 + 4)$ **49.** $(x - 6)(x - 1)$
51. $(2y - 1)(2y + 1)$ **53.** $2x(3x + 2)(x - 2)$ **55.** $3xy^2(2x - y + 1)$ **57.** $(u - 5)(u - v)$
59. $(x - 2y)(x^2 + 2xy + 4y^2)$ **61.** $2x(2y + x)(4y^2 - 2yx + x^2)$ **63.** $(x^2 + 2)^2$
65. $(x^3 - 4)(x + 1)(x^2 - x + 1)$ **67.** $(x - 2)(x + 2)(x^2 + 4)$ **69.** $(x^2 + 3)(x^4 - 3x^2 + 9)$
71. $(x - 1)(x + 1)(x^2 + 1)$ **73.** $(x - y)(x + y)(x^2 + y^2)$

EXERCISE 6-7

1. $3, 4$ **3.** $-6, 5$ **5.** $-4, \frac{2}{3}$ **7.** $-\frac{3}{4}, \frac{2}{5}$ **9.** $0, \frac{1}{4}$ **11.** $1, 5$ **13.** $1, 3$ **15.** $-2, 6$
17. $0, 3$ **19.** $0, 2$ **21.** $-5, 5$ **23.** $\frac{1}{2}, -3$ **25.** $\frac{2}{3}, 2$ **27.** $-4, 8$ **29.** $-\frac{2}{3}, 4$
31. Not factorable in the integers **33.** $3, -4$ **35.** $-3, 3$ **37.** 11 by 3 in. **39.** $5, -3$ **41.** $\frac{1}{2}, 2$
43. $2, 5$ **45.** $2, -4$ **47.** $\frac{2}{3}$ or $\frac{3}{2}$ **49.** 1 ft

EXERCISE 6-8

1. $x + 2$ **3.** $2x - 3$ **5.** $2x + 3, R = 5$ **7.** $m - 2$ **9.** $2x + 3$ **11.** $2x + 5, R = -2$
13. $x + 5, R = -2$ **15.** $x + 2$ **17.** $m + 3, R = 2$ **19.** $5c - 2, R = 8$ **21.** $3x + 2, R = -4$
23. $2y^2 + y - 3$ **25.** $x^2 + x + 1$ **27.** $x^3 - 2x^2 + 4x - 8$ **29.** $2y^2 - 5y + 13, R = -27$
31. $2x^3 - 3x^2 - 5, R = 5$ **33.** $2x^2 - 3x + 2, R = 4$ **35.** $4, 3, 1$ **37.** $-3, -2, -1$

REVIEW EXERCISE 6-9

1. $5x^2 + 3x - 4$ *(6-1)* **2.** $2x^2 - x + 7$ *(6-1)* **3.** $3x + 4, R = 2$ *(6-7)* **4.** $6x^2 + 11x - 10$ *(6-2)*
5. $6u^2 - uv - 12v^2$ *(6-2)* **6.** $3x^3 + x^2 - 3x + 6$ *(6-1)* **7.** $-3x^3 + 3x^2 - 3x - 4$ *(6-1)*
8. $(x - 7)(x - 2)$ *(6-4, 6-5)* **9.** $(3x - 4)(x - 2)$ *(6-4, 6-5)* **10.** Not factorable *(6-4, 6-5)*
11. $2xy(2x - 3y)$ *(6-3)* **12.** $x(x - 2)(x - 3)$ *(6-6)* **13.** $(2u - 3)(2u + 3)$ *(6-6)*
14. $(x - 1)(x + 3)$ *(6-3)* **15.** Not factorable *(6-6)* **16.** $-5, 2$ *(6-7)* **17.** $0, \frac{1}{3}$ *(6-7)*
18. $5, 1, 0$ *(6-1)* **19.** $2x^2 + 5x + 5$ *(6-1)* **20.** $x - 4, R = 3$ *(6-8)*
21. $3x^2 + 2x - 2, R = -2$ *(6-8)* **22.** $4x^3 - 12x^2 + 13x - 6$ *(6-1)*
23. $27x^4 + 63x^3 - 66x^2 - 28x + 24$ *(6-1)* **24.** $a^3 + b^3$ *(6-2)* **25.** $-2x + 20$ *(6-1)*
26. $3(u - 2)(u + 2)$ *(6-6)* **27.** $(2x - 3y)(x + y)$ *(6-4, 6-5)* **28.** Not factorable *(6-4, 6-5)*
29. $3y(2y - 5)(y + 3)$ *(6-6)* **30.** $2x(x^2 - 2xy - 5y^2)$ *(6-6)* **31.** $3xy(4x^2 + 9y^2)$ *(6-6)*
32. $(x - 1)(x - 3)(x + 3)$ *(6-6)* **33.** $(x - y)(x + 4)$ *(6-6)* **34.** $(x + y)(x - 3)$ *(6-6)*
35. $(2u - 3)(u + 3)$ *(6-3)* **36.** $(3x + 2)(2x - 1)$ *(6-3)* **37.** $-4, 1$ *(6-7)* **38.** $\frac{1}{2}, -2$ *(6-7)*
39. 0 *(6-1)* **40.** $x^3 - 3x^2 + 2x + 4, R = -20$ *(6-8)* **41.** $3xy(6x - 5y)(2x + 3y)$ *(6-6)*
42. $4u^3(3u - 3v - 5v^2)$ *(6-6)* **43.** $2(3a + 2b)(c - 2d)$ *(6-6)* **44.** $(4u - 5v))(3x - 1)$ *(6-6)*
45. $(2x + 1)(4x^2 - 2x + 1)$ *(6-6)* **46.** $-2, 2, -7, 7$ *(6-5)* **47.** $4, 2, -2$ *(6-8)*

CHAPTER 7   EXERCISE 7-1

1. $\dfrac{x}{3}$ **3.** $\dfrac{1}{A}$ **5.** $\dfrac{1}{x+3}$ **7.** $4(y-5)$ **9.** $\dfrac{x}{3(x+7)^2}$ **11.** $\dfrac{x}{2}$ **13.** $3-y$ **15.** $\dfrac{1}{n}$

17. $\dfrac{2x-1}{3x}$ **19.** $\dfrac{2x+1}{3x-7}$ **21.** $\dfrac{x+2}{2x}$ **23.** $\dfrac{x-3}{x+3}$ **25.** $\dfrac{x-2}{x-3}$ **27.** $\dfrac{x+3}{2x+1}$

29. $3x^2-x+2$ **31.** $\dfrac{2+m-3m^2}{m}$ **33.** $2m^2-mn+3n^2$ **35.** $x+2$ **37.** $\dfrac{2x-3y}{2xy}$ **39.** -1

41. $-y$ **43.** $\dfrac{-1}{x+2}$ **45.** $\dfrac{x+2}{x+y}$ **47.** $x-5$ **49.** $\dfrac{x+5}{2x}$ **51.** $\dfrac{x^2+2x+4}{x+2}$

EXERCISE 7-2

1. $\frac{5}{6}$ **3.** 2 **5.** $\dfrac{2y^3}{9u^2}$ **7.** $\dfrac{u^2w^2}{25y^2}$ **9.** $\dfrac{2}{x}$ **11.** $a+1$ **13.** $\dfrac{x-2}{2x}$ **15.** $8d^6$

17. $\dfrac{1}{y(x+4)}$ **19.** $\dfrac{1}{2y-1}$ **21.** $\dfrac{x}{x+5}$ **23.** $-3(x-2)$ or $6-3x$ **25.** $\dfrac{m+2}{m(m-2)}$

27. $\dfrac{x^2(x+y)}{(x-y)^2}$ **29.** All but one (namely, $x=1$)

31. Obtain $\dfrac{x^2-(x+2)^2}{(x+1)(x+5)-(x+3)^2}$, which simplifies to $x+1$. Since $x=108{,}641$, $x+1=108{,}642$, the answer.

EXERCISE 7-3

1. $\dfrac{1}{x}$ **3.** $\dfrac{2}{x^2}$ **5.** 2 **7.** $\dfrac{1}{x-1}$ **9.** $\dfrac{3(z+1)}{z(z+3)}$ **11.** $\dfrac{y+4}{(y+1)(y+2)}$ **13.** $\dfrac{3(x-3)}{x^2-1}$

15. $\dfrac{2x+1}{x(x+1)}$ **17.** $\dfrac{-1}{y-1}$ or $\dfrac{1}{1-y}$ **19.** $\dfrac{3x-7}{(x-1)(x-2)(x-3)}$ **21.** $\dfrac{-3}{(x+1)(x+2)}$

23. $\dfrac{-x-6}{(x-2)^2(x+2)}$ **25.** $\dfrac{5}{(x+3)(x-2)}$ **27.** $\dfrac{x^2+2x+3}{x^2}$ **29.** $\dfrac{6x+10}{(x+2)(x+1)(x+4)}$

31. $\dfrac{5}{x+1}$ **33.** $\dfrac{4x-1}{x(x^2-1)}$ **35.** $\dfrac{1}{1+y}$ **37.** $\dfrac{-3}{y-1}$ or $\dfrac{3}{1-y}$

EXERCISE 7-4

1. $x=-9$ **3.** $y=2$ **5.** $x=-4$ **7.** $t=4$ **9.** $L=-4$ **11.** No solution   **13.** $-\frac{6}{5}$
15. No solution   **17.** $x=8$ **19.** $n=\frac{53}{11}$ **21.** $x=1$ **23.** $x=-4$ **25.** 8

EXERCISE 7-5

1. $I = A - P$ **3.** $r = \dfrac{d}{t}$ **5.** $t = \dfrac{I}{Pr}$ **7.** $\pi = \dfrac{C}{D}$ **9.** $x = -\dfrac{b}{a}$ **11.** $t = \dfrac{s+5}{2}$

13. $y = \dfrac{3x - 12}{4}$ or $y = \frac{3}{4}x - 3$ **15.** $E = IR$ **17.** $R = \dfrac{E}{I}$ **19.** $B = \dfrac{CL}{100}$ **21.** $L = \dfrac{100B}{C}$

23. $m = \dfrac{d^2F}{GM}$ **25.** $d = \dfrac{M - P}{Mt}$ **27.** $M = \dfrac{P}{1 - dt}$ **29.** $F = \frac{9}{5}C + 32$

31. $f = \dfrac{ab}{a + b}$ or $f = \dfrac{1}{\dfrac{1}{a} + \dfrac{1}{b}}$ **33.** $x = \dfrac{y + 1}{2y - 3}$ **35.** $b = \dfrac{a + 2}{2a - 1}$ **37.** $y = \dfrac{xz + 3z}{1 - 2x}$

EXERCISE 7-6

1. $\frac{5}{6}$ **3.** $\frac{7}{8}$ **5.** $\dfrac{xz}{y}$ **7.** a^2c^2 **9.** $\dfrac{a^2}{b^2}$ **11.** $\dfrac{y(x + y)}{x}$ **13.** $\dfrac{x + 1}{x}$ **15.** $\dfrac{x + y}{y}$

17. $\dfrac{a - 1}{a}$ **19.** $\dfrac{xy}{x + y}$ **21.** $\dfrac{m - 3}{m(m - 2)}$ **23.** $\dfrac{(m + n)^2}{m^3}$ **25.** 1 **27.** $\dfrac{x^2 + xy + y^2}{xy}$ **29.** $-\frac{1}{2}$

31. $\dfrac{2x + 1}{x + 1}$ **33.** $\dfrac{rs}{r + s}$

REVIEW EXERCISE 7-7

1. $\dfrac{3x + 2}{3x}$ *(7-3)*   **2.** $\dfrac{2x + 11}{6x}$ *(7-3)*   **3.** $\dfrac{4x^2y^2}{9(x - 3)}$ *(7-2)*   **4.** $\dfrac{(d - 2)^2}{d + 2}$ *(7-2)*

5. $\dfrac{x + 1}{2x(3x - 1)}$ *(7-3)*   **6.** $\dfrac{4}{x - 4}$ *(7-3)*   **7.** $\frac{3}{10}$ *(7-6)*   **8.** $\frac{28}{9}$ *(7-6)*   **9.** $m = 5$ *(7-4)*

10. No solution *(7-4)*   **11.** $b = \dfrac{2A}{h}$ *(7-5)*   **12.** $\dfrac{y + 2}{y(y - 2)}$ *(7-2)*   **13.** 2 *(7-2)*

14. $\dfrac{-1}{(x + 2)(x + 3)}$ *(7-3)*   **15.** $\dfrac{5x - 3}{6x^2(x - 1)}$ *(7-3)*   **16.** $\dfrac{4m}{(m - 2)(m + 2)}$ *(7-3)*

17. $\dfrac{-2y}{(x - y)^2(x + y)}$ *(7-3)*   **18.** x *(7-6)*   **19.** $\dfrac{x - y}{x}$ *(7-6)*   **20.** $x = -2$ *(7-4)*

21. $x = -5$ *(7-4)*   **22.** $L = \dfrac{2x - an}{n}$ or $L = \dfrac{2s}{n} - a$ *(7-5)*   **23.** $A = \dfrac{M}{1 + x}$ *(7-5)*   **24.** $\frac{2}{3}$ *(7-4)*

25. -1 *(7-2)*   **26.** $\dfrac{y + 4}{2x - y}$ *(7-3)*   **27.** $\dfrac{6 - 3x}{2x}$ *(7-6)*   **28.** $\dfrac{x - 2}{x - 1}$ *(7-6)*

29. No solution *(7-4)*   **30.** $x = \dfrac{3y + 1}{2y - 3}$ *(7-5)*

CHAPTER 8   EXERCISE 8-1

1. x^{13} **3.** y^{15} **5.** x^{15} **7.** y^{15} **9.** x^8y^8 **11.** $(xy)^7$ **13.** $\dfrac{x^8}{y^8}$ **15.** $\left(\dfrac{x}{y}\right)^5$ **17.** x^6

19. $\dfrac{1}{x^8}$ **21.** $\dfrac{1}{y^4}$ **23.** y^6 **25.** 10^{15} **27.** 10^{12} **29.** 6×10^{11} **31.** 2×10^3

33. 1.5×10^6 **35.** -8 **37.** 9 **39.** $x^{20}y^8$ **41.** $27a^6b^3$ **43.** $6x^7$ **45.** $\dfrac{1}{2a^4}$ **47.** $\dfrac{3a^3}{b}$

49. a^8b^{11} **51.** $5x^4y^{12}$ **53.** $625x^4y^{12}$ **55.** x^2y^4 **57.** $-x^2y^4$ **59.** -16 **61.** -27

63. $16x^4y^{12}z^{16}$ **65.** $6a^{15}$ **67.** $324a^{20}$ **69.** $\dfrac{a^4b^7}{2}$ **71.** $-a^6b^9$ **73.** $-\dfrac{1}{a^2b^5}$ **75.** a^5

EXERCISE 8-2

1. 1 **3.** 1 **5.** $\frac{1}{8}$ **7.** 27 **9.** $\frac{1}{4}$ **11.** $-\frac{1}{27}$ **13.** $\dfrac{1}{a^5}$ **15.** b^7 **17.** $\dfrac{1}{3^7}$ **19.** $\dfrac{1}{4^3}$

21. x^{11} **23.** $\dfrac{1}{y^9}$ **25.** $\frac{1}{9}$ **27.** 3^4 **29.** 10^8 **31.** $\dfrac{1}{10^6}$ **33.** 10^4 **35.** $\dfrac{1}{x^6}$ **37.** y^8

39. $\dfrac{y^4}{x^2}$ **41.** $\dfrac{x^6}{y^3}$ **43.** a^2b **45.** x^4y^7 **47.** 10^2 **49.** a^6 **51.** $\dfrac{1}{x^2}$ **53.** $\dfrac{b}{9a^4}$ **55.** $\dfrac{3y^2}{x^3}$

57. $3ab$ **59.** $\frac{12}{7}$ **61.** $\frac{36}{25}$ **63.** $\dfrac{1,000}{11}$ **65.** $\dfrac{3y^2}{2x^3}$ **67.** $\dfrac{4x^6y^4}{9}$ **69.** $\dfrac{b^4}{2a^4}$ **71.** $\dfrac{1}{10a^3}$

73. $\dfrac{ab}{a+b}$ **75.** $\dfrac{x^4y^4}{(y^2-x^2)^2}$

EXERCISE 8-3

1. 2×10^3 **3.** 1.08×10^5 **5.** 4.12×10^2 **7.** 4.8×10^1 **9.** 6.3×10^{-1} **11.** 4.6×10^{-2}
13. 4.4×10^{-4} **15.** 9.5×10^{-5} **17.** 3×10^{-6} **19.** 1.8×10^{-6} **21.** 1×10^0 **23.** $30,000$
25. 0.004 **27.** 0.08 **29.** $3,400,000$ **31.** $480,000,000$ **33.** $0.000\,24$ **35.** $0.000\,003\,2$
37. 6.35×10^9 **39.** 8.45×10^{-10} **41.** 4.805×10^{-7} **43.** 5.87×10^{12} **45.** 3×10^{-23}
47. $52,500$ **49.** $0.004\,15$ **51.** $93,000,000$ **53.** $0.000\,075$ **55.** 1.5×10^2 **57.** 2.4×10^{-1}
59. 1.6×10^0 **61.** 1.1×10^4 **63.** 2×10^{13} or $20,000,000,000,000$ **65.** 5×10^{-7} or $0.000\,000\,5$
67. 3.3×10^{18} or $3,300,000,000,000,000,000$ **69.** 10^7 or $10,000,000$; 6×10^8 or $600,000,000$

EXERCISE 8-4

1. 4 **3.** -9 **5.** x **7.** $3m$ **9.** $2\sqrt{2}$ **11.** $x\sqrt{x}$ **13.** $3y\sqrt{2y}$ **15.** $\frac{1}{2}$ **17.** $-\frac{2}{3}$

19. $\dfrac{1}{x}$ **21.** $\dfrac{\sqrt{3}}{3}$ **23.** $\dfrac{\sqrt{3}}{3}$ **25.** $\dfrac{\sqrt{x}}{x}$ **27.** $\dfrac{\sqrt{x}}{x}$ **29.** $5xy^2$ **31.** $2x^2y\sqrt{xy}$

33. $2x^3y^3\sqrt{2x}$ **35.** $\dfrac{\sqrt{3y}}{3y}$ **37.** $2x\sqrt{2y}$ **39.** $\frac{2}{3}x\sqrt{3xy}$ **41.** $\dfrac{\sqrt{6}}{3}$ **43.** $\dfrac{\sqrt{6mn}}{2n}$

45. $\dfrac{2a\sqrt{3ab}}{3b}$ **47.** 4.24 **49.** 0.45 **51.** 4.06 **53.** $\dfrac{\sqrt{2}}{2}$ **55.** In simplest radical form

57. $x\sqrt{x^2 - 2}$ **59.** Yes, no **61.** $5^{1/2} = \sqrt{5}$

63. If $a^2 = b^2$, then a does not necessarily equal b. For example, let $a = 2$ and $b = -2$.

65. 1.92 seconds **67.** 24 centimeters

EXERCISE 8-5

1. $8\sqrt{2}$ **3.** $3\sqrt{x}$ **5.** $4\sqrt{7} - 3\sqrt{5}$ **7.** $-3\sqrt{y}$ **9.** $4\sqrt{5}$ **11.** $4\sqrt{x}$ **13.** $2\sqrt{2} - 2\sqrt{3}$

15. $2\sqrt{x} + 2\sqrt{y}$ **17.** $\sqrt{2}$ **19.** $-3\sqrt{3}$ **21.** $2\sqrt{2} + 6\sqrt{3}$ **23.** $-\sqrt{x}$ **25.** $2\sqrt{6} + \sqrt{3}$

27. $-\sqrt{6}/6$ **29.** $5\sqrt{2xy}/2$ **31.** $2\sqrt{3} - \dfrac{\sqrt{2}}{2}$ **33.** $3\sqrt{2}$

EXERCISE 8-6

1. $4\sqrt{5} + 8$ **3.** $10 - 2\sqrt{2}$ **5.** $2 + 3\sqrt{2}$ **7.** $5 - 4\sqrt{5}$ **9.** $2\sqrt{3} - 3$ **11.** $x - 3\sqrt{x}$

13. $3\sqrt{m} - m$ **15.** $2\sqrt{3} - \sqrt{6}$ **17.** $5\sqrt{2} + 5$ **19.** $2\sqrt{2} - 1$ **21.** $x - \sqrt{x} - 6$

23. $9 + 4\sqrt{5}$ **25.** $2 - 11\sqrt{2}$ **27.** $6x - 13\sqrt{x} + 6$

29. $(3 - \sqrt{2})^2 - 6(3 - \sqrt{2}) + 7 = 9 - 6\sqrt{2} + 2 - 18 + 6\sqrt{2} + 7 = 0$ **31.** $\dfrac{2 + \sqrt{2}}{3}$ **33.** $\dfrac{-1 - 2\sqrt{5}}{3}$

35. $2 - \sqrt{2}$ **37.** $\dfrac{\sqrt{11} - 3}{2}$ **39.** $\dfrac{\sqrt{5} - 1}{2}$ **41.** $\dfrac{y - 3\sqrt{y}}{y - 9}$ **43.** $\dfrac{7 + 4\sqrt{3}}{-1}$ or $-7 - 4\sqrt{3}$

45. $\dfrac{x + 5\sqrt{x} + 6}{x - 9}$ **47.** $4 + \sqrt{15}$ **49.** $3 + \sqrt{2} + \sqrt{3} + \sqrt{6}$

EXERCISE 8-7

1. 5 **3.** 5 **5.** No solution **7.** 0, 3 **9.** 0, 1 **11.** 0, 9 **13.** 0, 27 **15.** 1, 25

17. 5 **19.** 7 **21.** 4

REVIEW EXERCISE 8-8

1. **(A)** 16 **(B)** $\frac{1}{9}$ *(8-1, 8-2)* **2.** **(A)** 1 **(B)** 9 *(8-2)* **3.** $\dfrac{4x^4}{9y^6}$ *(8-1)* **4.** $\dfrac{y^3}{x^2}$ *(8-2)*

5. **(A)** 6×10^{-2} **(B)** 0.06 *(8-3)* **6.** -5 *(8-4)* **7.** $2xy^2$ *(8-4)* **8.** $\dfrac{5}{y}$ *(8-4)*

9. $-3\sqrt{x}$ *(8-5)* **10.** $5 + 2\sqrt{5}$ *(8-6)* **11.** 12 *(8-7)* **12.** 5 *(8-7)*

13. **(A)** 9 **(B)** $\frac{1}{100}$ *(8-2)* **14.** **(A)** $\frac{1}{27}$ **(B)** 1 *(8-2)* **15.** $\dfrac{4x^4}{y^6}$ *(8-2)* **16.** $\dfrac{m^2}{2n^5}$ *(8-2)*

17. **(A)** 2×10^{-3} **(B)** 0.002 *(8-3)* **18.** $6x^2y^3\sqrt{y}$ *(8-4)* **19.** $\dfrac{\sqrt{2y}}{2y}$ *(8-4)* **20.** $\dfrac{\sqrt{6xy}}{2y}$ *(8-4)*

21. $\dfrac{5\sqrt{6}}{6}$ *(8-5)*   **22.** $1 + \sqrt{3}$ *(8-6)*   **23.** $\dfrac{n^{10}}{9m^{10}}$ *(8-2)*   **24.** $\dfrac{xy}{x + y}$ *(8-2)*   **25.** $\dfrac{n^2\sqrt{6m}}{3}$ *(8-4)*

26. $3 + \sqrt{6}$ *(8-6)*   **27.** $\dfrac{x - 4\sqrt{x} + 4}{x - 4}$ *(8-5)*   **28.** $2x\sqrt{x^2 + 4}$ *(8-4)*   **29.** 1.036 cc *(8-3)*

30. $a^2 = b$ *(8-4)*   **31.** All real numbers *(8-4)*   **32.** 4 *(8-7)*

CHAPTER 9   EXERCISE 9-1

1. 3, 5   **3.** $-7, 4$ **5.** $-6, 7$ **7.** $-7, 3$ **9.** $-7, -4$ **11.** ± 4 **13.** ± 8 **15.** $\pm\sqrt{3}$

17. $\pm\sqrt{5}$ **19.** $\pm\sqrt{18}$ or $\pm 3\sqrt{2}$ **21.** $\pm\sqrt{12}$ or $\pm 2\sqrt{3}$ **23.** $\pm\frac{2}{3}$ **25.** $\pm\frac{2}{3}$ **27.** $\pm\frac{2}{3}$

29. $\pm\frac{2}{5}$ **31.** $\pm\sqrt{\dfrac{3}{4}}$ or $\pm\dfrac{\sqrt{3}}{2}$ **33.** $\pm\sqrt{\dfrac{5}{2}}$ or $\pm\dfrac{\sqrt{10}}{2}$ **35.** $\pm\sqrt{\dfrac{1}{3}}$ or $\pm\dfrac{\sqrt{3}}{3}$ **37.** $-1, 5$

39. 3, -7 **41.** $2 \pm \sqrt{3}$ **43.** $-1, 2$ **45.** No real solution   **47.** $\dfrac{3 \pm \sqrt{6}}{2}$ **49.** $-\frac{1}{2}, 3$

51. $-2, \frac{1}{3}$ **53.** $-2, \frac{1}{4}$ **55.** $\pm\sqrt{c^2 - a^2}$ **57.** 70 mph

EXERCISE 9-2

1. $x^2 - 8x + 16 = (x - 4)^2$ **3.** $x^2 + 10x + 25 = (x + 5)^2$ **5.** $x^2 - 10x + 25 = (x - 5)^2$ **7.** $4 \pm \sqrt{10}$

9. $-5 \pm \sqrt{26}$ **11.** $x^2 + 7x + \frac{49}{4} = (x + \frac{7}{2})^2$ **13.** $x^2 - 3x + \frac{9}{4} = (x - \frac{3}{2})^2$ **15.** $\dfrac{-7 \pm \sqrt{69}}{2}$

17. $\dfrac{3 \pm \sqrt{5}}{2}$ **19.** 4, 7   **21.** $\dfrac{-2 \pm \sqrt{14}}{2}$ **23.** $\dfrac{-5 \pm \sqrt{57}}{4}$ **25.** $-6 \pm \sqrt{6}$ **27.** $\dfrac{3 \pm \sqrt{6}}{3}$

29. 1, -3 **31.** 1, $\frac{3}{2}$

EXERCISE 9-3

1. $a = 1, b = 4, c = 2$ **3.** $a = 1, b = -3, c = -2$ **5.** $a = 3, b = -2, c = 1$

7. $a = 2, b = 3, c = -1$ **9.** $a = 2, b = -5, c = 0$ **11.** $-2 \pm \sqrt{2}$ **13.** $3 \pm 2\sqrt{3}$

15. $\dfrac{-3 \pm \sqrt{13}}{2}$ **17.** $\dfrac{3 \pm \sqrt{3}}{2}$ **19.** $\dfrac{-1 \pm \sqrt{13}}{6}$ **21.** No real solution   **23.** $\dfrac{3 \pm \sqrt{33}}{4}$

25. $\dfrac{4 \pm \sqrt{11}}{5}$ **27.** $\dfrac{2\sqrt{3}}{3}, -\dfrac{\sqrt{3}}{3}$ **29.** No real roots   **31.** One, $x = -\frac{1}{6}$ **33.** Two, $x = \dfrac{7 \pm \sqrt{13}}{6}$

35. No real roots   **37.** One, $x = \frac{3}{4}$ **39.** $-2, 3$ **41.** 0, -7 **43.** ± 4 **45.** $-1 \pm \sqrt{3}$

47. 0, 2   **49.** $1 \pm \sqrt{2}$ **51.** $\dfrac{3 \pm \sqrt{3}}{2}$ **53.** 0, 1   **55.** $\frac{1}{3}, -\frac{1}{2}$ **57.** $\pm 5\sqrt{2}$ **59.** $2 \pm \sqrt{3}$

61. No real solution   **63.** $-\frac{2}{3}, 3$ **65.** $-50, 2$

EXERCISE 9-4

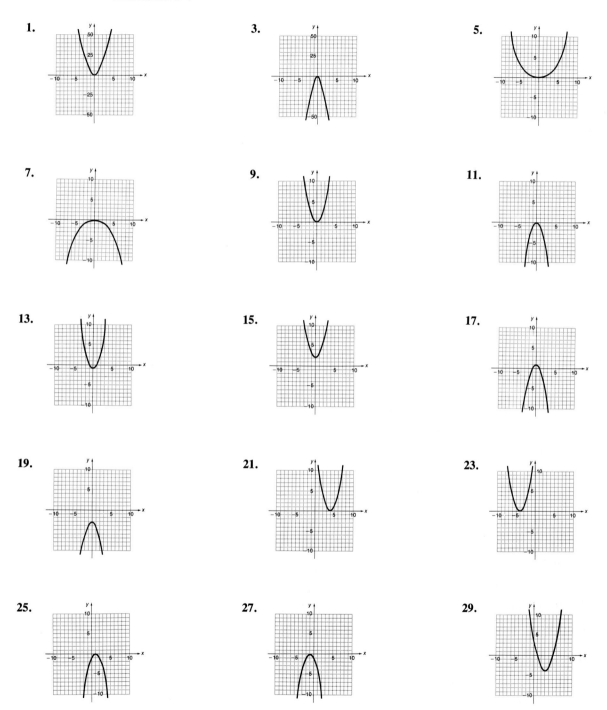

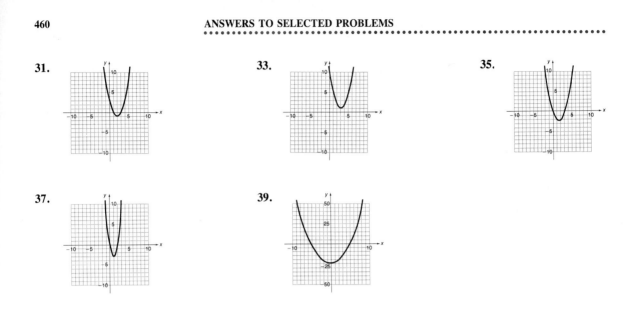

31.   **33.**   **35.**

37.   **39.**

EXERCISE 9-5

1. $t = \sqrt{\dfrac{2d}{g}}$ **3.** $r = -1 + \sqrt{\dfrac{A}{P}}$ **5.** 8   **7.** 0, 2   **9.** $\frac{1}{4}$, 4   **11.** 20%

13. 2,000 and 8,000 units   **15.** Approx. 9,854 or 3,146 units   **17.** 20

19. 3 meters, 4 meters, 5 meters   **21.** $(1 + \sqrt{2})$ in. $\approx$ 2.414 in.   **23.** 50 mph   **25.** 7 mph and 24 mph

27. 2 mph

REVIEW EXERCISE 9-6

1. ± 5 *(9-1)*   **2.** 0, 3 *(9-1)*   **3.** $-3, \frac{1}{2}$ *(9-1)*   **4.** 2, 3 *(9-1)*   **5.** $-3, 5$ *(9-1)*

6. $3x^2 + 4x - 2 = 0$; $a = 3$, $b = 4$, $c = -2$ *(9-1)*   **7.** $x = \dfrac{-b \pm \sqrt{b^2 - 4ac}}{2a}$ *(9-3)*

8. $\dfrac{-3 \pm \sqrt{5}}{2}$ *(9-3)*   **9.** $-5, 2$ *(9-1)*   **10.** 3, 9 *(9-1)*

11. *(9-4)*   **12.** $\pm 2\sqrt{3}$ *(9-1)*   **13.** 0, 2 *(9-1)*

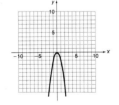

14. $-2, 6$ *(9-1)*   **15.** $-\frac{1}{3}, 3$ *(9-1)*   **16.** $\frac{1}{2}, -3$ *(9-1)*   **17.** $3 \pm 2\sqrt{3}$ *(9-2)*

18. $\dfrac{1 \pm \sqrt{7}}{3}$ *(9-3)*   **19.** 5, -4 *(9-1)*   **20.** 6, 12 *(9-1)*   **21.** 6 in. by 5 in. *(9-5)*

22. *(9-4)*   **23.** *(9-4)*

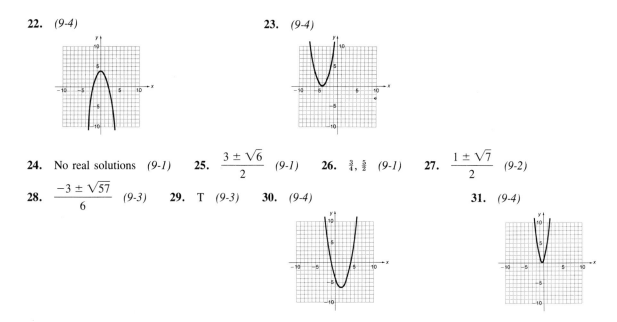

24. No real solutions *(9-1)*   **25.** $\dfrac{3 \pm \sqrt{6}}{2}$ *(9-1)*   **26.** $\frac{3}{4}, \frac{5}{2}$ *(9-1)*   **27.** $\dfrac{1 \pm \sqrt{7}}{2}$ *(9-2)*

28. $\dfrac{-3 \pm \sqrt{57}}{6}$ *(9-3)*   **29.** T *(9-3)*   **30.** *(9-4)*   **31.** *(9-4)*

32. $\dfrac{-1 + \sqrt{5}}{2}$ *(9-5)*

APPENDIX A   EXERCISE A

1. T   **3.** T   **5.** T   **7.** T   **9.** T   **11.** $5 \in P$ **13.** $6 \notin R$ **15.** $P = R$ **17.** $P \neq Q$

19. $\{6, 7, 8, 9\}$ **21.** $\varnothing$ **23.** $\{Su, M, T, W, Th, F, S\}$ **25.** $\{a, b, l\}$ **27.** $\varnothing$ **29.** $\{2, 4\}$

31. $\varnothing$ **33.** $\{1, 2, 3, 4, 5, 6, 7, 8\}$ **35.** $\{5, 6, 7, 8\}$ **37.** $\{2, 4, 6, 8\}$ **39.** $\{5, 7\}$ **41.** $\{5, 7\}$

43. $\varnothing, \{1\}, \{2\}, \{1, 2\}$ **45.**   **47.**   **49.**

APPENDIX C   EXERCISE C-1

1. Function   **3.** Not a function   **5.** Function   **7.** Function   **9.** Not a function   **11.** Function

13. Function   **15.** Function   **17.** Not a function   **19.** Not a function   **21.** Function

23. Function

25. Domain $= \{1, 2, 3\}$, Range $= \{1, 2, 3\}$; not a function

27. Domain = {−1, 0, 1, 2, 3, 4}, Range = {−2, −1, 0, 1, 2}; a function

29. Domain = {0, 1, 2, 3, 4}, Range = {−3, −1, 1, 3, 5}; a function

31. Domain = {0, 1, 4}, Range = {−2, −1, 0, 1, 2}; not a function

33. Domain = {−2, 0, 2}, Range = {−2, 0, 2}; not a function

EXERCISE C-2

1. 4   **3.** −8   **5.** −2   **7.** −2   **9.** −12   **11.** −6   **13.** −27   **15.** 2   **17.** 6
19. 25   **21.** 22   **23.** −91   **25.** 48   **27.** 0   **29.** −7   **31.** $\frac{1}{5}$, $-\frac{3}{5}$, not defined
33. $C(x) = 5x$ **35.** $C(F) = \frac{5}{9}(F - 32)$

INDEX

Basic Formulas

RECTANGLE

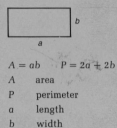

$A = ab \qquad P = 2a + 2b$

A   area
P   perimeter
a   length
b   width

CIRCLE

$A = \pi R^2 \qquad C = 2\pi R = \pi D \qquad D = 2R$

A   area
C   circumference
R   radius
D   diameter
π pi (≈ 3.14159)

SIMPLE INTEREST

$I = Prt \qquad A = P + Prt$

I   simple interest
P   principal
A   amount
r   rate
t   time

TEMPERATURE

$F = \frac{9}{5}C + 32 \qquad C = \frac{5}{9}(F - 32)$

F   degrees Fahrenheit
C   degrees Celsius

TRIANGLE

$A = \frac{1}{2}bh = \frac{bh}{2} \qquad P = a + b + c$

A   area
P   perimeter
b   base
h   height
a, c   sides

RECTANGULAR SOLID

$V = abc \qquad S = 2ab + 2ac + 2bc$

V   volume
S   surface area
a   length
b   width
c   height

RATE–TIME

$d = rt \qquad q = rt$

d   distance
q   quantity
r   rate
t   time